THERMODYNAMICS OF
SMALL SYSTEMS
PART II

FRONTIERS IN CHEMISTRY

Ronald Breslow and Martin Karplus, Editors
Columbia University

THERMODYNAMICS OF SMALL SYSTEMS: *Parts I and II*

T. L. Hill   *University of Oregon*

LECTURES ON QUANTUM THEORY OF MOLECULAR ELECTRONIC STRUCTURE

R. G. Parr   *The Johns Hopkins University*

OXIDATION MECHANISMS: Applications to Organic Chemistry

R. Stewart   *University of British Columbia*

THE BIOSYNTHESIS OF STEROIDS, TERPENES, AND ACETOGENINS

J. H. Richards   *California Institute of Technology*
J. B. Hendrickson   *Brandeis University*

THERMODYNAMICS
OF
SMALL SYSTEMS

PART II

TERRELL L. HILL
University of Oregon

W. A. BENJAMIN, INC., PUBLISHERS
New York   Amsterdam
1964

THERMODYNAMICS OF SMALL SYSTEMS: Part II

Copyright © 1964 by W. A. Benjamin, Inc.

All rights reserved

Library of Congress Catalog Card Number: 63–8157

Manufactured in the United States of America

The manuscript was put into production October 3, 1963, and this volume was published June 24, 1964

The publisher is pleased to acknowledge the assistance of William Prokos, who designed the book and the dust jacket

W. A. BENJAMIN, INC.

New York, New York

To my early and best teachers:

E. J. Albrecht
   (*High School Mathematics*)

J. H. Hildebrand
   (*Freshman Chemistry*)

E. A. Guggenheim
   (*through his books*)

PREFACE

This volume continues and completes the subject introduced in Part I of *Thermodynamics of Small Systems*, which appeared in 1963.

It was planned originally to publish, at this time, a combined volume containing Part II and a revised version of Part I. However, the necessary changes in Part I have proved to be minor. Therefore the author and publisher have decided to issue Part II as a separate work. But a list of corrections to be made in Part I is included here.

There are three areas covered in the present volume. First, Chapters 7 and 10 treat binding on macromolecules and aggregation (soap micelles, etc.) in such a way as to be applicable to both experimental and theoretical work in these fields. Second, Chapters 8, 9, and 10 complete the discussion of certain choices of environmental variables important in the analysis of statistical mechanical models of finite systems. Finally, Chapters 11 through 15 contain very brief summaries of certain special topics.

Chapter 10 includes a discussion of the partition function for completely open systems. It is believed that use of a finite system avoids the complications usually met with this partition function and provides the method of choice in applications of the partition function (to finite or macroscopic systems).

It is assumed in Part II that the reader is familiar with the notation and basic ideas introduced in Part I.

T.L.H.

Eugene, Oregon
March 1964

CONTENTS

CORRECTIONS AND COMMENTS
ON PART I

p. 10, Part I. The word "vanishes," following Eq. (1-11), should be replaced by "becomes negligible." See the discussion of $\mathscr{E}$ on p. 101.

p. 14, Part I. This is an addendum to Section 1-2, suggested by Eq. (10-35). The probability that any system of the ensemble contains exactly N molecules is

$$P(N) = \frac{Q(N, V, T)e^{N\mu/kT}}{\Xi}.$$

If $Q(0, V, T) = 1$ (as will usually be the case), the probability that any system is empty is $P(0) = 1/\Xi$. Therefore,

$$\hat{p}V = kT \ln \Xi = -kT \ln P(0).$$

Consider a *closed* ensemble (N_t = constant) of μ, V, T systems. Equation (1-4) becomes

$$dE_t = T\, dS_t - p\,\mathcal{N}\, dV - \hat{p}V\, d\mathcal{N}$$
$$= DQ' + DW'$$

where $DQ' = T\, dS_t$ and DW' is work done *on* the ensemble:

$$DW' = -p\,\mathcal{N}\, dV - \hat{p}V\, d\mathcal{N}.$$

In the special case in which V = constant and $d\mathcal{N} = -1$ (i.e., the molecules are forced out of one system of the ensemble and into the remaining $\mathcal{N} - 1$ systems), the work done on the system is

$$DW' = \hat{p}V = -kT \ln P(0).$$

This is analogous to the work required to create a cavity in a fluid.* But in our case the molecules of the system being evacuated have no intermolecular interaction with the surroundings.

p. 40, Part I. The second sentence should read: But, for a discrete variable such as N, the equations of Chapter 15 have to be used as a starting point.

* E. Helfand, H. L. Frisch, and J. L. Lebowitz, *J. Chem. Phys.*, **34**, 1037 (1961).

p. 43, Part I. See p. 195 in connection with the differentiation with respect to N.

p. 45, Part I. The first summation is over l.

p. 57, Part I. The second equation on this page is the same as Eq. (7-71). The footnote on this page is proved in Eq. (7-75).

p. 69, Part I. See p. 195 in connection with the differentiation with respect to N.

p. 69, Part I. Incompressible linear aggregate in an inert solvent: see Eq. (10-312)ff.

p. 70, Part I. An intrinsic partition function $j(T)^N$ may be included as a factor in Eq. (3-55) [see Eqs. (3-61) and (10-21)].

p. 70, Part I. Spherical crystallite in an inert solvent: see Eq. (10-312)ff.

p. 79, Part I. The superscript S has been changed to s in Part II.

p. 87, Part I. The treatment of an ideal binary mixture is corrected for discreteness of variables on p. 205.

p. 103, Part I. Change N_1 to N_1^S on pp. 103 and 104, Part I.

p. 105, Part I. Change $\hat{\mu}_1^0$ to μ_1^0.

p. 117, Part I. A real, macroscopic N, p, T system at a phase transition (e.g., ice + water in a heat bath) would not always be observed as all ice or all water because of the length of time required to switch from one state to the other. This time would be relatively short for small systems.

p. 142, Part I. See p. 196 in connection with the treatment of B as a continuous variable.

p. 143, Part I. The statistical mechanics of a finite lattice gas in the grand ensemble has been studied by a Monte Carlo procedure by Chesnut and Salsburg.*

p. 145, Part I. See p. 196 in connection with treatment of B and N as continuous variables.

p. 152, Part I. The reference to Section 8-1 should be changed to p. 198.

p. 166, Part I. Equation (157) is corrected in Eq. (14-5)ff.

---

* D. A. Chesnut and Z. W. Salsburg, *J. Chem. Phys.*, **38**, 2861 (1963).

CHAPTER 7

ENVIRONMENTAL VARIABLES N_1, μ_2, p, T

A polymer molecule in solution which binds small molecules or ions from the solution is representative of a class of small systems that is especially important in physical biochemistry. There are two components in this example. The system is closed with respect to component 1 (the polymer contains N_1 monomers) but open with respect to component 2 (the molecules being bound by the polymer have chemical potential μ_2 on the polymer and in the solution). The variables N_2, V, and E fluctuate about mean values.

A similar example is the binding or adsorption of molecules from solution or from the gas phase onto the surface of a colloidal particle.

If charged species are involved in these systems, the two components must be chosen in neutral combinations, as is usual in macroscopic thermodynamics. For example: component 1 = polyelectrolyte monomer + counterion; and component 2 = bound ion + counterion.

It should be recognized that the classification of molecules of component 2 into molecules in solution and "bound" molecules is an extrathermodynamic and, in principle at least, somewhat arbitrary procedure.[1] But in practice, if the binding forces are reasonably strong, this arbitrariness is unimportant.

The environment variables N_1, μ_2, p, T resemble N, p, T (Chapter 2) and μ, V, T (Chapter 6) in that each set has only one extensive variable. The analogy is still closer with N, p, T, ψ (Chapter 5), N, p, f, T, or μ_1, μ_2, V, T. If the pressure is dropped from the list of variables because of assumed incompressibility or other reasons, then a formal correspondence can easily be established between the variables N_1, μ_2, T on the one hand, and N, p, T or μ, V, T on the other. Thus the equations in Chapter 2 or, especially, those in Chapter 6 (including the discussion of phase transitions) can easily be transcribed[2] to the case N_1, μ_2, T.

---

[1] See T. L. Hill, *J. Chem. Phys.*, **23**, 623 (1955), Sec. III.
[2] The details are left to the interested reader. Equations (6-1) to (6-5) should be noted in this connection. See also Eq. (7-131), below.

In an N_1, μ_2, p, T system, the number of binding sites B (or, say, the area if the binding is not confined to definite sites) is not a further independent thermodynamic variable. In most cases B will be determined primarily by N_1. For example: binding on a linear polyelectrolyte, $B \propto N_1$; absorption in a spherical crystallite, $B \propto N_1$; adsorption on the surface of a spherical crystallite, $B \propto N_1^{2/3}$; hydrogen ion binding by the normal dicarboxylic acids or diamines, $B = 2 = $ constant ($N_1 = $ number of CH_2 groups in chain).

Binding on, say, a naturally occurring protein molecule, which is not composed of a variable number of identical units or monomers, must be treated as a μ_2, p, T system (Chapter 10). That is, N_1 is, in effect, always constant and hence drops out as a variable.

The elasticity of a polymer with binding is of some interest. The environmental variables are N_1, μ_2, p, f, T, or, if incompressibility is assumed, N_1, μ_2, f, T. In the latter case, f simply replaces p in the basic set N_1, μ_2, p, T.

Closely related to the elasticity problem, at least formally, and important experimentally, is the case of binding of molecules on a small system with an isomeric chemical equilibrium. An example is the hydrogen ion titration of synthetic polypeptides or polynucleotides, both of which have the possibility of a helix $\rightleftharpoons$ coil isomeric equilibrium (see Section 5-3). The environmental variables are N_1 (total number of monomers or units), μ_2, p, T, ψ, or N_1, μ_2, T, ψ (incompressibility).

Section 7-1 is concerned with the basic equations for an ensemble of N_1, μ_2, p, T systems. Small systems in solvent or gas are considered in Section 7-2. Isomeric equilibrium with binding is treated in Section 7-3.

7-I. BASIC EQUATIONS

The fundamental macroscopic equation, analogous to Eqs. (1-4) and (1-24), for an ensemble of $\mathcal{N}$ distinguishable and independent N_1, μ_2, p, T systems is

$$dE_t = T\,dS_t - p\,dV_t + \mu_1 \mathcal{N}\,dN_1 + \mu_2\,dN_{t2} + X\,d\mathcal{N}. \tag{7-1}$$

Integration gives

$$E_t = TS_t - pV_t + \mu_2 N_{t2} + X\mathcal{N},$$

or

$$X \equiv \hat{\mu}_1 N_1 = \bar{E} - TS + p\bar{V} - \mu_2 \bar{N}_2. \tag{7-2}$$

Then

$$\mathscr{E} \equiv \bar{E} - TS + p\bar{V} - \mu_1 N_1 - \mu_2 \bar{N}_2 = (\hat{\mu}_1 - \mu_1)N_1. \quad (7\text{-}3)$$

We substitute Eq. (7-2) for X in Eq. (7-1) and obtain

$$d\bar{E} = T\,dS - p\,d\bar{V} + \mu_1\,dN_1 + \mu_2\,d\bar{N}_2. \quad (7\text{-}4)$$

Also,

$$d(\hat{\mu}_1 N_1) = -S\,dT + \bar{V}\,dp + \mu_1\,dN_1 - \bar{N}_2\,d\mu_2 \quad (7\text{-}5)$$

$$d\mathscr{E} = -S\,dT + \bar{V}\,dp - N_1\,d\mu_1 - \bar{N}_2\,d\mu_2. \quad (7\text{-}6)$$

The relation to statistical mechanics is[1]

$$\Gamma(N_1, \mu_2, p, T) = \sum_{N_2, V} Q(N_1, N_2, V, T)e^{-pV/kT}e^{N_2\mu_2/kT} \quad (7\text{-}7)$$

$$N_1\hat{\mu}_1 = X = -kT \ln \Gamma. \quad (7\text{-}8)$$

This is a "semigrand" partition function appropriate to a semiopen system.

Several Legendre transformations will prove useful:

$$d(\hat{\mu}_1 N_1 + \mu_2\bar{N}_2) = dF = -S\,dT + \bar{V}\,dp + \mu_1\,dN_1 + \mu_2\,d\bar{N}_2 \quad (7\text{-}9)$$

$$d(\hat{\mu}_1 N_1 - p\bar{V}) = -S\,dT - p\,d\bar{V} + \mu_1\,dN_1 - \bar{N}_2\,d\mu_2 \quad (7\text{-}10)$$

$$d(\hat{\mu}_1 N_1 + \mu_2\bar{N}_2 - p\bar{V}) = dA = -S\,dT - p\,d\bar{V} + \mu_1\,dN_1 + \mu_2\,d\bar{N}_2. \quad (7\text{-}11)$$

One can write six Maxwell relations for each of Eqs. (7-4) to (7-6) and (7-9) to (7-11), and these, of course, by no means exhaust the possibilities. For example, from Eq. (7-5),

$$\left(\frac{\partial \mu_1}{\partial T}\right)_{p, N_1, \mu_2} = -\left(\frac{\partial S}{\partial N_1}\right)_{T, p, \mu_2}, \quad \left(\frac{\partial \mu_1}{\partial p}\right)_{T, N_1, \mu_2} = \left(\frac{\partial \bar{V}}{\partial N_1}\right)_{T, p, \mu_2},$$

$$\left(\frac{\partial \mu_1}{\partial \mu_2}\right)_{T, p, N_1} = -\left(\frac{\partial \bar{N}_2}{\partial N_1}\right)_{T, p, \mu_2}. \quad (7\text{-}12)$$

---

[1] See S.T., p. 363.

We find, from Eqs. (7-5), (7-6), and (7-12),

$$d\hat{\mu}_1 = -\frac{S}{N_1} dT + \frac{\bar{V}}{N_1} dp - \frac{\bar{N}_2}{N_1} d\mu_2 - \frac{\mathscr{E}}{N_1^2} dN_1 \qquad (7\text{-}13)$$

$$d\mu_1 = -\left(\frac{\partial S}{\partial N_1}\right)_{T,p,\mu_2} dT + \left(\frac{\partial \bar{V}}{\partial N_1}\right)_{T,p,\mu_2} dp - \left(\frac{\partial \bar{N}_2}{\partial N_1}\right)_{T,p,\mu_2} d\mu_2$$
$$-\frac{1}{N_1}\left(\frac{\partial \mathscr{E}}{\partial N_1}\right)_{T,p,\mu_2} dN_1. \qquad (7\text{-}14)$$

If we substitute Eq. (7-14) for $d\mu_1$ in Eq. (7-6), we have

$$d\mathscr{E} = -[S]_1 dT + [\bar{V}]_1 dp - [\bar{N}_2]_1 d\mu_2 + \left(\frac{\partial \mathscr{E}}{\partial N_1}\right)_{T,p,\mu_2} dN_1,$$
$$(7\text{-}15)$$

where

$$[G]_1 \equiv G - N_1\left(\frac{\partial G}{\partial N_1}\right)_{T,p,\mu_2}. \qquad (7\text{-}16)$$

Then we find, from Eq. (7-15),

$$\left(\frac{\partial S/N_1}{\partial N_1}\right)_{T,p,\mu_2} = \frac{1}{N_1^2}\left(\frac{\partial \mathscr{E}}{\partial T}\right)_{p,\mu_2,N_1} \qquad (7\text{-}17)$$

$$\left(\frac{\partial \bar{V}/N_1}{\partial N_1}\right)_{T,p,\mu_2} = -\frac{1}{N_1^2}\left(\frac{\partial \mathscr{E}}{\partial p}\right)_{T,\mu_2,N_1} \qquad (7\text{-}18)$$

$$\left(\frac{\partial \bar{N}_2/N_1}{\partial N_1}\right)_{T,p,\mu_2} = \frac{1}{N_1^2}\left(\frac{\partial \mathscr{E}}{\partial \mu_2}\right)_{T,p,N_1}. \qquad (7\text{-}19)$$

These also follow directly from Eq. (7-13). The last equation is concerned with the effect of the size of the small system on the amount of binding per unit. It is of interest especially when the number of binding sites is proportional to N_1.

EQUATION-OF-STATE RELATIONS.   We are interested here in derivatives involving the observable[1] quantities p, $\bar{V}$, T, N_1, $\bar{N}_2$, and

[1] Changes in μ_2 at constant p and T can be measured by means of a change in concentration, partial pressure, activity, etc., in the reservoir. However, when the temperature is not constant, the choice of the arbitrary zero of entropy in μ_2 becomes involved. Nonisothermal equations in the present section are correct but are not useful experimentally if μ_2 is concerned explicitly. See Eqs. (6-38) to (6-41) et seq. and Section 7-2.

μ_2, and the thermodynamic information that can be derived therefrom. There are a great many of these derivatives (in fact, 60). Equations (7-12b) and (7-12c) are examples. A few others are given below.

The effect of the environmental variables μ_2, p, and T on $\bar{N}_2$ and $\bar{V}$ is as follows:

$$\left(\frac{\partial \bar{N}_2}{\partial T}\right)_{p, N_1, \mu_2} = \left(\frac{\partial S}{\partial \mu_2}\right)_{T, p, N_1}, \qquad \left(\frac{\partial \bar{V}}{\partial T}\right)_{p, N_1, \mu_2} = -\left(\frac{\partial S}{\partial p}\right)_{T, N_1, \mu_2}$$

$$(7\text{-}20)$$

$$\left(\frac{\partial \bar{N}_2}{\partial p}\right)_{T, N_1, \mu_2} = -\left(\frac{\partial \bar{V}}{\partial \mu_2}\right)_{T, p, N_1} \tag{7-21}$$

$$\left(\frac{\partial \bar{N}_2}{\partial \mu_2}\right)_{T, p, N_1} = -\frac{(\partial \bar{N}_2/\partial N_1)_{T, p, \mu_2}}{(\partial \mu_2/\partial N_1)_{T, p, \bar{N}_2}} \tag{7-22}$$

$$\left(\frac{\partial \bar{V}}{\partial p}\right)_{T, N_1, \mu_2} = -\frac{(\partial \bar{V}/\partial N_1)_{T, \mu_2, p}}{(\partial p/\partial N_1)_{T, \mu_2, \bar{V}}}. \tag{7-23}$$

Two other quotients can be written on the right-hand side of each of Eqs. (7-22) and (7-23), replacing N_1 by T or p in the former case or by T or μ_2 in the latter [see, for example, Eq. (2-46)].

Four derivatives at constant temperature, which are of some interest in connection with phase transitions (see below) and otherwise, are

$$\left(\frac{\partial p}{\partial N_1}\right)_{T, V, \mu_2} = -\left(\frac{\partial \mu_1}{\partial \bar{V}}\right)_{T, N_1, \mu_2}, \qquad \left(\frac{\partial \mu_2}{\partial p}\right)_{T, \bar{V}, N_1} = \left(\frac{\partial \bar{V}}{\partial \bar{N}_2}\right)_{T, N_1, \mu_2}$$

$$(7\text{-}24)$$

$$\left(\frac{\partial \mu_2}{\partial N_1}\right)_{T, p, \bar{N}_2} = \left(\frac{\partial \mu_1}{\partial \bar{N}_2}\right)_{T, p, N_1}, \qquad \left(\frac{\partial \mu_2}{\partial p}\right)_{T, N_1, \bar{N}_2} = \left(\frac{\partial \bar{V}}{\partial \bar{N}_2}\right)_{T, p, N_1}.$$

$$(7\text{-}25)$$

Four nonisothermal derivatives of the same type are

$$\left(\frac{\partial p}{\partial T}\right)_{\bar{V}, N_1, \mu_2} = \left(\frac{\partial S}{\partial \bar{V}}\right)_{T, N_1, \mu_2}, \qquad \left(\frac{\partial \mu_2}{\partial T}\right)_{p, N_1, \bar{N}_2} = -\left(\frac{\partial S}{\partial \bar{N}_2}\right)_{T, p, N_1}$$

$$(7\text{-}26)$$

$$\left(\frac{\partial T}{\partial N_1}\right)_{p, \bar{V}, \mu_2} = \left(\frac{\partial \mu_1}{\partial S}\right)_{T, N_1, \mu_2}, \qquad \left(\frac{\partial T}{\partial N_1}\right)_{p, \mu_2, \bar{N}_2} = \left(\frac{\partial \mu_1}{\partial S}\right)_{T, p, N_1}.$$

$$(7\text{-}27)$$

A few other, possibly useful, relations are

$$\left(\frac{\partial \mu_2}{\partial N_1}\right)_{T,\,p,\,\bar{V}} = \left(\frac{\partial \mu_1}{\partial \bar{N}_2}\right)_{T,\,N_1,\,\mu_2}, \qquad \left(\frac{\partial \mu_2}{\partial T}\right)_{p,\,\bar{V},\,N_1} = -\left(\frac{\partial S}{\partial \bar{N}_2}\right)_{T,\,N_1,\,\mu_2}$$

$$(7\text{-}28)$$

$$\left(\frac{\partial p}{\partial N_1}\right)_{T,\,\mu_2,\,\bar{N}_2} = -\left(\frac{\partial \mu_1}{\partial \bar{V}}\right)_{T,\,p,\,N_1}, \qquad \left(\frac{\partial p}{\partial T}\right)_{N_1,\,\mu_2,\,\bar{N}_2} = \left(\frac{\partial S}{\partial \bar{V}}\right)_{T,\,p,\,N_1}.$$

$$(7\text{-}29)$$

Equations (7-20), (7-21), and (7-24) to (7-26) are Maxwell relations obtained from the appropriate independent variables. Equations (7-27) to (7-29) were deduced using, in addition, quotients of the type in Eqs. (7-22) and (7-23).

As an example of an application, suppose the amount bound, $\bar{N}_2$, is measured as a function of the reservoir concentration c^s, of this same component, from $c^s = 0$ to $c^s = c'$, for two values of N_1 not too far apart. Let $\bar{N}_2 = \bar{N}'_2$ (for the mean value of N_1) when $c^s = c'$. Pressure and temperature are constant and we assume $d\mu_2 = kT\,d \ln c^s$. Then for each value of $\bar{N}_2$ we can approximate the left-hand side of Eq. (7-25a) by (see Fig. 7-1)

$$\frac{(\Delta \mu_2)_{\bar{N}_2}}{\Delta N_1} = \frac{kT\,\Delta c^s}{c^s(\text{mean})\,\Delta N_1}.$$

This quantity is a function of $\bar{N}_2$, with p, T, and (the mean value of) N_1 constant. Hence integration of Eq. (7-25a) gives

$$\mu_1(\bar{N}'_2) - \mu_1(0) = kT \int_0^{\bar{N}'_2} \frac{1}{c^s} \frac{\Delta c^s}{\Delta N_1}\,d\bar{N}_2 \quad (T, p, N_1 \text{ constant}).$$

$$(7\text{-}30)$$

Also, using $\bar{N}_2(c^s)$ corresponding to the mean value of N_1,

$$N_1[\hat{\mu}_1(\bar{N}'_2) - \hat{\mu}_1(0)] = -kT \int_0^{c'} \frac{\bar{N}_2(c^s)}{c^s}\,dc^s \quad (T, p, N_1 \text{ constant}).$$

$$(7\text{-}31)$$

This follows from Eq. (7-5). We can combine Eqs. (7-30) and (7-31) to obtain $\mathscr{E}(\bar{N}'_2) - \mathscr{E}(0)$. Integration of $-[\bar{N}_2]_1\,d\mu_2$ in Eq. (7-15) provides a check.

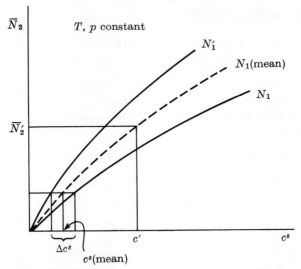

FIGURE 7-1. Schematic plot of amount bound $\bar{N}_2$ versus reservoir concentration c^s at two different values of N_1 for use in Eq. (7-30).

Example. Crystallite with Adsorption. For the crystallite, we use the model in Eqs. (2-68) to (2-71) but keep the surface term only. We assume that the partition function $\Delta(N_1, N_2, p, T)$ for a crystallite of N_1 molecules with N_2 molecules adsorbed has the simple form

$$\Delta(N_1, N_2, p, T) = \Delta(N_1, 0, p, T) \left[\frac{B! q^{N_2}}{N_2!(B - N_2)!} \right], \quad (7\text{-}32)$$

where $q(p, T)$ is the partition function of a bound molecule (including the energy of adsorption) and B is the number of independent and equivalent sites for adsorption ("Langmuir model"). We take $B = \alpha(p, T)N_1^{2/3}$, where α is a proportionality factor. That is, the sites are assumed to be on the surface of the crystallite. According to Eq. (2-68),

$$-kT \ln \Delta(N_1, 0, p, T) = N_1 f(p, T) + a(p, T)N_1^{2/3}. \quad (7\text{-}33)$$

From Eq. (7-7),

$$\Gamma = \sum_{N_2=0}^{M} \Delta(N_1, N_2, p, T)\lambda_2^{N_2}$$

$$= \Delta(N_1, 0, p, T)(1 + q\lambda_2)^B, \quad (7\text{-}34)$$

where $\lambda_2 = e^{\mu_2/kT}$. Then

$$N_1\hat{\mu}_1 = -kT \ln \Gamma = N_1 f(p, T) + a(p, T)N_1^{2/3}$$
$$- kT\alpha(p,T)N_1^{2/3} \ln[1 + q(p, T)\lambda_2]. \qquad (7\text{-}35)$$

The first term on the right, which has nothing to do with adsorption, is the only macroscopic term. This comes about because the adsorption is confined to the surface and the surface becomes relatively unimportant as $N_1 \to \infty$.

Equations (7-5) and (7-35) then lead, for example, to

$$\frac{\bar{N}_2}{B} = \frac{q\lambda_2}{1 + q\lambda_2} \qquad (7\text{-}36)$$

$$\mu_1 = f + \tfrac{2}{3}aN_1^{-1/3} - \tfrac{2}{3}kT\alpha N_1^{-1/3} \ln(1 + q\lambda_2) \qquad (7\text{-}37)$$

$$\bar{V} = N_1\frac{\partial f}{\partial p} + N_1^{2/3}\frac{\partial a}{\partial p} - kT\bar{N}_2\frac{\partial \ln q}{\partial p} - kT\frac{\partial \alpha}{\partial p}N_1^{2/3} \ln(1 + q\lambda_2). \qquad (7\text{-}38)$$

The reader may wish to use this model to verify some of the thermodynamic equations given earlier in this section.

TWO-STATE APPROXIMATION FOR PHASE TRANSITIONS.   There are two obvious possibilities for first-order phase transitions in N_1, μ_2, p, T systems. First, a small system of N_1 molecules may undergo a transition irrespective of the value of μ_2 or $\bar{N}_2$ (see Section 5-4). For example, a crystallite may melt irrespective of adsorption or binding on its surface, although of course the adsorption would be expected to perturb the melting somewhat. Second, the molecules being adsorbed or absorbed may themselves show a phase transition,[1] for example, from a dilute to a concentrated adsorbed layer (see Section 6-2). An absorption example would be expected in a colloidal H_2-Pt or H_2-Pd system.

Neither of the above types of phase transition would be anticipated in experimental linear (one-dimensional) polymer systems.

A two-state approximation should again often be useful here. With reference to Eq. (7-7), we define the function

$$P(N_2, V) = \frac{Q(N_1, N_2, V, T)e^{-pV/kT}e^{N_2\mu_2/kT}}{\Gamma}. \qquad (7\text{-}39)$$

[1] See, for example, J. R. Colvin, *Can. J. Chem.*, **30**, 320 (1952).

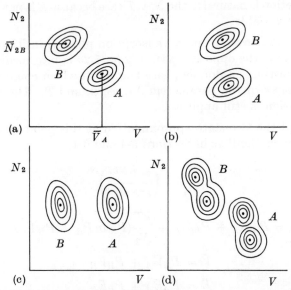

FIGURE 7-2. Schematic contour diagrams of the probability $P(N_2, V)$ of observing a small system with N_2 and V. The contour centers correspond to maximum probability. The two-state approximation is appropriate in all cases. In cases (a), (c), and (d), we have $\bar{V}_A > \bar{V}_B$. In cases (a), (b), and (d), $\bar{N}_{2B} > \bar{N}_{2A}$.

This is the probability of observing a small system with N_2 and V, for given values of N_1, μ_2, p, and T. In Fig. 7-2a, a two-state situation is illustrated by a schematic plot of $P(N_2, V)$ in the form of a contour diagram. There are two separated and more or less Gaussian peaks labeled states A and B. This figure is the analogue of Fig. 5-1c for an N, p, T system.

Incidentally, if we had defined [compare Eq. (5-113)]

$$P(E, V) = \frac{\Omega(N, V, E)e^{-E/kT}e^{-pV/kT}}{\Delta}$$

for an N, p, T system, a contour diagram of $P(E, V)$ in the E, V plane would also appear as in Fig. 7-2a. Figure 5-1c is a summation-projection of the E, V contour diagram onto the V axis:

$$P(V) = \sum_E P(E, V).$$

This projection is natural in the N, p, T case because E is not a readily observable variable.

Figure 7-2b shows a "pure" adsorption phase transition whereas Fig. 7-2c shows the opposite case. Figure 7-2a is intermediate. Figure 7-2d illustrates a double phase transition which could occur for certain choices of the parameters N_1, μ_2, p, and T. The two-state approximation is still applicable.

We adopt the two-state approximation at this point and deduce, by the same method[1] as in Sections 5-4 and 6-1,

$$\frac{\mathcal{N}_A}{\mathcal{N}_B} = \left(\frac{e^{-\hat{\mu}_{1A}/kT}}{e^{-\hat{\mu}_{1B}/kT}}\right)^{N_1} \tag{7-40}$$

$$\hat{\mu}_1 = P_A\hat{\mu}_{1A} + P_B\hat{\mu}_{1B} + \frac{kT}{N_1}(P_A \ln P_A + P_B \ln P_B) \tag{7-41}$$

$$\bar{V} = P_A\bar{V}_A + P_B\bar{V}_B \tag{7-42}$$

$$\bar{E} = P_A\bar{E}_A + P_B\bar{E}_B \tag{7-43}$$

$$\bar{N}_2 = P_A\bar{N}_{2A} + P_B\bar{N}_{2B} \tag{7-44}$$

$$\mu_1 = P_A\mu_{1A} + P_B\mu_{1B} \tag{7-45}$$

$$S = P_AS_A + P_BS_B - k(P_A \ln P_A + P_B \ln P_B). \tag{7-46}$$

Section 5-4 should be used as a guide to fill in some of the details that we are omitting here.

From the above results and Eq. (7-5) we arrive at the following conclusions: (1) an equal-area theorem and an equal-distance theorem both apply to a $\bar{V}$ versus p diagram (N_1, μ_2, T constant); and (2) both also apply to an $\bar{N}_2$ versus μ_2 diagram (N_1, p, T constant).

The $\bar{V}$ "fluctuation" equation (5-126) is unchanged here except that N_1, μ_2, and T are held constant in the derivatives. The corresponding $\bar{N}_2$ equation is

$$\left(\frac{\partial \bar{N}_2}{\partial \mu_2}\right)_{N_1, p, T} = P_A\left(\frac{\partial \bar{N}_{2A}}{\partial \mu_2}\right)_{N_1, p, T} + P_B\left(\frac{\partial \bar{N}_{2B}}{\partial \mu_2}\right)_{N_1, p, T}$$
$$+ \frac{P_AP_B}{kT}(\bar{N}_{2A} - \bar{N}_{2B})^2. \tag{7-47}$$

[1] See also the footnote on p. 149 of Part I concerning a derivation from statistical mechanics.

There are also cross relations:

$$\left(\frac{\partial \bar{V}}{\partial \mu_2}\right)_{N_1, p, T} = P_A\left(\frac{\partial \bar{V}_A}{\partial \mu_2}\right)_{N_1, p, T} + P_B\left(\frac{\partial \bar{V}_B}{\partial \mu_2}\right)_{N_1, p, T}$$

$$+ \frac{P_A P_B}{kT}(\bar{N}_{2A} - \bar{N}_{2B})(\bar{V}_A - \bar{V}_B), \tag{7-48}$$

or $\partial\bar{V}/\partial\mu_2$ can be replaced by $-(\partial\bar{N}_2/\partial p)_{N_1, \mu_2, T}$. These follow by differentiation of Eqs. (7-24) and (7-44), or on making use of

$$\overline{VN_2} - \bar{V}\bar{N}_2 = kT\left(\frac{\partial \bar{V}}{\partial \mu_2}\right)_{N_1, p, T} = -kT\left(\frac{\partial \bar{N}_2}{\partial p}\right)_{N_1, \mu_2, T}. \tag{7-49}$$

EQUATIONS OF THE CLAUSIUS-CLAPEYRON TYPE. The two metastable states A and B, in equilibrium,[1] have the same values of N_1, μ_2, p, T, and $\hat{\mu}_1$. They have different values of $\mu_1, \bar{N}_2, \bar{V}, S, \bar{E}$, and $\mathcal{E}$. If we regard $\hat{\mu}_1$ as a function of N_1, μ_2, p, and T, and shift the equilibrium state by variations in these variables, then from $d\hat{\mu}_{1A} = d\hat{\mu}_{1B}$ and Eq. (7-13),

$$\left(\frac{\partial p}{\partial T}\right)_{N_1, \mu_2} = \frac{\Delta S}{\Delta \bar{V}}, \qquad \left(\frac{\partial \mu_2}{\partial T}\right)_{p, N_1} = -\frac{\Delta S}{\Delta \bar{N}_2} \tag{7-50}$$

$$\left(\frac{\partial T}{\partial N_1}\right)_{p, \mu_2} = \frac{\Delta \mu_1}{\Delta S}, \qquad \left(\frac{\partial p}{\partial \mu_2}\right)_{T, N_1} = \frac{\Delta \bar{N}_2}{\Delta \bar{V}} \tag{7-51}$$

$$\left(\frac{\partial p}{\partial N_1}\right)_{T, \mu_2} = -\frac{\Delta \mu_1}{\Delta \bar{V}}, \qquad \left(\frac{\partial \mu_2}{\partial N_1}\right)_{T, p} = \frac{\Delta \mu_1}{\Delta \bar{N}_2}, \tag{7-52}$$

where Δ refers to the difference between the two metastable states A and B mentioned above. Only three of Eqs. (7-50) to (7-52) are independent. There are 4×6 other equations of this type which follow from $dN_{1A}(\mu_2, p, T, \hat{\mu}_1) = dN_{1B}(\mu_2, p, T, \hat{\mu}_1)$, etc. The relation between Eqs. (7-24) to (7-27) and (7-50) to (7-52) should be noted.

Of the above equations, only (7-52b) is ordinarily very practical to use. In fact, both sides of the first three of these equations depend

[1] We remind the reader that states A and B here are "metastable" in the sense that *all* small systems are in state A or *all* are in state B, whereas the stable equilibrium state of the ensemble is a mixture of small systems in states A and B, as determined by Eq. (7-40). Also, "in equilibrium" means simply that conditions are chosen so that the two metastable states have $\hat{\mu}_{1A} = \hat{\mu}_{1B}$. But we can take the alternative and equivalent point of view that Eqs. (7-50) to (7-54) refer to the single point $\mathcal{N}_A = \mathcal{N}_B$ on the stable equilibrium path.

on the choice of the zero of entropy for component 2 [compare Eqs. (6-38) and (6-39)].

The following relations are of interest:

$$\Delta(N_1\hat{\mu}_1) = 0 = \Delta\bar{E} - T\,\Delta S + p\,\Delta\bar{V} - \mu_2\,\Delta\bar{N}_2 \qquad (7\text{-}53)$$

$$\Delta\mathscr{E} = -N_1\,\Delta\mu_1. \qquad (7\text{-}54)$$

We cannot set $T\,\Delta S$ equal to a heat of transition Q because the process does not occur in a closed system ($\Delta\bar{N}_2 \neq 0$).

Example. Crystallite Melting with Adsorption. This is the example at the end of Chapter 5, but with adsorption on the surface of the small system from a solvent reservoir now included. Let us use Eq. (7-35) as the basic equation for both liquid and solid states, but we simplify matters by considering only the Henry's law adsorption region ($\lambda_2 \to 0$). Then we write

$$\hat{\mu}_1 = f + aN_1^{-1/3} - XN_1^{-1/3}\lambda_2 \qquad (7\text{-}55)$$

where $X = kT\alpha q$ and

$$\lambda_2 = m^s \exp\left[\frac{\mu^\Delta(p,\,T)}{kT}\right].$$

Here, m^s is the molality and μ^Δ the standard chemical potential of the adsorbate in the solvent.

As in Chapter 5, we take p_∞ and T_∞ as values of p and T at which the two macroscopic phases are in equilibrium. Our object is to find the first-order effect of finite N_1 [as in Eq. (5-152)] and of adsorption on the equilibrium pressure p and temperature T.

To find the effect on p, we start with

$$\Delta\hat{\mu}_1 = 0 = \Delta f(p,\,T_\infty) + N_1^{-1/3}$$

$$\times\left\{\Delta a(p,\,T_\infty) - m^s \exp\left[\frac{\mu^\Delta(p,\,T_\infty)}{kT_\infty}\right]\Delta X(p,\,T_\infty)\right\}.$$

On introduction of the expansions (about $p = p_\infty$)

$$\Delta f(p,\,T_\infty) = \Delta\mathrm{v}_\infty(p - p_\infty) + \cdots$$

$$\Delta a(p,\,T_\infty) = \Delta a(p_\infty,\,T_\infty) + \cdots$$

$$\Delta X(p,\,T_\infty) = \Delta X(p_\infty,\,T_\infty) + \cdots$$

$$\mu^\Delta(p,\,T_\infty) = \mu^\Delta(p_\infty,\,T_\infty) + \cdots,$$

we obtain the desired result:

$$p = p_\infty - \frac{N_1^{-1/3}[\Delta a(\infty) - m^s e^{\mu\Delta(\infty)/kT_\infty} \Delta\chi(\infty)]}{\Delta v_\infty}. \quad (7\text{-}56)$$

Thus, if there is more adsorption on the solid than on the liquid particles, $\Delta\chi = \chi_L - \chi_S$ is negative and an increase in m^s decreases the equilibrium pressure (assuming Δv_∞ is positive). This is confirmed by Eq. (7-51b), which states that $\partial p/\partial\mu_2$ has the same sign as $\Delta\bar{N}_2/\Delta\bar{V}$. In this example, according to Eq. (7-56),

$$\frac{\lambda_2}{kT}\left(\frac{\partial p}{\partial\lambda_2}\right)_{T,N} = \frac{N_1^{-1/3}\,\Delta\chi(\infty)\lambda_2}{kT\,\Delta v_\infty} = \frac{\Delta\bar{N}_2}{\Delta\bar{V}},$$

where

$$\Delta\bar{N}_2 = N_1^{2/3}\,\Delta\chi(\infty)\lambda_2/kT$$
$$\Delta\bar{V} = N_1\,\Delta v_\infty.$$

Equations (7-52a) and (7-56) give

$$\Delta\mu_1 = -\tfrac{1}{3}N_1^{-1/3}[\Delta a(\infty) - \lambda_2\,\Delta\chi(\infty)]. \quad (7\text{-}57)$$

By the same methods as above we also find

$$T = T_\infty + \frac{N_1^{-1/3}[\Delta a(\infty) - m^s e^{\mu\Delta(\infty)/kT_\infty} \Delta\chi(\infty)]}{\Delta s_\infty}. \quad (7\text{-}58)$$

7-2. SMALL SYSTEMS IN SOLVENT OR GAS

The starting point in Section 7-1 was, as usual, an ensemble of distinguishable and independent small systems. We now have to investigate whether the equations deduced there apply as well to infinitely dilute experimental small systems in a liquid or gas.

Real small systems with environmental variables N_1, μ_2, p, T will always exist in the presence of at least one other component, namely, molecules of the species being bound or adsorbed. The two most important cases are molecules being adsorbed from a gas onto small systems also in the gas phase, and molecules of a solute species in a liquid solution being bound on small systems suspended in the liquid.

We make use of the approach in Eqs. (2-121) to (2-123) for a mixed solvent, with the notational change for the solvent which is indicated at the end of Section 4-2.

The solvent may be liquid or gaseous and contains c components. For definiteness, suppose solvent component 1^s (s for solvent) is the species being bound—i.e., it is the same as component 2 in the small system. Thus $c \geqslant 1$. In the gas case mentioned above, usually $c = 1$; in the liquid case, usually $c \geqslant 2$.

The basic equation for the macroscopic solution containing solvent and (infinitely dilute) small systems is

$$dE_T = T\,dS_T - p\,dV_T + \sum_{i=1}^{c} \mu_i^s\,dN_i^s + \mu_2\,d(\mathcal{N}\bar{N}_2)$$
$$+ \mu^{\square\ddagger}\,d\mathcal{N} + \mu_1\mathcal{N}\,dN_1, \qquad (7\text{-}59)$$

or

$$dF_T = -S_T\,dT + V_T\,dp + \sum_{i=1}^{c} \mu_i^s\,dN_i^s + \mu_2\,d(\mathcal{N}\bar{N}_2)$$
$$+ \mu^{\square\ddagger}\,d\mathcal{N} + \mu_1\mathcal{N}\,dN_1. \qquad (7\text{-}60)$$

Equation (7-59) should be compared with Eq. (2-117) for an N, p, T system in a mixed solvent. The terms

$$\mu_1^s\,dN_1^s + \mu_2\,d(\mathcal{N}\bar{N}_2)$$

refer to the same component. The separation of this component into "free" (N_1^s) and "bound" ($\mathcal{N}\bar{N}_2$) molecules is, strictly speaking, a nonthermodynamic procedure, as already mentioned in the introduction to this chapter. The rigorous but uninformative "black-box" attitude would be that a total of $N_1^s + \mathcal{N}\bar{N}_2$ molecules of species 1^s has been introduced into the solution and there is no *thermodynamic* information concerning a division of the molecules into two classes. But it is implicit in our entire discussion of N_1, μ_2, p, T systems that some reliable, basically nonthermodynamic experimental technique is available to measure either $\mathcal{N}\bar{N}_2$ or N_1^s separately.

Consider the transfer of an infinitesimal amount of component 1^s from solvent to small systems, with the macroscopic solution closed, at equilibrium with respect to the transfer, and at constant T and p. Then N_1, $\mathcal{N}$, N_2^s, ..., N_c^s, and $N_1^s + \mathcal{N}\bar{N}_2$ are all constant, and

$$dF_T = 0 = \mu_1^s\,dN_1^s + \mu_2\,d(\mathcal{N}\bar{N}_2) = (\mu_1^s - \mu_2)\,dN_1^s.$$

Therefore $\mu_1^s = \mu_2$ at equilibrium as might have been expected. This equilibrium condition will not be introduced explicitly until we reach Eq. (7-80).

The chemical potential $\mu^{\square\ddagger}$ is defined formally as a differential coefficient, in terms of E_T by Eq. (7-59), or, from Eq. (7-60), by

$$\mu^{\square\ddagger} = \left(\frac{\partial F_T}{\partial \mathcal{N}}\right)_{T, p, N_i^s, \mathcal{N}\bar{N}_2, N_1}. \qquad (7\text{-}61)$$

In the process implicit here, $d\mathcal{N}$ "bare" small systems (i.e., with no adsorbed molecules) are added to the macroscopic solution, and the total $\mathcal{N}\bar{N}_2$ adsorbed molecules are redistributed over the $\mathcal{N} + d\mathcal{N}$ small systems. The double dagger on $\mu^{\square\ddagger}$ means "bare."

Let us rewrite Eq. (7-60) in a more convenient form:

$$dF_T = -S_T\, dT + V_T\, dp + \sum_{i=1}^{c} \mu_i^s\, dN_i^s$$
$$+ \mu^{\square}\, d\mathcal{N} + \mu_1 \mathcal{N}\, dN_1 + \mu_2 \mathcal{N}\, d\bar{N}_2, \qquad (7\text{-}62)$$

where

$$\mu^{\square} \equiv \mu^{\square\ddagger} + \mu_2 \bar{N}_2$$

or

$$\mu^{\square} = \left(\frac{\partial F_T}{\partial \mathcal{N}}\right)_{T, p, N_i^s, N_1, \bar{N}_2}. \qquad (7\text{-}63)$$

In this process the $d\mathcal{N}$ added small systems are not "bare": each has $\bar{N}_2$ adsorbed molecules.

SOLVENT CONTAINS TWO OR MORE COMPONENTS. In this case the composition of the macroscopic solution can be specified by $x' = \mathcal{N}/\Sigma_i N_i^s$ and $c-1$ solvent composition variables (denoted by sc). We choose, as one of these, the molality m_1^s of component 1^s, defined by $m_1^s = 1000 N_1^s/(N_2^s + \cdots + N_c^s)M$, where M is the mean molecular weight of the $N_2^s + \cdots + N_c^s$ molecules. The molality is used instead of the concentration to avoid taking into account the dependence of solvent density on pressure and temperature. We denote the remaining $c-2$ solvent composition variables, collectively, by sc'. These variables specify the composition of components $2^s, 3^s, ..., c^s$ relative to each other. In a typical case, 1^s would be the molecular species bound on the small systems, 2^s might be water, and 3^s might be, say, added salt. We shall hold sc' constant in all the equations below, but of course different sets of experiments can be done with different choices of sc'.

Corresponding to Eqs. (2-121) and (2-122), we now have

$$\mu^\square = \widetilde{\mathrm{E}}^\square - T\widetilde{\mathrm{s}}^\square + p\widetilde{\mathrm{v}}^\square \qquad (7\text{-}64)$$

and[1]

$$d\mu^\square = -\,\widetilde{\mathrm{s}}^\square\, dT + \widetilde{\mathrm{v}}^\square\, dp + \frac{\partial\mu^\square}{\partial x'}\, dx' + \frac{\partial\mu^\square}{\partial m_1^s}\, dm_1^s$$

$$+ \frac{\partial\mu^\square}{\partial N_1}\, dN_1 + \frac{\partial\mu^\square}{\partial \bar{N}_2}\, d\bar{N}_2 \qquad (sc') \qquad (7\text{-}65)$$

for the chemical potential of the small systems. We define F, $\hat{\mu}_1$, and $\mathscr{E}$ by the equations

$$\mu^\square = F(N_1, \bar{N}_2, p, T, sc) + kT \ln x' \qquad (7\text{-}66)$$

$$F = N_1\hat{\mu}_1(N_1, \bar{N}_2, p, T, sc) + \bar{N}_2\mu_2 = \mathscr{E} + N_1\mu_1 + \bar{N}_2\mu_2, \qquad (7\text{-}67)$$

and S by

$$\widetilde{\mathrm{s}}^\square = S - k \ln x'. \qquad (7\text{-}68)$$

Of course, at equilibrium, $\bar{N}_2$ is itself a function of N_1, p, T, and sc. If we write $\widetilde{\mathrm{E}}^\square = \bar{E}$ and $\widetilde{\mathrm{v}}^\square = \bar{V}$, Eq. (7-64) becomes

$$F = N_1\hat{\mu}_1 + \bar{N}_2\mu_2 = \bar{E} - TS + p\bar{V}. \qquad (7\text{-}69)$$

This is formally identical with Eq. (7-2).

Equation (7-65) requires a more detailed discussion. We show first that the coefficient $\partial\mu^\square/\partial N_1$ in this equation is equal to μ_1 in Eq. (7-62). From Eqs. (7-62) and (7-66), we have

$$\left(\frac{\partial\mu_k^s}{\partial\mathscr{N}}\right)_{T,\,p,\,N_i^s,\,N_1,\,\bar{N}_2} = \left(\frac{\partial\mu^\square}{\partial N_k^s}\right)_{T,\,p,\,N_j^s,\,\mathscr{N},\,N_1,\,\bar{N}_2}$$

$$= \left(\frac{\partial F}{\partial N_k^s}\right)_{T,\,p,\,N_j^s,\,N_1,\,\bar{N}_2} - \frac{kT}{N_1^s + \cdots + N_c^s}. \qquad (7\text{-}70)$$

Integration of Eq. (7-70) from $\mathscr{N} = 0$ to $\mathscr{N}$ gives

$$\mu_k^s = \mu_k^*(p, T, sc) + \left[(N_1^s + \cdots + N_c^s)\frac{\partial F}{\partial N_k^s} - kT\right]x', \qquad (7\text{-}71)$$

where μ_k^* refers to the pure solvent ($x' \to 0$). The Gibbs–Duhem equation for the macroscopic solution is

$$\sum_{k=1}^{c} N_k^s\, d\mu_k^s + \mathscr{N}\, d\mu^\square = 0 \qquad (T, p, N_1, \bar{N}_2 \text{ constant}).$$

[1] The notation (sc') following an equation is shorthand for $(sc'$ constant).

Then

$$0 = \sum_k N_k^s \left(\frac{\partial \mu_k^s}{\partial \mathcal{N}}\right)_{T,p,N_i^s,N_1,\bar{N}_2} + \mathcal{N}\left(\frac{\partial \mu^\square}{\partial \mathcal{N}}\right)_{T,p,N_i^s,\bar{N}_1,\bar{N}_2}$$

$$= \sum_k N_k^s \left(\frac{\partial F}{\partial N_k^s} - \frac{kT}{N_1^s + \cdots + N_c^s}\right) + kT = \sum_k N_k^s \frac{\partial F}{\partial N_k^s}. \qquad (7\text{-}72)$$

We now multiply Eq. (7-71) by N_k^s and sum, using Eq. (7-72):

$$\sum_k N_k^s \mu_k^s = \sum_k N_k^s \mu_k^* - \mathcal{N}kT. \qquad (7\text{-}73)$$

Finally, from Eqs. (7-62), (7-73), and

$$F_T = \sum_k N_k^s \mu_k^s + \mathcal{N}\mu^\square, \qquad (7\text{-}74)$$

we obtain

$$\mu_1 = \frac{1}{\mathcal{N}}\left(\frac{\partial F_T}{\partial N_1}\right)_{T,p,N_i^s,\mathcal{N},\bar{N}_2} = \left(\frac{\partial \mu^\square}{\partial N_1}\right)_{T,p,N_i^s,\mathcal{N},\bar{N}_2}$$

$$= \left(\frac{\partial \mu^\square}{\partial N_1}\right)_{T,p,\bar{N}_2,x',sc}. \qquad (7\text{-}75)$$

A completely analogous argument shows that $\mu_2 = \partial\mu^\square/\partial\bar{N}_2$. Hence Eq. (7-65) becomes

$$d\mu^\square = -\tilde{s}^\square\, dT + \tilde{v}^\square\, dp + kT\, d\ln x'$$
$$+ \beta\, dm_1^s + \mu_1\, dN_1 + \mu_2\, d\bar{N}_2 \qquad (sc'), \qquad (7\text{-}76)$$

where $\beta = (\partial F/\partial m_1^s)_{T,p,N_1,\bar{N}_2,sc}$. We now substitute Eqs. (7-66) to (7-68) and $\tilde{v}^\square = \bar{V}$ into the above relation and find

$$d(\hat{\mu}_1 N_1) = -S\, dT + \bar{V}\, dp + \mu_1\, dN_1 - \bar{N}_2\, d\mu_2 + \beta\, dm_1^s \qquad (sc')$$
$$(7\text{-}77)$$

$$dF = -S\, dT + \bar{V}\, dp + \mu_1\, dN_1 + \mu_2\, d\bar{N}_2 + \beta\, dm_1^s \qquad (sc'). \quad (7\text{-}78)$$

These equations should be compared with Eqs. (7-5) and (2-123), respectively. We see that the term in β is a new feature, not encountered before, and a complication. It arises essentially because we cannot change μ_2 and hence $\bar{N}_2$, the amount of binding, by an alteration in m_1^s without simultaneously changing the solvent environment of each small system. This will influence the small system thermodynamic functions, for example F, quite aside from binding effects (note that $\bar{N}_2$ is held constant in $\beta = \partial F/\partial m_1^s$).

An equivalent observation is that sc is constant in Eq. (2-123) but not in Eqs. (7-77) and (7-78): in these latter equations sc' is constant but m_1^s varies.

If the interaction between small systems and solvent is at the surface of the small system only, then in the macroscopic limit, $N_1 \to \infty$, the small system becomes a bulk phase and β (a surface effect) becomes negligible. But if, for example, the small system is a rodlike macromolecule, β becomes proportional to N_1 (i.e., β becomes an extensive property) as N_1 becomes large. In the former case we may drop $\beta \, dm_1^s$ in Eq. (7-78) in the macroscopic limit, but not in the latter case. In both cases $F = \mu_1 N_1 + \mu_2 \bar{N}_2$.

Thus we do not have an exact, formal correspondence between Eqs. (7-5) and (7-77) as we might have expected from our previous treatments of small systems in a solvent. Furthermore, this type of complication may be anticipated with any *experimental* open or semiopen small system. We encounter it again, for example, in Chapter 10.

Actually, in many experimental cases of interest, the binding of the species 1^s on the small systems is strong, so that m_1^s is quite small over the whole range of values of interest. In this case, as we shall see below, the term in β may be dropped, and Eq. (7-77) becomes

$$d(\hat{\mu}_1 N_1) = -S \, dT + \bar{V} \, dp + \mu_1 \, dN_1 - \bar{N}_2 \, d\mu_2 \qquad (m_1^s \to 0, \, sc').$$

$$(7\text{-}79)$$

This equation is identical with Eq. (7-5).

We return now to Eq. (7-77). Since $\mu_2 = \mu_1^s$ at equilibrium and μ_1^s is a function of m_1^s, we want to eliminate $d\mu_2$ from this equation in favor of the more directly measurable quantity dm_1^s. At the same time this will avoid any arbitrariness, in later equations, associated with the choice of the zeros of energy and entropy in μ_2. Such arbitrariness would otherwise arise, for example, in equations in which the temperature is varied holding μ_2 constant.[1]

We are always interested in the limit $x' \to 0$ (isolated small systems) and retain the lowest-order term in x' possible. For this reason, $\mu_2 = \mu_1^s$ in Eq. (7-77) should be taken as $\mu_1^*(p, T, m_1^s, sc')$, the chemical potential of 1^s in the solvent ($x' = 0$). Thus

$$d\mu_2 = d\mu_1^* = -\tilde{s}_1^* \, dT + \tilde{v}_1^* \, dp + \left(\frac{\partial \mu_1^*}{\partial m_1^s}\right)_{T, \, p, \, sc'} dm_1^s \qquad (sc'). \quad (7\text{-}80)$$

[1] See the footnote on p. 4.

If we substitute Eq. (7-80) in Eq. (7-77), we obtain

$$d(\hat{\mu}_1 N_1) = -(S - \bar{N}_2 \tilde{s}_1^*) \, dT + (\bar{V} - \bar{N}_2 \tilde{v}_1^*) \, dp$$

$$+ \mu_1 \, dN_1 + \left[\beta - \bar{N}_2 \left(\frac{\partial \mu_1^*}{\partial m_1^s} \right)_{T, p, sc'} \right] dm_1^s \quad (sc'). \quad (7\text{-}81)$$

The independent variables in Eq. (7-81) are the "equilibrium" set T, p, N_1, m_1^s, and sc', which recognize explicitly the existence of the binding equilibrium. That is, the redundancies (at equilibrium) in independent variables (μ_2 and $\bar{N}_2$, respectively) which occur in Eqs. (7-77) and (7-78) do not appear here. For $\mu_2(= \mu_1^*)$ is determined by T, p, m_1^s, and sc', and $\bar{N}_2$ is determined by these variables and N_1 in addition. Equations (7-77) and (7-78), as they stand (without the equilibrium condition $\mu_2 = \mu_1^*$), apply to a binary small system in a solvent, with variations in solvent composition (m_1^s) included.

From the list of independent variables in Eq. (7-81) it is apparent that an alternative expression for the coefficient of dm_1^s must be

$$\beta - \bar{N}_2 \left(\frac{\partial \mu_1^*}{\partial m_1^s} \right)_{T, p, sc'} = \left(\frac{\partial \hat{\mu}_1 N_1}{\partial m_1^s} \right)_{T, p, N_1, sc'}. \quad (7\text{-}82)$$

Still another form is

$$\left(\frac{\partial \hat{\mu}_1 N_1}{\partial m_1^s} \right)_{T, p, N_1, sc'} = \left(\frac{\partial \hat{\mu}_1 N_1}{\partial m_1^s} \right)_{T, p, N_1, \bar{N}_2, sc'}$$

$$+ \left(\frac{\partial \hat{\mu}_1 N_1}{\partial \bar{N}_2} \right)_{T, p, N_1, sc} \left(\frac{\partial \bar{N}_2}{\partial m_1^s} \right)_{T, p, N_1, sc'}. \quad (7\text{-}83)$$

The first derivative on the right can be written (from $N_1 \hat{\mu}_1 = F - \bar{N}_2 \mu_2$) as

$$\left(\frac{\partial \hat{\mu}_1 N_1}{\partial m_1^s} \right)_{T, p, N_1, \bar{N}_2, sc'} = \beta - \bar{N}_2 \left(\frac{\partial \mu_2}{\partial m_1^s} \right)_{T, p, N_1, \bar{N}_2, sc'}. \quad (7\text{-}84)$$

We also have, from Eqs. (7-77) and (7-78), respectively,

$$\left(\frac{\partial \hat{\mu}_1 N_1}{\partial \bar{N}_2} \right)_{T, p, N_1, sc} = - \bar{N}_2 \left(\frac{\partial \mu_2}{\partial \bar{N}_2} \right)_{T, p, N_1, sc}$$

$$\left(\frac{\partial \mu_2}{\partial m_1^s} \right)_{T, p, N_1, \bar{N}_2, sc'} = \left(\frac{\partial \beta}{\partial \bar{N}_2} \right)_{T, p, N_1, sc}. \quad (7\text{-}85)$$

If we use Eqs. (7-84) and (7-85) in Eq. (7-83), we obtain

$$\left(\frac{\partial \hat{\mu}_1 N_1}{\partial m_1^s}\right)_{T, p, N_1, sc'} = \beta - \bar{N}_2 \left(\frac{\partial \beta}{\partial \bar{N}_2}\right)_{T, p, N_1, sc}$$

$$- \bar{N}_2 \left(\frac{\partial \bar{N}_2}{\partial m_1^s}\right)_{T, p, N_1, sc'} \left(\frac{\partial \mu_2}{\partial \bar{N}_2}\right)_{T, p, N_1, sc} . \qquad (7\text{-}86)$$

An expression for the dependence of the equilibrium amount of binding $\bar{N}_2$ on m_1^s follows on combining Eqs. (7-82) and (7-86):

$$\left(\frac{\partial \bar{N}_2}{\partial m_1^s}\right)_{T, p, N_1, sc'}$$

$$= \left[\left(\frac{\partial \mu_1^*}{\partial m_1^s}\right)_{T, p, sc'} - \left(\frac{\partial \beta}{\partial \bar{N}_2}\right)_{T, p, N_1, sc}\right] \bigg/ \left(\frac{\partial \mu_2}{\partial \bar{N}_2}\right)_{T, p, N_1, sc} . \qquad (7\text{-}87)$$

A more direct derivation of this relation will be given below.

When the solvent is very dilute in 1^s, as will often either be the case or be assumed for simplicity [see Eq. (7-79)],

$$\mu_1^* = \mu_1^\Delta(p, T, sc') + kT \ln m_1^s \qquad (m_1^s \to 0) \qquad (7\text{-}88)$$

$$\left(\frac{\partial \mu_1^*}{\partial m_1^s}\right)_{T, p, sc'} = \frac{kT}{m_1^s} \qquad (m_1^s \to 0), \qquad (7\text{-}89)$$

where μ^Δ is a "standard" chemical potential for component 1^s in the solvent. Now β can be expressed as a power series in m_1^s and it becomes a function of N_1, $\bar{N}_2$, p, T, and sc' in the limit $m_1^s \to 0$. Statistical mechanical considerations show that, for small m_1^s, the ratio of β to kT/m_1^s in the last term of Eq. (7-81) has the order of magnitude of the ratio of the "van der Waals volume" of a small system to the volume per molecule (V_T/N_1^s) of species 1^s. This ratio becomes small as $m_1^s \to 0$. The ratio of β to $\bar{N}_2 kT/m_1^s$ is of course even smaller (we are assuming strong binding so that ordinarily $\bar{N}_2 > 1$ or $\bar{N}_2 \gg 1$ even though m_1^s is small). Hence we drop β in Eq. (7-81) with the result

$$d(\hat{\mu}_1 N_1) = -(S - \bar{N}_2 \tilde{s}_1^\square) dT + (\bar{V} - \bar{N}_2 \tilde{v}_1^\square) dp + \mu_1 dN_1$$

$$- \bar{N}_2 kT \, d \ln m_1^s \qquad (m_1^s \to 0, \quad sc'), \qquad (7\text{-}90)$$

where $\tilde{s}_1^\square$ and $\tilde{v}_1^\square$ are partial molal quantities for 1^s in the solvent in the limit $m_1^s \to 0$ (that is, $\tilde{s}_1^* \to \tilde{s}_1^{\square}$, etc.). This equation is completely equivalent to but is a more practical form of Eq. (7-79). It is therefore also identical with Eq. (7-5).

Similarly, when $m_1^s \to 0$, Eq. (7-87) becomes

$$\left(\frac{\partial \bar{N}_2}{\partial m_1^s}\right)_{T,\,p,\,N_1,\,sc'} = \frac{kT}{m_1^s} \Bigg/ \left(\frac{\partial \mu_2}{\partial \bar{N}_2}\right)_{T,\,p,\,N_1,\,sc'} \qquad (m_1^s \to 0). \quad (7\text{-}91)$$

Measurement of $\partial \bar{N}_2 / \partial m_1^s$ and m_1^s allows evaluation of $\partial \mu_2 / \partial \bar{N}_2$. If m_1^s is so small that the amount of binding is also small ($\bar{N}_2 \to 0$), then, according to Eq. (4-68), $\partial \mu_2 / \partial \bar{N}_2 = kT / \bar{N}_2$. Therefore

$$\bar{N}_2 = k_1^s(T,\,p,\,N_1,\,sc')m_1^s, \qquad (7\text{-}92)$$

where k_1^s is an integration constant. This is Henry's law.

Equation (7-78) can obviously be rewritten with the same independent variables as in Eq. (7-81):

$$dF = \left[-S + \mu_1^*\left(\frac{\partial \bar{N}_2}{\partial T}\right)_{p,\,N_1,\,sc}\right] dT + \left[\bar{V} + \mu_1^*\left(\frac{\partial \bar{N}_2}{\partial p}\right)_{T,\,N_1,\,sc}\right] dp$$

$$+ \left[\mu_1 + \mu_1^*\left(\frac{\partial \bar{N}_2}{\partial N_1}\right)_{T,\,p,\,sc}\right] dN_1 + \left[\beta + \mu_1^*\left(\frac{\partial \bar{N}_2}{\partial m_1^s}\right)_{T,\,p,\,N_1,\,sc'}\right] dm_1^s \quad (sc')$$

$$(7\text{-}93)$$

where

$$\beta + \mu_1^*\left(\frac{\partial \bar{N}_2}{\partial m_1^s}\right)_{T,\,p,\,N_1,\,sc'} = \left(\frac{\partial F}{\partial m_1^s}\right)_{T,\,p,\,N_1,\,sc'}. \quad (7\text{-}94)$$

An explicit expression for $\partial \bar{N}_2 / \partial m_1^s$ is given in Eq. (7-87). Similar relations for $\partial \bar{N}_2 / \partial T$, etc., will be derived below.

Equation (7-81) results from Eq. (7-77) on elimination of μ_2 as an independent variable. If, instead, we eliminate m_1^s using Eq. (7-80), we find

$$d(\hat{\mu}_1 N_1) = \left[-S + \tilde{s}_1^*\left(\frac{\partial F}{\partial \mu_1^*}\right)_{T,\,p,\,N_1,\,\bar{N}_2,\,sc'}\right] dT$$

$$+ \left[\bar{V} - \tilde{v}_1^*\left(\frac{\partial F}{\partial \mu_1^*}\right)_{T,\,p,\,N_1,\,\bar{N}_2,\,sc'}\right] dp + \mu_1\, dN_1$$

$$+ \left[\left(\frac{\partial F}{\partial \mu_1^*}\right)_{T,\,p,\,N_1,\,\bar{N}_2,\,sc'} - \bar{N}_2\right] d\mu_1^* \quad (sc'), \quad (7\text{-}95)$$

where

$$\left(\frac{\partial F}{\partial \mu_1^*}\right)_{T,\,p,\,N_1,\,\bar{N}_2,\,sc'} - \bar{N}_2 = \left(\frac{\partial \hat{\mu}_1 N_1}{\partial \mu_1^*}\right)_{T,\,p,\,N_1,\,sc'}. \qquad (7\text{-}96)$$

In the special case $m_1^s \to 0$, $\partial F/\partial \mu_1^*$ becomes negligible and

$$\frac{\partial \hat{\mu}_1 N_1}{\partial \mu_1^*} \to -\bar{N}_2. \qquad (7\text{-}97)$$

Hence Eq. (7-79) is again recovered.

So far in this subsection we have been concerned primarily with analogues of the fundamental Eq. (7-5). We can summarize the work thus far as follows.

If we use the same definitions of thermodynamic functions for a two-component small system in a solvent as in Section 4-2, we find that in the present problem Eq. (7-2) is satisfied by these functions but Eq. (7-5) is satisfied only in the limit $m_1^s \to 0$ [see Eq. (7-90)]. However, this limit is a common special case and even otherwise is a useful approximation. Extensions of Eq. (7-5) [for example, Eq. (7-81)] must be employed when the limit $m_1^s \to 0$ is not appropriate.

Finally, in this subsection, we deduce a number of other relations that follow directly from the condition $d\mu_2 = d\mu_1^*$. Equation (7-80) contains an explicit expression for $d\mu_1^*$. We now consider $d\mu_2$ and related topics. Section 4-1 is applicable here, with the added complication that m_1^s may vary (sc = constant is understood in Section 4-1; see Section 4-2). Thus

$$d\mu_2 = -\tilde{s}_2\, dT + \tilde{v}_2\, dp + \left(\frac{\partial \mu_2}{\partial N_1}\right)_{T,\,p,\,\bar{N}_2,\,sc} dN_1$$
$$+ \left(\frac{\partial \mu_2}{\partial \bar{N}_2}\right)_{T,\,p,\,N_1,\,sc} d\bar{N}_2 + \left(\frac{\partial \mu_2}{\partial m_1^s}\right)_{T,\,p,\,N_1,\,\bar{N}_2,\,sc'} dm_1^s \quad (sc'), \qquad (7\text{-}98)$$

where $\tilde{s}_2 = (\partial S/\partial \bar{N}_2)_{T,\,p,\,N_1,\,sc}$, etc. These are partial molal quantities for the small system, not the solvent. In view of Eq. (7-85b) and the cross relation $\partial \mu_2/\partial N_1 = \partial \mu_1/\partial \bar{N}_2$, we can also write

$$d\mu_2 = -\tilde{s}_2\, dT + \tilde{v}_2\, dp + \left(\frac{\partial \mu_1}{\partial \bar{N}_2}\right)_{T,\,p,\,N_1,\,sc} dN_1$$
$$+ \left(\frac{\partial \mu_2}{\partial \bar{N}_2}\right)_{T,\,p,\,N_1,\,sc} d\bar{N}_2 + \tilde{\beta}_2\, dm_1^s \quad (sc'). \qquad (7\text{-}99)$$

The Gibbs–Duhem relation is

$$d\mathscr{E} = -S\,dT + \bar{V}\,dp - N_1\,d\mu_1 - \bar{N}_2\,d\mu_2 + \beta\,dm_1^s \qquad (sc').$$

$$(7\text{-}100)$$

A special case is

$$\left(\frac{\partial \mathscr{E}}{\partial \bar{N}_2}\right)_{T, p, N_1, sc} = -N_1\left(\frac{\partial \mu_1}{\partial \bar{N}_2}\right)_{T, p, N_1, sc} - \bar{N}_2\left(\frac{\partial \mu_2}{\partial \bar{N}_2}\right)_{T, p, N_1, sc}.$$

$$(7\text{-}101)$$

If we put this in Eq. (7-99), we have

$$d\mu_2 = -\tilde{s}_2\,dT + \tilde{v}_2\,dp - \frac{1}{N_1}\left(\frac{\partial \mathscr{E}}{\partial \bar{N}_2}\right)_{T, p, N_1, sc} dN_1$$

$$+ \left(\frac{\partial \mu_2}{\partial \bar{N}_2/N_1}\right)_{T, p, N_1, sc} d\left(\frac{\bar{N}_2}{N_1}\right) + \tilde{\beta}_2\,dm_1^s \qquad (sc'). \quad (7\text{-}102)$$

If we now set $d\mu_1^*$ in Eq. (7-80) equal to $d\mu_2$ in Eq. (7-102), five variables (T, p, N_1, $\bar{N}_2/N_1$, m_1^s) appear in the resulting equation. Ten different pairs may be chosen out of the five variables and hence there are ten equations of the "Clausius—Clapeyron" type that can be derived (only four are independent). Equation (7-87) is one of these. A few others are

$$\left(\frac{\partial \bar{N}_2/N_1}{\partial N_1}\right)_{T, p, sc} = \frac{1}{N_1}\left(\frac{\partial \mathscr{E}}{\partial \bar{N}_2}\right)_{T, p, N_1, sc}\bigg/\left(\frac{\partial \mu_2}{\partial \bar{N}_2/N_1}\right)_{T, p, N_1, sc}$$

$$= \frac{1}{N_1^2}\left(\frac{\partial \mathscr{E}}{\partial \mu_2}\right)_{T, p, N_1, sc} \quad (7\text{-}103)$$

$$\left(\frac{\partial \bar{N}_2}{\partial T}\right)_{p, N_1, sc} = \frac{\tilde{s}_2 - \tilde{s}_1^*}{\left(\dfrac{\partial \mu_2}{\partial \bar{N}_2}\right)_{T, p, N_1, sc}} \quad (7\text{-}104)$$

$$\left(\frac{\partial m_1^s}{\partial T}\right)_{p, N_1, \bar{N}_2, sc'} = \frac{\tilde{s}_1^* - \tilde{s}_2}{\left(\dfrac{\partial \mu_1^*}{\partial m_1^s}\right)_{T, p, sc} - \tilde{\beta}_2} \quad (7\text{-}105)$$

$$\left(\frac{\partial p}{\partial T}\right)_{N_1, \bar{N}_2, sc} = \frac{\tilde{s}_1^* - \tilde{s}_2}{\tilde{v}^* - \tilde{v}_2}, \quad (7\text{-}106)$$

where $\tilde{s}_1^* - \tilde{s}_2$ can also be written as $(\tilde{H}_1^* - \tilde{H}_2)/T$ [see Eq. (4-17)]. We see from Eqs. (7-91) and (7-103) that measurement of $\partial \bar{N}_2/\partial m_1^s$ and $\partial \bar{N}_2/\partial N_1$ (or $\partial m_1^s/\partial N_1$) will give $\partial \mathscr{E}/\partial \bar{N}_2$. When the solvent is dilute in 1^s, Eq. (7-105) becomes

$$\left(\frac{\partial \ln m_1^s}{\partial T}\right)_{p,\,N_1,\,\bar{N}_2,\,sc'} = \frac{\tilde{s}_1^{\square} - \tilde{s}_2}{kT} = \frac{\tilde{H}_1^{\square} - \tilde{H}_2}{kT^2} \qquad (m_1^s \to 0). \quad (7\text{-}107)$$

Thus, measurement of $\partial \ln m_1/\partial T$ makes $\tilde{s}_1^{\square} - \tilde{s}_2$ and $\tilde{H}_1^{\square} - \tilde{H}_2$ accessible. Equation (7-107) is the analogue of the "isosteric heat equation" familiar in gas adsorption work. It is easy to show that $(\tilde{H}_1^{\square} - \tilde{H}_2)\, dN_1^s$ is the heat adsorbed by the closed macroscopic solution in the transfer of dN_1^s molecules of component 1^s from the bound state to the solvent, at equilibrium and at constant pressure and temperature.

There is an alternative form of Eqs. (7-105) and (7-107) that is of some interest. In Eq. (7-77), we use the notation $\hat{\mu}_{10}$, S_0, etc., to indicate values of these functions when[1] $\bar{N}_2 = 0$. Then, on subtracting $d(\hat{\mu}_{10} N_1)$ from $d(\hat{\mu}_1 N_1)$ and solving for $d\mu_2$,

$$d\mu_2 = -\frac{S - S_0}{\bar{N}_2}\, dT + \frac{\beta - \beta_0}{\bar{N}_2}\, dm_1^s - \frac{N_1}{\bar{N}_2}\, d(\hat{\mu}_1 - \hat{\mu}_{10})$$

$$(p,\, N_1,\, sc' \text{ constant}). \quad (7\text{-}108)$$

We set this equal to $d\mu_1^*$ in Eq. (7-80) and find

$$\left(\frac{\partial m_1^s}{\partial T}\right)_{p,\,N_1,\,sc',\,\hat{\mu}_1 - \hat{\mu}_{10}} = \frac{\tilde{s}_1^* - \dfrac{S - S_0}{\bar{N}_2}}{\left(\dfrac{\partial \mu_1^*}{\partial m_1^s}\right)_{T,\,p,\,sc'} - \dfrac{\beta - \beta_0}{\bar{N}_2}}. \quad (7\text{-}109)$$

When m_1^s is small,

$$\left(\frac{\partial \ln m_1^s}{\partial T}\right)_{p,\,N_1,\,sc',\,\hat{\mu}_1 - \hat{\mu}_{10}} = \frac{1}{kT}\left(\tilde{s}_1^{\square} - \frac{S - S_0}{\bar{N}_2}\right) \qquad (m_1^s \to 0). \quad (7\text{-}110)$$

These equations give the entropy $S - S_0$ rather than $\partial S/\partial \bar{N}_2$, as in Eq. (7-105). There is an analogous equation, useful in gas adsorption work, in which the surface pressure (the analogue of $\hat{\mu}_{10} - \hat{\mu}_1$) is held constant.

[1] These functions refer to "bare" small systems in the presence of solvent with $m_1^s \neq 0$. See p. 15.

In order to find $\hat{\mu}_1 - \hat{\mu}_{10}$ from experimental data, we put Eq. (7-108) in the form

$$d(\hat{\mu}_1 - \hat{\mu}_{10}) = \left[-\frac{\bar{N}_2}{N_1}\left(\frac{\partial \mu_1^*}{\partial m_1^s}\right)_{T,p,sc'} + \frac{\beta - \beta_0}{N_1} \right] dm_1^s$$

$$(T, p, N_1, sc' \text{ constant}). \qquad (7\text{-}111)$$

This equation is not very practical to use as it stands, but when the solvent is dilute in 1^s,

$$d(\hat{\mu}_1 - \hat{\mu}_{10}) = -\frac{\bar{N}_2 kT}{N_1 m_1^s} dm_1^s \qquad (m_1^s \to 0; T, p, N_1, sc' \text{ constant}).$$

$$(7\text{-}112)$$

Then, if $\bar{N}_2(m_1^s)$ is measured experimentally between $\bar{N}_2 = 0$ at $m_1^s = 0$ and $\bar{N}_2 = N'$ at $m_1^s = m'$,

$$\hat{\mu}_1(N') - \hat{\mu}_{10} = -\frac{kT}{N_1}\int_0^{m'} \frac{\bar{N}_2(m_1^s)}{m_1^s} dm_1^s \qquad (m_1^s \to 0; T, p, N_1, sc' \text{ constant}).$$

$$(7\text{-}113)$$

This is the analogue of the "Gibbs adsorption isotherm." One can calculate $\hat{\mu}_1 - \hat{\mu}_{10}$ from Eq. (7-113) for use[1] in Eq. (7-110). In the Henry's law region, $\bar{N}_2 = k_1^s m_1^s$, as in Eq. (7-92), and

$$-[\hat{\mu}_1(\bar{N}_2) - \hat{\mu}_{10}] = \frac{kT\bar{N}_2}{N_1} \qquad (\bar{N}_2 \to 0). \qquad (7\text{-}114)$$

This is the analogue of an ideal equation of state.[2]

"BLACK-BOX" POINT OF VIEW. Here we consider exactly the same system as above but adopt the alternative point of view that we are unaware of the fact that binding is taking place. That is, the binding will now be included implicitly but not explicitly. The fundamental equations are [see Eq. 7-60]:

$$dF_T = -S_T dT + V_T dp + \mu_1^s d(N_1^s + \mathcal{N}\bar{N}_2)$$

$$+ \sum_{j=2}^{c} \mu_j^s dN_j^s + \mu^{\square\ddagger} d\mathcal{N} + \mu_1\mathcal{N} dN_1 \qquad (7\text{-}115)$$

[1] Compare T. L. Hill, P. H. Emmett, and L. G. Joyner, J. Am. Chem. Soc., 73, 5102 (1951), for the gas adsorption case.
[2] Compare T. L. Hill, J. Am. Chem. Soc., 79, 4885 (1957), Eq. (15), for the macroscopic solution case.

and

$$d\mu^{\square\ddagger} = -\tilde{s}^{\square\ddagger}\, dT + \tilde{v}^{\square\ddagger}\, dp + kT\, d\ln x' + \mu_1\, dN_1 \qquad (sc) \qquad (7\text{-}116)$$

where

$$x' = \frac{\mathcal{N}}{N_1^s + \mathcal{N}\bar{N}_2 + \sum\limits_j N_j^s}.$$

This is the same as the earlier definition, $x' = \mathcal{N}/\Sigma_i N_i^s$, in the limit $\mathcal{N} \to 0$. Equations (7-115) and (7-116) are essentially the same as Eqs. (2-117) and (2-122), respectively. The partial molal quantities, $\mu^{\square\ddagger}$, $\tilde{s}^{\square\ddagger}$, etc., refer to the addition of "bare" small systems to the macroscopic solution [that is $\partial F_T/\partial \mathcal{N}$, $\partial S_T/\partial \mathcal{N}$, etc., as in Eq. (7-61)]. From Eqs. (7-66), (7-67), and the equation following (7-62), we have

$$\mu^{\square\ddagger} = N_1\hat{\mu}_1 + kT\ln x'.$$

Also, we define (as in Section 2-3 for a one-component small system)

$$S^{\ddagger} = \tilde{s}^{\square\ddagger} + k\ln x', \qquad \bar{E}^{\ddagger} = \tilde{E}^{\square\ddagger}, \qquad \bar{V}^{\ddagger} = \tilde{v}^{\square\ddagger}.$$

With these definitions, Eq. (7-116) becomes

$$d(\hat{\mu}_1 N_1) = -S^{\ddagger}\, dT + \bar{V}^{\ddagger}\, dp + \mu_1\, dN_1 \qquad (sc). \qquad (7\text{-}117)$$

This is equivalent to Eq. (2-123) and identical with Eq. (7-81) when m_1^s and sc' (that is, sc) are both constant. Thus the physical significance of the coefficients of dT and dp in Eq. (7-81) is seen to be

$$\begin{aligned} S - \bar{N}_2\tilde{s}_1^* &= S^{\ddagger} = \tilde{s}^{\square\ddagger} + k\ln x' \\ \bar{V} - \bar{N}_2\tilde{v}_1^* &= \bar{V}^{\ddagger} = \tilde{v}^{\square\ddagger}. \end{aligned} \qquad (7\text{-}118)$$

These are the ("bare") small system thermodynamic functions which would be obtained if the binding were ignored in the thermodynamics, even though it is known, on extrathermodynamic grounds, to exist. This result should be expected since the introduction of the concept of binding adds a degree of freedom (μ_2 or $\bar{N}_2$), but this degree of freedom is taken away again when the binding equilibrium condition ($\mu_2 = \mu_1^*$) is introduced explicitly as in Eq. (7-81). Of course, the complete Eq. (7-81) is more general than Eq. (7-117) in that the former equation allows variations in m_1^s. Such variations are essential in an explicit study of a binding equilibrium.

Naturally, the discussion of the relation $d\mu_2 = d\mu_1^*$, beginning with Eq. (7-98), has no parallel from the "black-box" point of view since binding is included explicitly in $d\mu_2$.

Note that Eqs. (7-118) are consistent with

$$\mu^\square - \mu^{\square\ddagger} = (\tilde{E}^\square - \tilde{E}^{\square\ddagger}) - T(\tilde{S}^\square - \tilde{S}^{\square\ddagger}) + p(\tilde{v}^\square - \tilde{v}^{\square\ddagger})$$
$$= \bar{N}_2\mu_1^* = \bar{N}_2(\tilde{E}_1^* - T\tilde{S}_1^* + {}_p\tilde{v}_1^*). \qquad (7\text{-}119)$$

If $S^\ddagger$, $\bar{V}^\ddagger$, and $\bar{E}^\ddagger$ are measured, ignoring binding, then

$$S = S^\ddagger + \bar{N}_2\tilde{s}_1^*$$
$$\bar{V} = \bar{V}^\ddagger + \bar{N}_2\tilde{v}_1^* \qquad (7\text{-}120)$$
$$\bar{E} = \bar{E}^\ddagger + \bar{N}_2\tilde{E}_1^*.$$

ONE-COMPONENT SOLVENT. If the solvent consists of only one component (1^s) and this component is bound to some extent on the small systems, then Eq. (7-65) simplifies somewhat to

$$d\mu^\square = - \tilde{s}^\square \, dT + \tilde{v}^\square \, dp + \frac{\partial\mu^\square}{\partial x'} \, dx' + \mu_1 \, dN_1 + \mu_2 \, d\bar{N}_2, \qquad (7\text{-}121)$$

where $x' = \mathcal{N}/N_1^s$. Examples are the hydration of a macromolecule and the adsorption of a gas onto gaseous colloidal particles. We use the same definitions as in Eqs. (7-66) to (7-68), although now there is no dependence of F, etc., on solvent composition. Then

$$F = N_1\hat{\mu}_1 + \bar{N}_2\mu_2 = \bar{E} - TS + p\bar{V} \qquad (7\text{-}122)$$

$$d(\hat{\mu}_1 N_1) = - S \, dT + \bar{V} \, dp + \mu_1 \, dN_1 - \bar{N}_2 \, d\mu_2. \qquad (7\text{-}123)$$

These are the same as Eqs. (7-2) and (7-5). However, because of the binding equilibrium, there is redundancy in the independent variables in Eq. (7-123), since $\mu_2 = \mu_1^*$ and μ_1^* is a function of p and T. We substitute

$$d\mu_1^* = - s_1^* \, dT + v_1^* \, dp$$

for $d\mu_2$ in Eq. (7-123) and obtain

$$d(\hat{\mu}_1 N_1) = - (S - \bar{N}_2 s_1^*) \, dT + (\bar{V} - \bar{N}_2 v_1^*) \, dp + \mu_1 \, dN_1. \qquad (7\text{-}124)$$

The quantities μ_1^*, s_1^*, etc., are properties per molecule of the pure solvent at p and T. The independent "equilibrium" variables are in this case T, p, and N_1.

If the binding is ignored ("black-box" point of view),

$$d(\hat{\mu}_1 N_1) = - S^{\ddagger} dT + \bar{V}^{\ddagger} dp + \mu_1 dN_1, \qquad (7\text{-}125)$$

as in Eq. (7-117). Thus $S = S^{\ddagger} + \bar{N}_2 s_1^*$, etc. Equation (7-125) is equivalent to Eq. (2-114).

If the solvent is a liquid or dense gas,[1] the pressure effect on the small system in Eq. (7-124) is hydrostatic in nature. But if the solvent is a very dilute gas ($p \to 0$), $\bar{V} = v_1^* = kT/p$ and

$$d(\hat{\mu}_1 N_1) = - (S - \bar{N}_2 s_1^{\square}) dT - (\bar{N}_2 - 1)kT \, d \ln p + \mu_1 dN_1$$
$$(p \to 0). \qquad (7\text{-}126)$$

In this case the hydrostatic pressure on the small system is negligible but p serves as a measure of the chemical potential of the species, 1^s, being adsorbed. The entropy per molecule $s_1^{\square}$ is that of 1^s in the ideal-gas state at T and p.

In the very dilute gas case just mentioned, there is a close relation to Section 3-3, as might be expected. Let us denote small system thermodynamic functions defined as in Section 3-3 by the superscript[(3)]. Then

$$\mu^{\square} = N_1 \hat{\mu}_1^{(3)} + \bar{N}_2 \mu_2 + kT \ln \frac{\mathcal{N}}{\mathcal{N}^{\dagger}}$$
$$\qquad (7\text{-}127)$$
$$\tilde{s}^{\square} = S^{(3)} + k - k \ln \frac{\mathcal{N}}{\mathcal{N}^{\dagger}},$$

so that

$$N_1 \hat{\mu}_1 = N_1 \hat{\mu}_1^{(3)} + kT \ln \frac{N_1^s}{\mathcal{N}^{\dagger}}$$
$$\qquad (7\text{-}128)$$
$$S = S^{(3)} + k + k \ln \frac{\mathcal{N}^{\dagger}}{N_1^s}.$$

If we put Eqs. (7-128) and $\bar{V} = kT/p$ in Eqs. (7-69) and (7-126), we find

$$d(\hat{\mu}_1^{(3)} N_1) = - (S^{(3)} - \bar{N}_2 s_1^{\square}) dT - \bar{N}_2 kT \, d \ln p + \mu_1 dN_1 \quad (p \to 0)$$
$$(7\text{-}129)$$
$$N_1 \hat{\mu}_1^{(3)} + \bar{N}_2 \mu_2 = \bar{E} - TS^{(3)}. \qquad (7\text{-}130)$$

---

[1] See the footnote on p. 55 of Part I.

Equation (7-129) can be written as

$$d(\hat{\mu}_1^{(3)} N_1) = - S^{(3)} dT - \bar{N}_2 d\mu_2 + \mu_1 dN_1. \qquad (7\text{-}131)$$

Equations (7-130) and (7-131) are two-component equivalents of Eqs. (3-29) and (3-31).

Equations (7-129) to (7-131) are unaltered if the very dilute gas contains other (very dilute) species 2^s, 3^s, ... But the pressure p in $d \ln p$ and $s_1^{\square}(p)$ is then the partial pressure of 1^s.

As a final topic in this subsection, we note, as we did beginning with Eq. (7-98), various deductions which can be made from the relation $d\mu_2 = d\mu_1^*$. We have first

$$- \tilde{s}_2 dT + \tilde{v}_2 dp - \frac{1}{N_1}\left(\frac{\partial \mathscr{E}}{\partial \bar{N}_2}\right)_{T, p, N_1} dN_1$$
$$+ \left(\frac{\partial \mu_2}{\partial \bar{N}_2/N_1}\right)_{T, p, N_1} d\left(\frac{\bar{N}_2}{N_1}\right) = - s_1^* dT + v_1^* dp.$$

There are six equations of the Clausius–Clapeyron type that now follow, three of which are independent. Thus

$$\left(\frac{\partial p}{\partial T}\right)_{N_1, \bar{N}_2} = \frac{s_1^* - \tilde{s}_2}{v_1^* - \tilde{v}_2}, \qquad \left(\frac{\partial \bar{N}_2}{\partial T}\right)_{p, N_1} = \frac{\tilde{s}_2 - s_1^*}{\left(\dfrac{\partial \mu_2}{\partial \bar{N}_2}\right)_{T, p, N_1}} \qquad (7\text{-}132)$$

$$\left(\frac{\partial \bar{N}_2}{\partial p}\right)_{T, N_1} = \frac{v_1^* - \tilde{v}_2}{\left(\dfrac{\partial \mu_2}{\partial \bar{N}_2}\right)_{T, p, N_1}} \qquad (7\text{-}133)$$

$$\left(\frac{\partial \bar{N}_2/N_1}{\partial N_1}\right)_{T, p} = \frac{1}{N_1}\left(\frac{\partial \mathscr{E}}{\partial \bar{N}_2}\right)_{T, p, N_1} \bigg/ \left(\frac{\partial \mu_2}{\partial \bar{N}_2/N_1}\right)_{T, p, N_1}$$
$$= \frac{1}{N_1^2}\left(\frac{\partial \mathscr{E}}{\partial \mu_2}\right)_{T, p, N_1}. \qquad (7\text{-}134)$$

In the very dilute gas case, $\tilde{v}_2 = 0$ and $v_1^* = kT/p$, so that

$$\left(\frac{\partial \ln p}{\partial T}\right)_{N_1, \bar{N}_2} = \frac{s_1^{\square} - \tilde{s}_2}{kT} = \frac{H_1^{\square} - \tilde{E}_2}{kT^2} \qquad (p \to 0) \qquad (7\text{-}135)$$

$$\left(\frac{\partial \bar{N}_2}{\partial \ln p}\right)_{T, N_1} = \frac{kT}{\left(\dfrac{\partial \mu_2}{\partial \bar{N}_2}\right)_{T, N_1}} \qquad (p \to 0) \qquad (7\text{-}136)$$

$$\left(\frac{\partial \bar{N}_2/N_1}{\partial N_1}\right)_{T,\,p} = \frac{1}{N_1}\left(\frac{\partial \mathscr{E}}{\partial \bar{N}_2}\right)_{T,\,N_1}\left(\frac{\partial \mu_2}{\partial \bar{N}_2/N_1}\right)_{T,\,N_1}$$

$$= \frac{1}{N_1^2}\left(\frac{\partial \mathscr{E}}{\partial \mu_2}\right)_{T,\,N_1}. \qquad (7\text{-}137)$$

The analogue of Eq. (7-108) is most conveniently written in the notation

$$d\mu_2 = -\frac{S^{(3)} - S_0^{(3)}}{\bar{N}_2}\,dT - \frac{N_1}{\bar{N}_2}\,d(\hat{\mu}_1^{(3)} - \hat{\mu}_{10}^{(3)}) \qquad (N_1 \text{ constant}).$$

Then, from $d\mu_2 = d\mu_1^*$,

$$\left(\frac{\partial \ln p}{\partial T}\right)_{N_1,\,\Delta\hat{\mu}_1^{(3)}} = \frac{1}{kT}\left(\mathrm{s}_1^{\square} - \frac{S^{(3)} - S_0^{(3)}}{\bar{N}_2}\right) \qquad (p \to 0). \qquad (7\text{-}138)$$

To find $\Delta\hat{\mu}_1^{(3)}$, we use

$$\hat{\mu}_1^{(3)}(N') - \hat{\mu}_{10}^{(3)} = -\frac{kT}{N_1}\int_0^{p'}\frac{\bar{N}_2(p)}{p}\,dp \qquad (p \to 0;\, T.\, N_1 \text{ constant}),$$

$$(7\text{-}139)$$

where $\bar{N}_2 = N'$ when $p = p'$. Measurement of $\bar{N}_2$ as a function of p, starting from $p = 0$ (with the aid of extrapolation), at several temperatures and values of N_1, will yield $\mathrm{s}_1^{\square} - \tilde{\mathrm{s}}_2$, $\mathrm{H}_1^{\square} - \tilde{\mathrm{E}}_2$, $\partial\mu_2/\partial\bar{N}_2$, $\Delta\hat{\mu}_1^{(3)}(\bar{N}_2)$, $\mathrm{s}_1^{\square} - [(S^{(3)} - S_0^{(3)})/\bar{N}_2]$, and $\partial\mathscr{E}/\partial\bar{N}_2$. Incidentally, it is easy to see that $\tilde{\mathrm{s}}_2 = \tilde{\mathrm{s}}_2^{(3)}$.

ANALOGUES OF SECTION 7-1. Much of Section 7-1 is concerned with deductions from the fundamental equation

$$d(\hat{\mu}_1 N_1) = -S\,dT + \bar{V}\,dp + \mu_1\,dN_1 - \bar{N}_2\,d\mu_2, \quad (7\text{-}140)$$

which has the environmental variables as independent variables. We have derived several corresponding expressions for $d(\hat{\mu}_1 N_1)$ in the present section, applicable to experimental small systems in solvent or gas. We now want to indicate a few consequences of two of these expressions that parallel some of the deductions from Eq. (7-140) referred to above.

The two basic equations with which we begin are

(7-90): $d(\hat{\mu}_1 N_1) = - (S - \bar{N}_2 \tilde{s}_1^{\square}) \, dT + (\bar{V} - \bar{N}_2 \tilde{v}_1^{\square}) \, dp$

$\qquad\qquad + \mu_1 \, dN_1 - \bar{N}_2 kT \, d \ln m_1^s \qquad (m_1^s \to 0; sc')$ (7-141)

(7-129): $d(\hat{\mu}_1^{(3)} N_1) = - (S^{(3)} - \bar{N}_2 \tilde{s}_1^{\square}) \, dT + \mu_1 \, dN_1$

$\qquad\qquad\qquad - \bar{N}_2 kT \, d \ln p \qquad (p \to 0).$ (7-142)

Both of these are equivalent in form to Eq. (7-140), whereas the more general but less practical Eq. (7-81), for example, is not equivalent because of the term in β. Equations (7-141) and (7-142) have the advantage over Eq. (7-140) of being expressed in terms of "operational" independent variables. One consequence of this is that arbitrariness associated with the choice of the zero of entropy is avoided.

We can replace $d \ln m_1^s$ in Eq. (7-141) by $d \ln c_1^s$ (concentration) if we make the approximation that the density of the 2^s, 3^s, ..., c^s solvent is independent of p and T.

To avoid separate discussion of the two cases above, we shall write both Eqs. (7-141) and (7-142) in the notation

$$d(\hat{\mu}_1 N_1) = - S' \, dT + V' \, dp + \mu_1 \, dN_1 - \bar{N}_2 kT \, d \ln a_1^s, \qquad (7\text{-}143)$$

with the following interpretations:

Liquid solvent, dilute component 1^s, Eq. (7-141):

$$S' = S - \bar{N}_2 \tilde{s}_1^{\square}, \quad V' = \bar{V} - \bar{N}_2 \tilde{v}_1^{\square}, \quad a_1^s = m_1^s \quad \text{or} \quad c_1^s. \qquad (7\text{-}144)$$

Dilute gaseous solvent, Eq. (7-142):

$$\hat{\mu}_1 = \hat{\mu}_1^{(3)}, \qquad S' = S^{(3)} - \bar{N}_2 \tilde{s}_1^{\square}, \qquad V' = 0, \quad a_1^s = p. \qquad (7\text{-}145)$$

A few Legendre transformations on Eq. (7-143) are useful:

$$d\mathscr{E} = d[(\hat{\mu}_1 - \mu_1) N_1] = - S' \, dT + V' \, dp - N_1 \, d\mu_1 - \bar{N}_2 kT \, d \ln a_1^s$$
$$(7\text{-}146)$$

$$d(\hat{\mu}_1 N_1 - pV') = - S' \, dT - p \, dV' + \mu_1 \, dN_1 - \bar{N}_2 kT \, d \ln a_1^s$$
$$(7\text{-}147)$$

$$d(\hat{\mu}_1 N_1 + \bar{N}_2 kT \ln a_1^s) = - S'' \, dT + V' \, dp + \mu_1 \, dN_1$$
$$+ (kT \ln a_1^s) \, d\bar{N}_2, \qquad (7\text{-}148)$$

where

$$S'' = S' - \bar{N}_2 k \ln a_1^s. \qquad (7\text{-}149)$$

We now follow Section 7-1, more or less, and rewrite in "operational" form some of the equations to be found there.

The six Maxwell relations from Eq. (7-143) are

$$\left(\frac{\partial \mu_1}{\partial T}\right)_{p, N_1, a_1^s} = - \left(\frac{\partial S'}{\partial N_1}\right)_{T, p, a_1^s}, \qquad \left(\frac{\partial \mu_1}{\partial p}\right)_{T, N_1, a_1^s} = \left(\frac{\partial V'}{\partial N_1}\right)_{T, p, a_1^s},$$

$$\left(\frac{\partial \mu_1}{\partial \ln a_1^s}\right)_{T, p, N_1} = - kT\left(\frac{\partial \bar{N}_2}{\partial N_1}\right)_{T, p, a_1^s} \qquad (7\text{-}150)$$

$$\left(\frac{\partial V'}{\partial T}\right)_{p, N_1, a_1^s} = - \left(\frac{\partial S'}{\partial p}\right)_{T, N_1, a_1^s},$$

$$\left(\frac{\partial V'}{\partial \ln a_1^s}\right)_{T, p, N_1} = - kT\left(\frac{\partial \bar{N}_2}{\partial p}\right)_{T, N_1, a_1^s} \qquad (7\text{-}151)$$

$$\left(\frac{\partial S'}{\partial \ln a_1^s}\right)_{T, p, N_1} = \bar{N}_2 k + kT\left(\frac{\partial \bar{N}_2}{\partial T}\right)_{p, N_1, a_1^s}. \qquad (7\text{-}152)$$

Equation (7-150c) is essentially unchanged from Section 7-1. This is because both T and p are held constant in both derivatives. Equation (7-152) is a good example of an "operational" equation; it should be contrasted with Eq. (7-20a), both sides of which depend on the arbitrary choice of the zero of entropy.

For a solvent dilute in component 1^s: Eq. (7-150c) is equivalent to Eq. (7-103); Eq. (7-152) is equivalent to Eq. (7-104); and Eq. (7-151b) is equivalent to Eq. (7-104) divided by Eq. (7-106).

Equations (7-143), (7-146), and (7-150) give

$$d\hat{\mu}_1 = - \frac{S'}{N_1} dT + \frac{V'}{N_1} dp - \frac{\bar{N}_2 kT}{N_1} d\ln a_1^s - \frac{\mathscr{E}}{N_1^2} dN_1 \quad (7\text{-}153)$$

$$d\mu_1 = - \left(\frac{\partial S'}{\partial N_1}\right)_{T, p, a_1^s} dT + \left(\frac{\partial V'}{\partial N_1}\right)_{T, p, a_1^s} dp$$

$$- kT\left(\frac{\partial \bar{N}_2}{\partial N_1}\right)_{T, p, a_1^s} d\ln a_1^s - \frac{1}{N_1}\left(\frac{\partial \mathscr{E}}{\partial N_1}\right)_{T, p, a_1^s} dN_1 \quad (7\text{-}154)$$

$$d\mathscr{E} = - \left[S' - N_1\left(\frac{\partial S'}{\partial N_1}\right)_{T, p, a_1^s}\right] dT + \left[V' - N_1\left(\frac{\partial V'}{\partial N_1}\right)_{T, p, a_1^s}\right] dp$$

$$- kT\left[\bar{N}_2 - N_1\left(\frac{\partial \bar{N}_2}{\partial N_1}\right)_{T, p, a_1^s}\right] d\ln a_1^s + \left(\frac{\partial \mathscr{E}}{\partial N_1}\right)_{T, p, a_1^s} dN_1.$$

$$(7\text{-}155)$$

Equations analogous to (7-24) and (7-26a) follow from Eq. (7-147). Similarly, analogues of Eqs. (7-25) and (7-26b) are consequences of Eq. (7-148).

Equations (7-27) are modified here to

$$\left(\frac{\partial T}{\partial N_1}\right)_{p, V', a_1^s} = \left(\frac{\partial \mu_1}{\partial S'}\right)_{T, N_1, a_1^s} \tag{7-156}$$

$$\left(\frac{\partial N_1}{\partial T}\right)_{p, a_1^s, \bar{N}_2} = \left(\frac{\partial S'}{\partial \mu_1}\right)_{T, p, N_1} - \bar{N}_2 k \left(\frac{\partial \ln a_1^s}{\partial \mu_1}\right)_{T, p, N_1}. \tag{7-157}$$

Also, Eqs. (7-28b) and (7-29) become

$$\left(\frac{\partial \ln a_1^s}{\partial T}\right)_{p, V', N_1} = - \frac{1}{kT} \left(\frac{\partial S'}{\partial \bar{N}_2}\right)_{T, N_1, a_1^s} \tag{7-158}$$

$$\left(\frac{\partial p}{\partial N_1}\right)_{T, a_1^s, \bar{N}_2} = - \left(\frac{\partial \mu_1}{\partial V'}\right)_{T, p, N_1} \tag{7-159}$$

$$\left(\frac{\partial p}{\partial T}\right)_{N_1, a_1^s, \bar{N}_2} = \left(\frac{\partial S'}{\partial V'}\right)_{T, p, N_1} - \bar{N}_2 k \left(\frac{\partial \ln a_1^s}{\partial V'}\right)_{T, p, N_1}. \tag{7-160}$$

In Eqs. (7-150) to (7-152) and (7-156) to (7-160), and in the many others of this sort that can be written, the "equation-of-state" variables which are easiest to measure are p, T, N_1, $\bar{N}_2$, and a_1^s (V' is accessible, but not so directly). In these equations one will therefore generally evaluate experimentally those derivatives involving only the variables mentioned, and thus obtain information about the less accessible or inaccessible derivatives. Furthermore, the variables listed above are just those which occur on the left-hand sides of Eqs. (7-103) to (7-107), etc. Hence equations involving derivatives with these variables may be derived in either of two ways [i.e., from $d\mu_2 = d\mu_1^*$, or from Eq. (7-143)ff.]. We have already mentioned three examples of this [Eq. (7-150c), etc.]. In addition, for a solvent dilute in component 1^s: Eq. (7-160) is equivalent to Eq. (7-106); Eq. (7-157) is equivalent to Eq. (7-104) divided by Eq. (7-103); and Eq. (7-159) is equivalent to

$$\left(\frac{\partial p}{\partial N_1}\right)_{T, \bar{N}_2, sc} = \frac{(\partial \mu_1 / \partial \bar{N}_2)_{T, p, N_1, sc}}{\tilde{v}_1^* - \tilde{v}_2}, \tag{7-161}$$

which follows from Eqs. (7-80) and (7-99).

TWO-STATE APPROXIMATION. We consider here the two-state approximation for small systems in a solvent. We have, as in Eqs. (5-130) and (7-62),

$$dF_T = -S_T\, dT + V_T\, dp + \sum_{i=1}^{c} \mu_i^s\, dN_i^s + \mu_A^{\square}\, d\mathcal{N}_A + \mu_B^{\square}\, d\mathcal{N}_B$$

$$+ (\mu_{1A}\mathcal{N}_A + \mu_{1B}\mathcal{N}_B)\, dN_1 + \mu_{2A}\mathcal{N}_A\, d\bar{N}_{2A} + \mu_{2B}\mathcal{N}_B\, d\bar{N}_{2B}.$$
$$(7\text{-}162)$$

Both types of small systems, A and B, are infinitely dilute in the macroscopic solution. If the macroscopic solution is closed, the following quantities are constant:

$$N_1, \quad \mathcal{N}_A + \mathcal{N}_B, \quad N_2^s, ..., N_c^s,$$
$$\text{and} \quad N_1^s + \mathcal{N}_A\bar{N}_{2A} + \mathcal{N}_B\bar{N}_{2B}. \quad (7\text{-}163)$$

At equilibrium, at constant T and p, $dF_T = 0$. Equation (7-162), together with Eq. (7-163), then gives, for the conditions of equilibrium,

$$\mu_1^s = \mu_{2A} = \mu_{2B} \quad (\equiv \mu_2)$$
$$\mu_A^{\square} - \mu_{2A}\bar{N}_{2A} = \mu_B^{\square} - \mu_{2B}\bar{N}_{2B}. \quad (7\text{-}164)$$

We define $\hat{\mu}_{1A}$ and $\hat{\mu}_{1B}$ by

$$\mu_A^{\square} = N_1\hat{\mu}_{1A} + \bar{N}_{2A}\mu_{2A} + kT \ln \frac{\mathcal{N}_A}{\sum_i N_i^s}$$

$$\mu_B^{\square} = N_1\hat{\mu}_{1B} + \bar{N}_{2B}\mu_{2B} + kT \ln \frac{\mathcal{N}_B}{\sum_i N_i^s}, \quad (7\text{-}165)$$

as in Eqs. (7-66) and (7-67). According to Eqs. (7-164) and (7-165), the equilibrium ratio of A systems to B systems is

$$\frac{\mathcal{N}_A}{\mathcal{N}_B} = \left(\frac{e^{-\hat{\mu}_{1A}/kT}}{e^{-\hat{\mu}_{1B}/kT}}\right)^{N_1}, \quad (7\text{-}166)$$

just as in Eq. (7-40). Equations (7-41) to (7-46) also follow.

The metastable states A and B, at equilibrium, have the same values of T, p, N_1, m_1^s, $\hat{\mu}_1$, and sc'. We could therefore set $d(\hat{\mu}_{1A}N_1) = d(\hat{\mu}_{1B}N_1)$, using Eq. (7-81), in order to obtain equations of the Clausius–Clapeyron type for the transition $B \to A$. But for simplicity we assume in the remainder of this subsection that m_1^s

is small, use Eq. (7-143) or (7-153), and obtain, instead of Eqs. (7-50) to (7-52),

$$\left(\frac{\partial p}{\partial T}\right)_{N_1,\,sc} = \frac{\Delta S'}{\Delta V'}, \qquad \left(\frac{\partial \ln m_1^s}{\partial T}\right)_{p,\,N_1,\,sc'} = -\frac{\Delta S'}{kT\,\Delta \bar{N}_2}$$

$$(7\text{-}167)$$

$$\left(\frac{\partial T}{\partial N_1}\right)_{p,\,sc} = \frac{\Delta \mu_1}{\Delta S'}, \qquad \left(\frac{\partial p}{\partial \ln m_1^s}\right)_{T,\,N_1,\,sc'} = \frac{kT\,\Delta \bar{N}_2}{\Delta V'} \qquad (7\text{-}168)$$

$$\left(\frac{\partial p}{\partial N_1}\right)_{T,\,sc} = -\frac{\Delta \mu_1}{\Delta V'}, \qquad \left(\frac{\partial \ln m_1^s}{\partial N_1}\right)_{T,\,p,\,sc'} = \frac{\Delta \mu_1}{kT\,\Delta \bar{N}_2}. \quad (7\text{-}169)$$

We can replace m_1^s by c_1^s in the approximation already referred to above. All derivatives (only three are independent), as well as $\Delta \bar{N}_2$ and $\Delta V'$, can be measured. Then $\Delta S'$ and $\Delta \mu_1$ may be calculated. From Eqs. (7-144),

$$\Delta S' = \Delta S - \tilde{s}_1^{\square} \Delta \bar{N}_2, \qquad \Delta V' = \Delta \bar{V} - \tilde{v}_1^{\square} \Delta \bar{N}_2. \qquad (7\text{-}170)$$

If we define E' by $\bar{E} - \bar{N}_2 \tilde{e}_1^{\square}$, in analogy with S' and V', Eq. (7-53) becomes

$$0 = \Delta E' + p\,\Delta V' - T\,\Delta S' \qquad (7\text{-}171)$$

or

$$\Delta H' = T\,\Delta S'. \qquad (7\text{-}172)$$

As pointed out on pages 126 of Part I and 11 of Part II, the above equations also refer to the single point $\mathscr{N}_A = \mathscr{N}_B$ on the stable equilibrium path. That is, we consider only those variations in T, p, N_1, and m_1^s consistent with the maintenance of $\mathscr{N}_A = \mathscr{N}_B$.

If the phase transition between the metastable states A and B occurs at equilibrium between these states,[1] and if we include the macroscopic solvent as well as the small systems in our reckoning, then the macroscopic solution is closed and is at constant pressure and temperature. The heat of the over-all process (i.e., phase transition plus transfer of component 1^s from or to the solvent), per small system, is

$$Q_T = \Delta H_T = T\,\Delta S_T = T(\Delta S - \tilde{s}_1^{\square} \Delta \bar{N}_2) = T\,\Delta S' = \Delta H'. \quad (7\text{-}173)$$

[1] In other words, in a solution with T, p, N_1, and m_1^s chosen so that $\hat{\mu}_{1A} = \hat{\mu}_{1B}$, the initial state in the process under consideration has all small systems in state B and the final state has all of them in state A.

The heat Q_T refers to a metastable process and hence would ordinarily not be measurable. Expressions can be derived for the heat of the over-all process, *along* the *stable* equilibrium path, where the process takes place by virtue of a variation in p or T in a closed macroscopic solution (see page 127 of Part I). There are three contributions to DQ_T in this case, and these cannot be disentangled experimentally: (a) heat absorbed by small systems undergoing the transition; (b) heat absorbed by adsorption (or desorption) of 1^s molecules on small systems of the two types (transition frozen); and (c) heat absorbed at constant solution composition (transition and adsorption frozen). We shall not set down these rather complicated expressions. A simpler situation is the one in which the small systems adsorb 1^s molecules, but there is no $B \to A$ transition. Then if the pressure or temperature is varied and the closed macroscopic solution absorbs heat,

$$DQ_T = T \, dS_T \quad (N_2^s, \, ..., \, N_c^s, \quad \mathscr{N}, \quad N_1, \quad N_1^s + \mathscr{N} \bar{N}_2 \text{ constant}).$$

One finds

$$\left(\frac{DQ_T}{\partial p}\right)_{T, \text{ closed}} = T\left(\frac{\partial S_T}{\partial p}\right)_{T, \, N_i^s, \, \bar{N}_2, \, \mathscr{N}, \, N_1}$$

$$+ \, T\mathscr{N}(\tilde{s}_2 - \tilde{s}_1^{\square})\left(\frac{\partial \bar{N}_2}{\partial p}\right)_{T, \text{ closed}}, \qquad (7\text{-}174)$$

or

$$\left(\frac{DQ_T}{\partial T}\right)_{p, \text{ closed}} = T\left(\frac{\partial S_T}{\partial T}\right)_{p, \, N_i^s, \, \bar{N}_2, \, \mathscr{N}, \, N_1}$$

$$+ \, T\mathscr{N}(\tilde{s}_2 - \tilde{s}_1^{\square})\left(\frac{\partial \bar{N}_2}{\partial T}\right)_{p, \text{ closed}}, \qquad (7\text{-}175)$$

where

$$T(\tilde{s}_2 - \tilde{s}_1^{\square}) = \tilde{H}_2 - \tilde{H}_1^{\square}.$$

In the above equations for $DQ_T/\partial p$ and $DQ_T/\partial T$, the first term is a constant composition term (adsorption frozen) whereas the second term arises from a shift in the adsorption equilibrium.

It is easy to see from Eqs. (7-42), (7-44), (7-46), and (7-143) that: (1) an equal-area theorem and an equal-distance theorem both apply to a V' versus p diagram (T, N_1, m_1^s constant) and to an $\bar{N}_2$ versus $\ln m_1^s$ diagram (T, p, N_1 constant); (2) on an S' versus T diagram (p, N_1, m_1^s constant), there is an equal-area theorem but not an exact equal-distance theorem [the same usually negligible term $k \ln 2$ appears which was mentioned following Eq. (5-129)]; and (3) on $\bar{V}$ versus T, V' versus T, or $\bar{N}_2$ versus T diagrams (p, N_1, m_1^s constant), or on a $\bar{V}$ versus p diagram (T, N_1, m_1^s constant), there are equal-distance but not equal-area theorems.

A convenient way to derive some important relations that pertain to the stable equilibrium situation [as determined by Eq. (7-166)] is to make explicit use of the condition

$$d(\mu_A^{\square} - \mu_1^* \bar{N}_{2A}) = d(\mu_B^{\square} - \mu_1^* \bar{N}_{2B}), \qquad (7\text{-}176)$$

which follows from Eqs. (7-164). Equations (7-76) and (7-80) give, for small m_1^s,

$$d(\mu_A^{\square} - \mu_1^* \bar{N}_{2A}) = (-\tilde{s}_A^{\square} + \bar{N}_{2A}\tilde{s}_1^{\square})\, dT + (\tilde{v}_A^{\square} - \bar{N}_{2A}\tilde{v}_1^{\square})\, dp$$
$$+ kT\, d\ln x_A' + \mu_{1A}\, dN_1 - \bar{N}_{2A}kT\, d\ln m_1^s \qquad (sc'), \quad (7\text{-}177)$$

and there is an analogous equation for B. Then, from Eq. (7-176),

$$\frac{dP_A}{P_A P_B} = \frac{\Delta H'}{kT^2}\, dT - \frac{\Delta V'}{kT}\, dp - \frac{\Delta \mu_1}{kT}\, dN_1 + \Delta \bar{N}_2\, d\ln m^s \qquad (sc'),$$
$$(7\text{-}178)$$

where $P_A = \mathcal{N}_A / \mathcal{N}$ and $P_B = 1 - P_A$. It should be emphasized that $\Delta H'$, $\Delta V'$, etc., in this equation refer to differences between A and B properties in an arbitrary (P_A) stable equilibrium mixture of A and B systems. This is not the case in Eqs. (7-167) to (7-173), which pertain to the metastable transition or to $\mathcal{N}_A = \mathcal{N}_B$ (that is, $P_A = \frac{1}{2}$ = constant). Thus we have here, for example,

$$N_1\, \Delta\bar{\mu}_1 = \Delta H' - T\, \Delta S' = -kT \ln \frac{\mathcal{N}_A}{\mathcal{N}_B} = -kT \ln \frac{P_A}{P_B}. \qquad (7\text{-}179)$$

These relations follow from Eqs. (7-69) and (7-166). They should be contrasted with Eq. (7-172). We also note that there is one more degree of freedom in the present case. We may consider each of T, p, N_1, and m_1^s as independent variables here, but the metastable equilibrium condition (or $\mathcal{N}_A = \mathcal{N}_B$) is more restrictive and only three of these variables can be independent in Eqs. (7-167) to (7-169). In fact, if we put $P_A = \frac{1}{2}$ = constant and therefore $dP_A = 0$ in Eq. (7-178), we recover Eqs. (7-167) to (7-169).

Equation (7-178) gives us the following explicit relations showing how the equilibrium between A and B systems depends on the independent variables:

$$\left(\frac{\partial P_A}{\partial T}\right)_{p, N_1, sc} = \frac{P_A P_B \, \Delta H'}{kT^2}, \qquad \left(\frac{\partial P_A}{\partial p}\right)_{T, N_1, sc} = -\frac{P_A P_B \, \Delta V'}{kT}$$

(7-180)

$$\left(\frac{\partial P_A}{\partial N_1}\right)_{T, p, sc} = -\frac{P_A P_B \, \Delta \mu_1}{kT}, \qquad \left(\frac{\partial P_A}{\partial \ln m_1^s}\right)_{T, p, N_1, sc'} = P_A P_B \, \Delta \bar{N}_2.$$

(7-181)

If desired, one can substitute in these equations

$$\frac{dP_A}{P_A P_B} = d \ln \frac{P_A}{1 - P_A} = d \ln \frac{\mathcal{N}_A}{\mathcal{N}_B}.$$

The last quotient has the form of an equilibrium constant. Analogues of Eqs. (7-180) and (7-181a) were encountered in Section 5-4, derived by a different method.

Six equations with the appearance of Eqs. (7-167) to (7-169) also follow from Eq. (7-178), if we take $P_A =$ constant (we have already mentioned the special case $P_A = \frac{1}{2}$).

Simple Example. Dibasic Long-Chain Acid. This is an example of simple binding, not of a phase transition. Consider a linear polymer molecule in solution, made up of N_1 monomers and containing one site for binding H^+ at each end of the chain. Examples are $NH_2(CH_2)_{N_1}COO^-$, $NH_2(CH_2)_{N_1}NH_2$, etc. The solution is assumed dilute in both polymer molecule and H^+. Then the titration curve may be expressed in the familiar form

$$\bar{N}_2 = \frac{\dfrac{c_1^s}{K_{(2)}} + \dfrac{2(c_1^s)^2}{K_{(1)}K_{(2)}}}{1 + \dfrac{c_1^s}{K_{(2)}} + \dfrac{(c_1^s)^2}{K_{(1)}K_{(2)}}},$$

(7-182)

where $K_{(1)}$ and $K_{(2)}$ are the successive thermodynamic dissociation constants, c_1^s is the H^+ concentration in solution, and $\bar{N}_2$ is the average number of bound hydrogen ions per polymer: $0 \leqslant \bar{N}_2 \leqslant 2$. If $K_{(1)}$ and $K_{(2)}$ are measured as functions of N_1 and T (ignoring pressure effects), we then have $\bar{N}_2$ as a function of the environmental variables c_1^s, N_1, and T. Hence, for example, from Eqs. (7-91), (7-103), (7-104), and (7-110), we can obtain information about the dependence of μ_2, S, and $\mathscr{E}$ on $\bar{N}_2$.

In the limit $N_1 \to \infty$ (assuming that the polymer is still soluble enough to measure $K_{(1)}$ and $K_{(2)}$): (a) the hydrogen ion binding becomes relatively insignificant ($\bar{N}_2 \ll N_1$) and the system, in effect, approaches an N_1, T system; and (b)

$$K_{(1)} \to K_1 + K_2$$

and

$$\frac{1}{K_{(2)}} \to \frac{1}{K_1} + \frac{1}{K_2},$$

where K_1 and K_2 are "intrinsic" dissociation constants for the two end groups, which dissociate independently of each other in this limit. If the end groups are the same, $K_1 = K_2$ and $K_{(1)}/K_{(2)} = 4$.

7-3. ISOMERIC EQUILIBRIUM WITH BINDING

In this section we consider the thermodynamics of binding or adsorption on a small system with an isomeric equilibrium. The most obvious example is hydrogen ion binding on a macromolecule with a helix-coil transition.

As usual, we shall begin by writing the basic equations for an ensemble of distinguishable systems. Because of the fact that we merely have to combine the treatments in Sections 5-3 and 7-1, we shall proceed directly to small system equations, without explicit discussion of the ensemble.

The small system consists of N_1 molecules, monomers, or units of component 1 and $\bar{N}_2$ bound or adsorbed molecules of component 2 at chemical potential μ_2. The units of component 1 are of two types which are in an isomeric equilibrium with each other: $A_1^{(1)} \rightleftharpoons A_1^{(2)}$. The numbers of these units are designated $N_1^{(1)}$ and $N_1^{(2)}$, with $N_1^{(1)} + N_1^{(2)} = N_1$. For convenience, we write $N_1^{(1)} = n$ and $N_1^{(2)} = N_1 - n$. Also, we define $\psi = \mu_1^{(2)} - \mu_1^{(1)}$, where the latter quantities are chemical potentials. The environmental variables are then N_1, μ_2, p, T, and ψ. It is easy to show that the equilibrium value of ψ is $\psi = 0$, but we permit arbitrary values of ψ in many equations. There are fluctuations in N_2, V, E, and n.

We now have five independent variables. This means that there will be an extremely large number of possible thermodynamic relations. We shall derive only a few of these in this section and leave it to the interested reader to pursue this case further.

The fundamental equations for a small system are

$$d\bar{E} = T\,dS - p\,d\bar{V} + \mu_1^{(1)}\,d\bar{N}_1^{(1)} + \mu_1^{(2)}\,d\bar{N}_1^{(2)} + \mu_2\,d\bar{N}_2$$

$$= T\,dS - p\,d\bar{V} - \psi\,d\bar{n} + \mu_1^{(2)}\,dN_1 + \mu_2\,d\bar{N}_2 \tag{7-183}$$

$$\bar{E} = TS - p\bar{V} - \psi\bar{n} + \mu_1^{(2)}N_1 + \mu_2\bar{N}_2 + \mathscr{E} \tag{7-184}$$

$$d\mathscr{E} = -S\,dT + \bar{V}\,dp - N_1\,d\mu_1^{(2)} - \bar{N}_2\,d\mu_2 + \bar{n}\,d\psi \tag{7-185}$$

$$d(\mu_1^{(2)}N_1 + \mathscr{E}) = d(\hat{\mu}_1 N_1) = -S\,dT + \bar{V}\,dp$$

$$+ \mu_1^{(2)}\,dN_1 - \bar{N}_2\,d\mu_2 + \bar{n}\,d\psi \tag{7-186}$$

$$d\hat{\mu}_1 = -\frac{S}{N_1}\,dT + \frac{\bar{V}}{N_1}\,dp - \frac{\mathscr{E}}{N_1^2}\,dN_1 - \frac{\bar{N}_2}{N_1}\,d\mu_2 + \frac{\bar{n}}{N_1}\,d\psi.$$

The last equations have the environmental variables as independent variables. We have introduced here the notation $\hat{\mu}_1 N_1 \equiv \mu_1^{(2)}N_1 + \mathscr{E}$.

As usual we define

$$F = \bar{E} - TS + p\bar{V}, \qquad H = \bar{E} + p\bar{V}, \qquad F = H - TS, \tag{7-187}$$

so that

$$F = -\psi\bar{n} + \hat{\mu}_1 N_1 + \mu_2\bar{N}_2 \tag{7-188}$$

and

$$dF = -S\,dT + \bar{V}\,dp + \mu_1^{(2)}\,dN_1 + \mu_2\,d\bar{N}_2 - \psi\,d\bar{n}. \tag{7-189}$$

The appropriate statistical mechanical partition function is

$$Z(N_1, \mu_2, p, T, \psi) = \sum_{n,\,N_2} \Delta(N_1^{(1)}, N_1^{(2)}, N_2, p, T)e^{-n\psi/kT}e^{N_2\mu_2/kT}, \tag{7-190}$$

where $N_1^{(1)} = n$ and $N_1^{(2)} = N_1 - n$. Then

$$\hat{\mu}_1 N_1 = -kT\ln Z. \tag{7-191}$$

From Eqs. (7-186) and (7-190),

$$\bar{n} = -kT\left(\frac{\partial \ln Z}{\partial \psi}\right)_{T,\,p,\,N_1,\,\mu_2} \tag{7-192}$$

and

$$\overline{n^2} - \bar{n}^2 = -kT\left(\frac{\partial \bar{n}}{\partial \psi}\right)_{T,\,p,\,N_1,\,\mu_2}. \tag{7-193}$$

When a solvent is present, Δ in Eq. (7-190) will be more complicated [see Eqs. (1-32) and (2-124), for example] but the factor $e^{-n\psi/kT}$ will still be present and hence Eqs. (7-192) and (7-193) will still obtain.

SMALL SYSTEMS IN SOLVENT. Let us turn at this point to the practical case of interest: the small systems are in a solvent. Our task is to superimpose on Section 7-2 the complication of an isomeric equilibrium.

We start with an obvious generalization of Eq. (7-62):

$$dF_T = - S_T \, dT + V_T \, dp + \sum_{i=1}^{c} \mu_i^s \, dN_i^s + \mu^\square \, d\mathcal{N}$$
$$+ \mu_1^{(1)} \mathcal{N} \, d\bar{N}_1^{(1)} + \mu_1^{(2)} \mathcal{N} \, d\bar{N}_1^{(2)} + \mu_2 \mathcal{N} \, d\bar{N}_2. \qquad (7\text{-}194)$$

If the macroscopic system is closed, is held at constant T and p, and is at equilibrium, then

$$N_1^s + \mathcal{N} \bar{N}_2, \qquad N_2^s, ..., N_c^s, \qquad \mathcal{N}, \qquad \text{and} \quad \bar{N}_1^{(1)} + \bar{N}_1^{(2)}$$

are constant and

$$dF_T = 0 = (\mu_1^s - \mu_2) \, dN_1^s + \mathcal{N}(\mu_1^{(1)} - \mu_1^{(2)}) \, d\bar{N}_1^{(1)}.$$

Thus, at equilibrium, $\mu_1^s = \mu_2$ and $\mu_1^{(1)} = \mu_1^{(2)}$.

As above, we introduce the notation

$$\psi = \mu_1^{(2)} - \mu_1^{(1)}, \qquad n = N_1^{(1)}, \qquad N_1 - n = N_1^{(2)}.$$

Thus Eq. (7-194) becomes

$$dF_T = - S_T \, dT + V_T \, dp + \sum_i \mu_i^s \, dN_i^s + \mu^\square \, d\mathcal{N}$$
$$+ \mu_1^{(2)} \mathcal{N} \, dN_1 + \mu_2 \mathcal{N} \, d\bar{N}_2 - \psi \mathcal{N} \, d\bar{n}. \qquad (7\text{-}195)$$

Integration of this equation, holding intensive properties and $N_1, \bar{N}_2$, and $\bar{n}$ (parameters characterizing the small systems) constant, gives

$$F_T = \sum_i \mu_i^s N_i^s + \mu^\square \mathcal{N} = E_T - TS_T + pV_T. \qquad (7\text{-}196)$$

Also,

$$\mu^\square = \left(\frac{\partial F_T}{\partial \mathcal{N}} \right)_{T, \, p, \, N_i^s, \, N_1, \, \bar{N}_2, \, \bar{n}} = \widetilde{\mathrm{E}}^\square - T\widetilde{\mathrm{s}}^\square + p\widetilde{\mathrm{v}}^\square, \qquad (7\text{-}197)$$

where $\widetilde{\mathrm{E}}^\square$, etc., are defined by similar derivatives.

We define F by

$$\mu^\square = F(N_1, \bar{N}_2, \bar{n}, p, T, sc) + kT \ln x' \qquad (7\text{-}198)$$

and then $\mathscr{E}$ and $\hat{\mu}_1$ by

$$F = N_1 \mu_1^{(2)} + \bar{N}_2 \mu_2 - \psi\bar{n} + \mathscr{E} = N_1\hat{\mu}_1 + \bar{N}_2\mu_2 - \psi\bar{n}. \qquad (7\text{-}199)$$

Further definitions are

$$S = \tilde{s}^\square + k \ln x', \qquad \bar{E} = \tilde{\mathrm{E}}^\square, \qquad \text{and} \qquad \bar{V} = \tilde{\mathrm{v}}^\square. \qquad (7\text{-}200)$$

Then Eq. (7-197) becomes

$$F = \bar{E} - TS + p\bar{V}. \qquad (7\text{-}201)$$

As in Eq. (7-65), we have from Eq. (7-195),

$$d\mu^\square = -\tilde{s}^\square\, dT + \tilde{\mathrm{v}}^\square\, dp + \frac{\partial\mu^\square}{\partial x'}\, dx' + \frac{\partial\mu^\square}{\partial m_1^s}\, dm_1^s$$

$$+ \frac{\partial\mu^\square}{\partial N_1}\, dN_1 + \frac{\partial\mu^\square}{\partial \bar{N}_2}\, d\bar{N}_2 + \frac{\partial\mu^\square}{\partial \bar{n}}\, d\bar{n} \qquad (sc'). \qquad (7\text{-}202)$$

From Eq. (7-198), we know that $\partial\mu^\square/\partial x' = kT/x'$. Also, we define β by

$$\beta = \left(\frac{\partial\mu^\square}{\partial m_1^s}\right)_{T,\, p,\, x',\, N_1,\, \bar{N}_2,\, \bar{n},\, sc'} = \left(\frac{\partial F}{\partial m_1^s}\right)_{T,\, p,\, N_1,\, \bar{N}_2,\, \bar{n},\, sc'}. \qquad (7\text{-}203)$$

The next coefficient, $\partial\mu^\square/\partial N_1$, can be shown to be equal to $\mu_1^{(2)}$ in Eq. (7-195). The argument is unchanged from that in Eqs. (7-70) to (7-75) except that $\bar{n}$ must be held constant in all the derivatives. Similarly, $\partial\mu^\square/\partial \bar{N}_2$ is equal to μ_2. Finally, using Eqs. (7-73) and (7-74),

$$-\psi = \frac{1}{\mathscr{N}}\left(\frac{\partial F_T}{\partial \bar{n}}\right)_{T,\, p,\, N_i^s,\, \mathscr{N},\, N_1,\, \bar{N}_2} = \left(\frac{\partial\mu^\square}{\partial \bar{n}}\right)_{T,\, p,\, x',\, N_1,\, \bar{N}_2,\, sc}.$$

Thus, in summary,

$$d\mu^\square = -\tilde{s}^\square\, dT + \tilde{\mathrm{v}}^\square\, dp + kT\, d\ln x' + \beta\, dm_1^s$$

$$+ \mu_1^{(2)}\, dN_1 + \mu_2\, d\bar{N}_2 - \psi\, d\bar{n} \qquad (sc'). \qquad (7\text{-}204)$$

If we now introduce the definitions of F, S, and $\bar{V}$ into this relation, we find

$$dF = -S\, dT + \bar{V}\, dp + \mu_1^{(2)}\, dN_1 + \mu_2\, d\bar{N}_2$$

$$- \psi\, dn + \beta\, dm_1^s \qquad (sc'). \qquad (7\text{-}205)$$

Legendre transformations give

$$d(\hat{\mu}_1 N_1) = -S\,dT + \bar{V}\,dp + \mu_1^{(2)}\,dN_1 - \bar{N}_2\,d\mu_2$$

$$+ \bar{n}\,d\psi + \beta\,dm_1^s \qquad (sc') \qquad (7\text{-}206)$$

$$d(\hat{\mu}_1 N_1 + \mu_2\bar{N}_2) = d(F + \bar{n}\psi) = -S\,dT + \bar{V}\,dp + \mu_1^{(2)}\,dN_1$$

$$+ \mu_2\,d\bar{N}_2 + \bar{n}\,d\psi + \beta\,dm_1^s \qquad (sc') \qquad (7\text{-}207)$$

$$d(\hat{\mu}_1 N_1 - \bar{n}\psi) = d(F - \mu_2\bar{N}_2) = -S\,dT + \bar{V}\,dp + \mu_1^{(2)}\,dN_1$$

$$- \bar{N}_2\,d\mu_2 - \psi\,d\bar{n} + \beta\,dm_1^s \qquad (sc'). \qquad (7\text{-}208)$$

Equation (7-206) is the most important of these. It differs from Eq. (7-186) in that there is an extra term, $\beta\,dm_1^s$, here. The discussion of this type of term on page 17 should be referred to. Equation (7-206) becomes the same as Eq. (7-186) in the special case $m_1^s \to 0$.

Up to this point in this subsection, we have not made use of the fact that we have a binding equilibrium ($\mu_1^s = \mu_2$). To take this into account, we substitute Eq. (7-80) for $d\mu_2$ in Eq. (7-206) and obtain

$$d(\hat{\mu}_1 N_1) = -(S - \bar{N}_2\tilde{s}_1^*)\,dT + (\bar{V} - \bar{N}_2\tilde{v}_1^*)\,dp + \mu_1^{(2)}\,dN_1$$

$$+ \bar{n}\,d\psi + \left[\beta - \bar{N}_2\left(\frac{\partial\mu_1^*}{\partial m_1^s}\right)_{T,\,p,\,sc'}\right]dm_1^s \qquad (\delta,sc'). \qquad (7\text{-}209)$$

This simplifies as in Eq. (7-90) when m_1^s is small.

Actually, we have used $d(\mu_2 - \mu_1^s) = 0$ to deduce Eq. (7-209); that is, $\mu_2 - \mu_1^s = $ constant. Hence Eq. (7-209) is a little more general than indicated above ($\mu_1^s = \mu_2$), although of course the experimentally significant value of $\mu_2 - \mu_1^s = $ constant is zero. This is obviously analogous to considering, for generality, $\psi = $ constant, not necessarily zero. To emphasize this analogy, we define $\delta = \mu_2 - \mu_1^s$ and we shall indicate explicitly that $\delta = $ constant in some of the deductions we make from Eq. (7-209). We did not do this in Section 7-2; it was simply understood there that $\delta = 0$.

By taking cross-derivatives in Eq. (7-209) we can obtain expressions for the variation of the extent of reaction $\bar{n}$ with T, p, N_1, and m_1^s. For example,

$$\left(\frac{\partial \bar{n}}{\partial T}\right)_{p,\,N_1,\,\psi,\,\delta,\,sc} = -\left(\frac{\partial S}{\partial \psi}\right)_{T,\,p,\,N_1,\,\delta,\,sc} + \tilde{s}_1^*\left(\frac{\partial \bar{N}_2}{\partial \psi}\right)_{T,\,p,\,N_1,\,\delta,\,sc}$$

$$(7\text{-}210)$$

$$\left(\frac{\partial \bar{n}}{\partial m_1^s}\right)_{T,\,p,\,N_1,\,\psi,\,\delta,\,sc'} = \left(\frac{\partial \beta}{\partial \psi}\right)_{T,\,p,\,N_1,\,\delta,\,sc}$$

$$- \left(\frac{\partial \mu_1^*}{\partial m_1^s}\right)_{T,\,p,\,sc'}\left(\frac{\partial \bar{N}_2}{\partial \psi}\right)_{T,\,p,\,N_1,\,\delta,\,sc} \qquad (7\text{-}211)$$

$$\left(\frac{\partial \bar{n}}{\partial N_1}\right)_{T,\,p,\,\psi,\,\delta,\,sc} = \left(\frac{\partial \mu_1^{(2)}}{\partial \psi}\right)_{T,\,p,\,N_1,\,\delta,\,sc}. \qquad (7\text{-}212)$$

All of these derivatives are of course to be evaluated at $\psi = 0$, $\delta = 0$. Where T, p, and sc are all held constant in a derivative, μ_1^s is constant. With δ also constant, μ_2 is then constant. Hence the set of constant variables T, p, sc, δ could be replaced by T, p, sc, μ_2.

The derivatives on the left, above, are measurable. The derivatives with respect to ψ, on the right, can all be rewritten as

$$\left(\frac{\partial}{\partial \psi}\right)_{T,\,p,\,N_1,\,\delta,\,sc} = \left(\frac{\partial \bar{n}}{\partial \psi}\right)_{T,\,p,\,N_1,\,\delta,\,sc}\left(\frac{\partial}{\partial \bar{n}}\right)_{T,\,p,\,N_1,\,\delta,\,sc},$$

where

$$\left(\frac{\partial \bar{n}}{\partial \psi}\right)_{T,\,p,\,N_1,\,\delta,\,sc} = -\frac{\overline{n^2} - \bar{n}^2}{kT}, \qquad (7\text{-}213)$$

as in Eq. (7-193).

If the solution is dilute with respect to 1^s, we put $\tilde{s}_1^* = \tilde{s}_1^\square$, $\partial \beta / \partial \psi = 0$, and $\partial \mu_1^* / \partial m_1^s = kT/m_1^s$ in Eqs. (7-210) and (7-211).

Next, we find expressions for the dependence of $\bar{N}_2$, the amount of binding, on several variables of interest. We shall do this by setting $d\mu_2 = d\mu_1^*$, where μ_2 is regarded as a function of T, p, N_1, $\bar{N}_2$, ψ, and sc. This choice of variables is convenient because it contains $\bar{N}_2$ and we can easily put $d\psi = 0$. We start with

$$d\mu_2 = \frac{\partial \mu_2}{\partial T}\,dT + \frac{\partial \mu_2}{\partial p}\,dp + \frac{\partial \mu_2}{\partial N_1}\,dN_1 + \frac{\partial \mu_2}{\partial \bar{N}_2}\,d\bar{N}_2$$

$$+ \frac{\partial \mu_2}{\partial \psi}\,d\psi + \frac{\partial \mu_2}{\partial m_1^s}\,dm_1^s \qquad (sc'). \qquad (7\text{-}214)$$

Using Eq. (7-207), this becomes

$$d\mu_2 = -\frac{\partial S}{\partial \bar{N}_2} dT + \frac{\partial \bar{V}}{\partial \bar{N}_2} dp + \frac{\partial \mu_1^{(2)}}{\partial \bar{N}_2} dN_1 + \frac{\partial \mu_2}{\partial \bar{N}_2} d\bar{N}_2$$

$$+ \frac{\partial \mu_2}{\partial \psi} d\psi + \frac{\partial \beta}{\partial \bar{N}_2} dm_1^s \quad (sc'), \qquad (7\text{-}215)$$

where all derivatives with respect to $\bar{N}_2$ are with T, p, N_1, ψ, and sc held constant. These are not quite small system partial molal quantities, as previously defined, because ψ is constant rather than $\bar{n}$. But it should be pointed out that if we were unaware of the isomeric equilibrium, or chose to ignore its existence (the "black-box" attitude), Eq. (7-215) with $\psi = 0$ would be identical with Eq. (7-98), and the derivatives with respect to $\bar{N}_2$ would then be partial molal quantities [for a small system of two components $(N_1, \bar{N}_2)$ instead of three $(N_1^{(1)}, N_1^{(2)}, \bar{N}_2)$].

In this connection, one can state quite generally that any deductions made here concerning the amount of binding and other properties at $\psi = 0$ (equilibrium with respect to the isomeric reaction) must be formally identical with corresponding results in Section 7-2 where an isomeric reaction is not taken into account.

We now set $d\mu_2$ in Eq. (7-215) equal to $d\mu_1^*$ in Eq. (7-80), take $d\psi = 0$, and find

$$\left(-\frac{\partial S}{\partial \bar{N}_2} + \tilde{s}_1^*\right) dT + \left(\frac{\partial \bar{V}}{\partial \bar{N}_2} - \tilde{v}_1^*\right) dp + \frac{\partial \mu_1^{(2)}}{\partial \bar{N}_2} dN_1 + \frac{\partial \mu_2}{\partial \bar{N}_2} d\bar{N}_2$$

$$+ \left(\frac{\partial \beta}{\partial \bar{N}_2} - \frac{\partial \mu_1^*}{\partial m_1^s}\right) dm_1^s = 0 \qquad (\psi, \delta, sc'). \qquad (7\text{-}216)$$

We can deduce ten equations of the Clausius–Clapeyron type from Eq. (7-216) [just as in Eqs. (7-103) to (7-106)]. Four of these are expressions for derivatives of $\bar{N}_2$ with respect to T, p, N_1, and m_1^s. For example,

$$\left(\frac{\partial \bar{N}_2}{\partial m_1^s}\right)_{T,\, p,\, N_1,\, \psi,\, \delta,\, sc'}$$

$$= \left[\left(\frac{\partial \mu_1^*}{\partial m_1^s}\right)_{T,\, p,\, sc'} - \left(\frac{\partial \beta}{\partial \bar{N}_2}\right)_{T,\, p,\, N_1,\, \psi,\, sc}\right] \Bigg/ \left(\frac{\partial \mu_2}{\partial \bar{N}_2}\right)_{T,\, p,\, N_1,\, \psi,\, sc}. $$

$$(7\text{-}217)$$

When m_1^s is small, this equation simplifies as in Eq. (7-91).

Another deduction from Eq. (7-216) is

$$\left(\frac{\partial m_1^s}{\partial T}\right)_{p, N_1, \bar{N}_2, \psi, \delta, sc'} = \frac{\left(\dfrac{\partial S}{\partial \bar{N}_2}\right)_{T, p, N_1, \psi, sc} - \tilde{s}_1^*}{\left(\dfrac{\partial \beta}{\partial \bar{N}_2}\right)_{T, p, N_1, \psi, sc} - \left(\dfrac{\partial \mu_1^*}{\partial m_1^s}\right)_{T, p, sc'}}.$$

When m_1^s is small,

$$kT\left(\frac{\partial \ln m_1^s}{\partial T}\right)_{p, N_1, \bar{N}_2, \psi, \delta, sc'}$$

$$= \tilde{s}_1^\square - \left(\frac{\partial S}{\partial \bar{N}_2}\right)_{T, p, N_1, \psi, sc} \qquad (m_1^s \to 0). \qquad (7\text{-}218)$$

These equations are the generalizations of Eqs. (7-105) and (7-107).

The quantity $\tilde{s}_1^* - (\partial S/\partial \bar{N}_2)$, which occurs, for example, in the equations for $\partial m_1^s/\partial T$, $\partial \bar{N}_2/\partial T$, and $\partial p/\partial T$, is equal to $[\tilde{h}_1^* - (\partial H/\partial \bar{N}_2)]/T$ when $\psi = 0$ and $\delta = 0$. This follows from

$$\mu_1^* = \tilde{h}_1^* - T\tilde{s}_1^*$$

$$= \mu_2 = \left[\frac{\partial(F + \bar{n}\psi)}{\partial \bar{N}_2}\right]_{T, p, N_1, \psi, sc} \qquad (\delta = 0)$$

$$= \left(\frac{\partial H}{\partial \bar{N}_2}\right)_{T, p, N_1, \psi, sc} - T\left(\frac{\partial S}{\partial \bar{N}_2}\right)_{T, p, N_1, \psi, sc} + \psi\left(\frac{\partial \bar{n}}{\partial \bar{N}_2}\right)_{T, p, N_1, \psi, sc}$$

$$= \frac{\partial H}{\partial \bar{N}_2} - T\frac{\partial S}{\partial \bar{N}_2} \qquad (\psi = 0, \delta = 0).$$

An alternative, more complicated, but equivalent way of deducing the derivatives with respect to $\bar{n}$ and $\bar{N}_2$ found above, as well as other relations, is to use the two simultaneous equations

$$d\mu_2(T, p, N_1, \bar{N}_2, \bar{n}, sc) = d\mu_1^*(T, p, sc), \qquad d\psi(T, p, N_1, \bar{N}_2, \bar{n}, sc) = 0,$$

$$(7\text{-}219)$$

with the independent variables indicated. On employing cross-derivatives in Eq. (7-205), we find for $d\mu_2$,

$$d\mu_2 = -\,\tilde{s}_2\,dT + \tilde{v}_2\,dp + \left(\frac{\partial\mu_2}{\partial N_1}\right)_{T,\,p,\,\bar{N}_2,\,\bar{n},\,sc} dN_1$$

$$+ \left(\frac{\partial\mu_2}{\partial\bar{N}_2}\right)_{T,\,p,\,N_1,\,\bar{n},\,sc} d\bar{N}_2 - \tilde{\psi}_2\,d\bar{n} + \tilde{\beta}_2\,dm_1^s \qquad (sc'), \quad (7\text{-}220)$$

where

$$\tilde{s}_2 = \left(\frac{\partial S}{\partial\bar{N}_2}\right)_{T,\,p,\,N_1,\,\bar{n},\,sc}, \text{ etc.}$$

These are small system partial molal quantities. For $d\psi$ we have

$$d\psi = \frac{\partial\psi}{\partial T}\,dT + \frac{\partial\psi}{\partial p}\,dp + \frac{\partial\psi}{\partial N_1}\,dN_1 + \frac{\partial\psi}{\partial\bar{N}_2}\,d\bar{N}_2$$

$$+ \frac{\partial\psi}{\partial\bar{n}}\,d\bar{n} + \frac{\partial\psi}{\partial m_1^s}\,dm_1^s \qquad (sc')$$

$$= \frac{\partial S}{\partial\bar{n}}\,dT - \frac{\partial\bar{V}}{\partial\bar{n}}\,dp - \frac{\partial\mu_1^{(2)}}{\partial\bar{n}}\,dN_1 - \frac{\partial\mu_2}{\partial\bar{n}}\,d\bar{N}_2$$

$$+ \frac{\partial\psi}{\partial\bar{n}}\,d\bar{n} - \frac{\partial\beta}{\partial\bar{n}}\,dm_1^s \qquad (sc'), \quad (7\text{-}221)$$

where all the derivatives with respect to $\bar{n}$ are at constant T, p, N_1, $\bar{N}_2$, and sc. If we now put Eqs. (7-80), (7-220), and (7-221) into Eqs. (7-219), we obtain two linear simultaneous equations in the quantities dT, dp, dN_1, $d\bar{N}_2$, $d\bar{n}$, and dm_1^s, with δ, ψ, and sc' constant. Hence four of the six variables listed can be independent, just as in Eq. (7-217) where T, p, N_1, and m_1^s are independent variables and $\bar{N}_2$ is a dependent variable. For example, one might solve $d\psi = 0$ for $d\bar{N}_2$, use this expression to eliminate $d\bar{N}_2$ from Eq. (7-219a), and then obtain, say, an expression for the derivative $\partial\bar{n}/\partial T$:

$$\left(\frac{\partial\bar{n}}{\partial T}\right)_{p,\,N_1,\,\psi,\,\delta,\,sc} = \frac{\tilde{s}_2 - \tilde{s}_1^* - (\partial\mu_2/\partial\bar{N}_2)_{T,\,p,\,N_1,\,\bar{n},\,sc}}{(\partial\mu_2/\partial\bar{N}_2)_{T,\,p,\,N_1,\,\bar{n},\,sc}(\partial\bar{n}/\partial\mu_2)_{T,\,p,\,N_1,\,\bar{N}_2,\,sc}} \cdot$$

$$\times \frac{(\partial\bar{n}/\partial\mu_2)_{T,\,p,\,N_1,\,\bar{N}_2,\,sc}(\partial S/\partial\bar{n})_{T,\,p,\,N_1,\,\bar{N}_2,\,sc}}{}$$

$$\times (\partial\psi/\partial\bar{n})_{T,\,p,\,N_1,\,\bar{N}_2,\,sc} - \tilde{\psi}_2$$

This can be shown to reduce to Eq. (7-210). Alternatively, $d\psi = 0$ may be used to eliminate $d\bar{n}$ rather than $d\bar{N}_2$ from Eq. (7-219a).

We define the equilibrium constant K' by

$$K' = \frac{\bar{N}_1^{(2)}}{\bar{N}_1^{(1)}} = \frac{N_1 - \bar{n}}{\bar{n}} \quad \text{at} \quad \psi = 0, \quad \delta = 0. \quad (7\text{-}222)$$

In general, $\bar{n}$ is a function of T, p, N_1, ψ, and m_1^s (δ, sc' constant), as in Eqs. (7-210) to (7-212), and hence K' is also. But the operationally significant value of K' is its value at $\psi = 0$ and $\delta = 0$, and this quantity is a function of T, p, N_1, and m_1^s (sc' constant). In a macroscopic system, it would be a function of T, p, and m_1^s (sc' constant).

The equilibrium constant defined above is not a "constant" in the conventional sense, for the value of the ratio $\bar{N}_1^{(2)}/\bar{N}_1^{(1)}$, at equilibrium, is influenced by the amount ($\bar{N}_2$) of component 2 present. But we take the more practical point of view that m_1^s, like p and T, is an externally controllable, intensive parameter on which K' at $\psi = 0$, $\delta = 0$ depends, and hence K' is a useful "constant."

The temperature derivative of $\ln K'$ is

$$\left(\frac{\partial \ln K'}{\partial T}\right)_{p, N_1, \psi, \delta, sc} = -\frac{N_1}{\bar{n}(N_1 - \bar{n})}\left(\frac{\partial \bar{n}}{\partial T}\right)_{p, N_1, \psi, \delta, sc}, \quad (7\text{-}223)$$

where $\partial \bar{n}/\partial T$ is given by Eq. (7-210). According to Eq. (7-208),

$$\frac{\partial(F - \mu_2 \bar{N}_2)}{\partial \bar{n}} = -\psi = \frac{\partial H}{\partial \bar{n}} - T\frac{\partial S}{\partial \bar{n}} - \mu_2 \frac{\partial \bar{N}_2}{\partial \bar{n}}, \quad (7\text{-}224)$$

with all derivatives at constant T, p, N_1, μ_2, and sc. At equilibrium, $\psi = 0$ and $\mu_2 = \mu_1^* = \tilde{h}_1^* - T\tilde{s}_1^*$. Then

$$\frac{\partial H}{\partial \bar{n}} - \tilde{h}_1^* \frac{\partial \bar{N}_2}{\partial \bar{n}} = T\left(\frac{\partial S}{\partial \bar{n}} - \tilde{s}_1^* \frac{\partial \bar{N}_2}{\partial \bar{n}}\right) \quad (\psi = 0), \quad (7\text{-}225)$$

with all derivatives[1] at constant T, p, N_1, and sc, and with $\delta = 0$. Let us call this quantity $-\Delta H$. We now combine Eqs. (7-210),

---

[1] As in Eq. (5-26), for example, the change dn may be regarded as having been brought about by a variation $d\psi$ at $\psi = 0$ as the system approaches equilibrium with respect to the isomeric reaction.

(7-213), (7-223), and (7-225) to find

$$\left(\frac{\partial \ln K'}{\partial T}\right)_{p, N_1, \psi, \delta, sc} = \frac{\Delta H}{kT^2}\left[\frac{N_1(\overline{x^2} - \bar{x}^2)}{\bar{x}(1 - \bar{x})}\right] \qquad (\psi = 0, \delta = 0), \quad (7\text{-}226)$$

where

$$x = \frac{n}{N_1} = \frac{N_1^{(1)}}{N_1^{(1)} + N_1^{(2)}}.$$

The heat of reaction and binding, and its relation to ΔH, will be discussed in the next subsection because some digression is required.

For the pressure derivative of $\ln K'$, we find

$$\left(\frac{\partial \ln K'}{\partial p}\right)_{T, N_1, \psi, \delta, sc}$$

$$= \frac{1}{kT}\left[\left(\frac{\partial \bar{V}}{\partial \bar{n}}\right)_{T, p, N_1, \delta, sc} - \tilde{v}_1^*\left(\frac{\partial \bar{N}_2}{\partial \bar{n}}\right)_{T, p, N_1, \delta, sc}\right]\left[\frac{N_1(\overline{x^2} - \bar{x}^2)}{\bar{x}(1 - \bar{x})}\right].$$

$$(7\text{-}227)$$

To find the effect of the size (N_1) of the small system on K', we need the Gibbs–Duhem equation

$$d\mathcal{E} = d[(\hat{\mu}_1 - \mu_1^{(2)})N_1]$$

$$= - (S - \bar{N}_2 \tilde{s}_1^*)\,dT + (\bar{V} - \bar{N}_2 \tilde{v}_1^*)\,dp - N_1\,d\mu_1^{(2)} + \bar{n}\,d\psi$$

$$+ \left[\beta - \bar{N}_2\left(\frac{\partial \mu_1^*}{\partial m_1^s}\right)_{T, p, sc'}\right]dm_1^s \qquad (\delta, sc'), \qquad (7\text{-}228)$$

which follows from Eq. (7-209). Using this and Eq. (7-212), we deduce

$$\left(\frac{\partial \ln K'}{\partial N_1}\right)_{T, p, \psi, \delta, sc} = - \frac{1}{N_1 kT}\left(\frac{\partial \mathcal{E}}{\partial \bar{n}}\right)_{T, p, N_1, \delta, sc}\left[\frac{N_1(\overline{x^2} - \bar{x}^2)}{\bar{x}(1 - \bar{x})}\right].$$

$$(7\text{-}229)$$

Also, from Eq. (7-211),

$$\left(\frac{\partial \ln K'}{\partial m_1^s}\right)_{T, p, N_1, \psi, \delta, sc'}$$

$$= \frac{1}{kT}\left[\left(\frac{\partial \beta}{\partial \bar{n}}\right)_{T, p, N_1, \delta, sc} - \left(\frac{\partial \mu_1^*}{\partial m_1^s}\right)_{T, p, sc'}\left(\frac{\partial \bar{N}_2}{\partial \bar{n}}\right)_{T, p, N_1, \delta, sc}\right]$$

$$\times \left[\frac{N_1(\overline{x^2} - \bar{x}^2)}{\bar{x}(1 - \bar{x})}\right]. \qquad (7\text{-}230)$$

When m_1^s is small,

$$\left(\frac{\partial \ln K'}{\partial \ln m_1^s}\right)_{T, p, N_1, \psi, \delta, sc'} = -\left(\frac{\partial \bar{N}_2}{\partial \bar{n}}\right)_{T, p, N_1, \delta, sc}\left[\frac{N_1(\overline{x^2} - \bar{x}^2)}{\bar{x}(1 - \bar{x})}\right].$$

$$(7\text{-}231)$$

Finally, there is the somewhat less practical relation

$$\left(\frac{\partial \ln K'}{\partial \psi}\right)_{T, p, N_1, \delta, sc} = \frac{1}{kT}\left[\frac{N_1(\overline{x^2} - \bar{x}^2)}{\bar{x}(1 - \bar{x})}\right]. \qquad (7\text{-}232)$$

If in Eq. (7-227) we measure (at $\psi = 0$) $\partial \ln K'/\partial p$, $\partial \bar{V}/\partial \bar{n}$, and $\tilde{v}_1^*(\partial \bar{N}_2/\partial \bar{n})$, or if in Eq. (7-231) we measure $\partial \ln K'/\partial \ln m_1^s$ and $\partial \bar{N}_2/\partial \bar{n}$, [ ] may be calculated. From [ ] we can then find $\partial \ln K'/\partial \psi$, from [ ] and $\partial \ln K'/\partial N_1$ we get $\partial \mathscr{E}/\partial \bar{n}$, and from [ ] and $\partial \ln K'/\partial T$ we obtain ΔH.

We can combine Eqs. (7-226) [or (7-223)], (7-227), (7-229), and (7-231), in pairs, to obtain derivatives at constant K' (or $\bar{n}/N_1$). For example,

$$\left(\frac{\partial N_1}{\partial T}\right)_{p, \psi, \delta, K', sc}$$

$$= -N_1\left[\left(\frac{\partial S}{\partial \mathscr{E}}\right)_{T, p, N_1, \delta, sc} - \tilde{s}_1^*\left(\frac{\partial \bar{N}_2}{\partial \mathscr{E}}\right)_{T, p, N_1, \delta, sc}\right]. \quad (7\text{-}233)$$

Another Legendre transformation of Eq. (7-209) is

$$d(\hat{\mu}_1 N_1 - \bar{n}\psi) = -(S - \bar{N}_2\tilde{s}_1^*)\, dT + (\bar{V} - \bar{N}_2\tilde{v}_1^*)\, dp + \mu_1^{(2)}\, dN_1$$

$$- \psi\, d\bar{n} + \left[\beta - \bar{N}_2\left(\frac{\partial \mu_1^*}{\partial m_1^s}\right)_{T, p, sc}\right] dm_1^s \qquad (\delta, sc'). \quad (7\text{-}234)$$

From this we can deduce, for example,

$$\left(\frac{\partial \psi}{\partial T}\right)_{p, N_1, \bar{n}, \delta, sc} = \left(\frac{\partial S}{\partial \bar{n}}\right)_{T, p, N_1, \delta, sc} - \tilde{s}_1^*\left(\frac{\partial \bar{N}_2}{\partial \bar{n}}\right)_{T, p, N_1, \delta, sc} \qquad (7\text{-}235)$$

$$\left(\frac{\partial \psi}{\partial p}\right)_{T, N_1, \bar{n}, \delta, sc} = -\left(\frac{\partial \bar{V}}{\partial \bar{n}}\right)_{T, p, N_1, \delta, sc} + \tilde{v}_1^*\left(\frac{\partial \bar{N}_2}{\partial \bar{n}}\right)_{T, p, N_1, \delta, sc}$$

$$(7\text{-}236)$$

$$\left(\frac{\partial \psi}{\partial N_1}\right)_{T, p, \bar{n}, \delta, sc} = -\left(\frac{\partial \mu_1^{(2)}}{\partial \bar{n}}\right)_{T, p, N_1, \delta, sc}. \qquad (7\text{-}237)$$

Equation (7-235) also follows from Eq. (7-210). On combining Eqs. (7-235) and (7-237), we get

$$\left(\frac{\partial N_1}{\partial T}\right)_{p,\,\bar{n},\,\psi,\,\delta,\,sc} = \left(\frac{\partial S}{\partial \mu_1^{(2)}}\right)_{T,\,p,\,N_1,\,\delta,\,sc} - \tilde{\mathrm{s}}_1^* \left(\frac{\partial \bar{N}_2}{\partial \mu_1^{(2)}}\right)_{T,\,p,\,N_1,\,\delta,\,sc}.$$

(7-238)

This differs from Eq. (7-233) in that $\bar{n}$ rather than $\bar{n}/N_1$ is constant here.

There are, of course, a vast number of other relations which can be derived. We have presented what we hope is a reasonable sample.

HEAT OF REACTION AND BINDING. Because of the binding of component 2 from solution, the small systems are not closed. We therefore consider the whole macroscopic solution in discussing the heat of reaction and binding. For the macroscopic solution [compare Eq. (7-195)],

$$dE_T = T\,dS_T - p\,dV_T + \sum_i \mu_i^s\,dN_i^s + \mu^\square\,d\mathcal{N}$$

$$+ \mu_1^{(2)}\mathcal{N}\,dN_1 + \mu_2\mathcal{N}\,d\bar{N}_2 - \psi\mathcal{N}\,d\bar{n}. \qquad (7\text{-}239)$$

For an infinitesimal, reversible process occurring in the closed macroscopic system, the following quantities are constant:

$$N_2^s, ..., N_c^s, \qquad N_1^s + \mathcal{N}\bar{N}_2, \qquad \mathcal{N}, \qquad N_1. \qquad (7\text{-}240)$$

In such a process, $DQ_T = T\,dS_T$.

A general expression for dS_T, which we shall use below, is

$$dS_T = \frac{\partial S_T}{\partial T}\,dT + \frac{\partial S_T}{\partial p}\,dp + \sum_i \frac{\partial S_T}{\partial N_i^s}\,dN_i^s + \frac{\partial S_T}{\partial \bar{N}_2}\,d\bar{N}_2$$

$$+ \frac{\partial S_T}{\partial \bar{N}_1^{(1)}}\,d\bar{N}_1^{(1)} + \frac{\partial S_T}{\partial \bar{N}_1^{(2)}}\,d\bar{N}_1^{(2)} + \frac{\partial S_T}{\partial \mathcal{N}}\,d\mathcal{N}. \qquad (7\text{-}241)$$

From this point on we consider specifically the heat of the process in which the reaction proceeds to an extent $d\bar{n}$ (at $\psi = 0$, $\delta = 0$) with the macroscopic system closed and with p and T constant. This process could be realized experimentally by following the closed macroscopic system at constant p and T in its approach to isomeric equilibrium ($\psi \to 0$) and noting the heat absorbed by the macroscopic system at the last stage $d\bar{n}$ of this approach. For the process just described,

$$DQ_T = T\,dS_T = T\left(-\mathcal{N}\frac{\partial S_T}{\partial N_1^s} + \frac{\partial S_T}{\partial \bar{N}_2}\right)d\bar{N}_2$$

$$+ T\left(\frac{\partial S_T}{\partial \bar{N}_1^{(1)}} - \frac{\partial S_T}{\partial \bar{N}_1^{(2)}}\right)d\bar{n}, \qquad (7\text{-}242)$$

where we have used Eqs. (7-240) and (7-241). From

$$S_T = \mathcal{N}(S - k\ln x') + \sum_i N_i^s \tilde{s}_i^s$$

we find

$$DQ_T = T\,dS_T = \mathcal{N}T\left[\left(\frac{\partial S}{\partial \bar{N}_2}\right)_{T,\,p,\,N_1,\,\bar{n},\,sc} - \tilde{s}_1^*\right]d\bar{N}_2$$

$$+ \mathcal{N}T\left(\frac{\partial S}{\partial \bar{n}}\right)_{T,\,p,\,N_1,\,\bar{N}_2,\,sc}d\bar{n}. \qquad (7\text{-}243)$$

The term in $d\bar{N}_2$ is the heat of binding, whereas the term in $d\bar{n}$ is the heat of reaction.

In the above process, although an average of $d\bar{N}_2$ molecules of component 1^s are removed from the solution and bound on each small system, the chemical potential μ_1^* in the solution remains effectively constant. This follows because the number of small systems is so small ($\mathcal{N} \to 0$) relative to the amount of solvent that N_1^s is virtually constant. Since $\delta = 0$ and $\mu_1^* = $ constant, $\mu_2 = $ constant.

Thus Eq. (7-243) can be written

$$\left(\frac{DQ_T}{\partial \bar{n}}\right)_{p,\,T,\,\text{closed}} = \mathcal{N}T\left[\left(\frac{\partial S}{\partial \bar{N}_2}\right)_{T,\,p,\,N_1,\,\bar{n},\,sc} - \tilde{s}_1^*\right]$$

$$\times \left(\frac{\partial \bar{N}_2}{\partial \bar{n}}\right)_{T,\,p,\,N_1,\,\mu_2,\,sc} + \mathcal{N}T\left(\frac{\partial S}{\partial \bar{n}}\right)_{T,\,p,\,N_1,\,\bar{N}_2,\,sc} \qquad (\psi = 0, \delta = 0).$$
$$(7\text{-}244)$$

If we employ

$$\left(\frac{\partial S}{\partial \bar{n}}\right)_{T,\,p,\,N_1,\,\mu_2,\,sc} = \left(\frac{\partial S}{\partial \bar{n}}\right)_{T,\,p,\,N_1,\,\bar{N}_2,\,sc}$$

$$+ \left(\frac{\partial S}{\partial \bar{N}_2}\right)_{T,\,p,\,N_1,\,\bar{n},\,sc}\left(\frac{\partial \bar{N}_2}{\partial \bar{n}}\right)_{T,\,p,\,N_1,\,\mu_2,\,sc},$$

Eq. (7-244) becomes

$$\left(\frac{DQ_T}{\partial \bar{n}}\right)_{p, T, \text{ closed}}$$

$$= \mathscr{N}T\left[\left(\frac{\partial S}{\partial \bar{n}}\right)_{T, p, N_1, \delta, sc} - \tilde{s}_1^*\left(\frac{\partial \bar{N}_2}{\partial \bar{n}}\right)_{T, p, N_1, \delta, sc}\right] \quad (\psi = 0, \delta = 0).$$

$$(7\text{-}245)$$

Finally, from Eq. (7-226),

$$\left(\frac{\partial \ln K'}{\partial T}\right)_{p, N_1, \psi, \delta, sc} = -\left[\frac{N_1(\overline{x^2} - \bar{x}^2)}{\bar{x}(1 - \bar{x})}\right]$$

$$\times \frac{1}{\mathscr{N}kT^2}\left(\frac{DQ_T}{\partial \bar{n}}\right)_{p, T, \text{ closed}} \quad (\psi = 0, \delta = 0). \quad (7\text{-}246)$$

Example. Helix-Coil Transition. Independent Helix and Coil Units. We assume here, as in Eqs. (2-99) and (5-107), that any one of the N_1 units in the chain can be of helix or coil type, independently. When there are n helix units and no binding of component 2 on the chain, the canonical ensemble partition function is

$$Q = \frac{q_H^n q_C^{N_1 - n} N_1!}{n!(N_1 - n)!}, \quad (7\text{-}247)$$

where $q_H(T)$ and $q_C(T)$ are individual unit partition functions.

Now let us assume further that each unit has one site for binding one molecule of component 2. All sites are independent; all H sites are equivalent, as are all C sites. The partition function for a bound molecule is $j_H(T)$ on an H site and $j_C(T)$ on a C site. Then for a chain with n helix units, N_{2H} component 2 molecules bound on H sites, and N_{2C} component 2 molecules bound on C sites,

$$Q(n, N_1, N_{2H}, N_{2C}, T) = \frac{q_H^n q_C^{N_1 - n} N_1!}{n!(N_1 - n)!} \frac{j_H^{N_{2H}} n!}{N_{2H}!(n - N_{2H})!}$$

$$\times \frac{j_C^{N_{2C}}(N_1 - n)!}{N_{2C}!(N_1 - n - N_{2C})!}. \quad (7\text{-}248)$$

The partition function Z of Eq. (7-190) is in this case

$$Z(N_1, \mu_2, T, \psi) = \sum_{n=0}^{N_1} \sum_{N_{2H}=0}^{n} \sum_{N_{2C}=0}^{N_1-n} Q(n, N_1, N_{2H}, N_{2C}, T)$$
$$\times\ e^{-n\psi/kT}e^{(N_{2H}+N_{2C})\mu_2/kT}$$
$$= [q_C(1 + j_C\lambda_2) + q_H e^{-\psi/kT}(1 + j_H\lambda_2)]^{N_1},$$
$$(7\text{-}249)$$

where $\lambda_2 = e^{\mu_2/kT}$. This is a special case of Eqs. (7-64) and (7-68) in S.T. From Eq. (7-191),

$$\hat{\mu}_1 N_1 = -N_1 kT \ln[\ ] \qquad (7\text{-}250)$$

where [ ] is the expression in brackets in Eq. (7-249).

Equation (7-186) then gives the thermodynamic functions. Thus we find

$$\mathscr{E} = 0 \qquad (7\text{-}251)$$

$$\frac{\bar{n}}{N_1} = \frac{q_H e^{-\psi/kT}(1 + j_H\lambda_2)}{[\ ]} \qquad (7\text{-}252)$$

$$K' = \frac{N_1 - \bar{n}}{\bar{n}} = \frac{q_C(1 + j_C\lambda_2)}{q_H(1 + j_H\lambda_2)} \qquad \text{at}\ \ \psi = 0 \qquad (7\text{-}253)$$

$$\frac{\bar{N}_2}{N_1} = \frac{\bar{N}_{2C}}{N_1} + \frac{\bar{N}_{2H}}{N_1}$$

$$= \frac{q_C j_C\lambda_2}{[\ ]} + \frac{q_H e^{-\psi/kT}j_H\lambda_2}{[\ ]}$$

$$= \frac{N_1 - \bar{n}}{N_1}\frac{j_C\lambda_2}{1 + j_C\lambda_2} + \frac{\bar{n}}{N_1}\frac{j_H\lambda_2}{1 + j_H\lambda_2}. \qquad (7\text{-}254)$$

These results are simple and their interpretation self-evident. Also, from Eq. (7-193),

$$\frac{\overline{n^2} - \bar{n}^2}{\bar{n}^2} = \frac{N_1 - \bar{n}}{N_1\bar{n}} = O\!\left(\frac{1}{N_1}\right). \qquad (7\text{-}255)$$

This is the same as Eq. (5-111).

All-or-None Model. This is essentially the model in Eq. (2-95), but here we introduce binding of component 2 on H and C units as in Eq. (7-248) above. Without binding,

$$Q = q_C^{N_1} + q_H^{N_1}. \qquad (7\text{-}256)$$

With binding,

$$Q(n, N_1, N_{2H}, N_{2C}, T) = Q_C + Q_H$$

$$= \frac{q_C^{N_1} j_C^{N_{2C}} N_1!}{N_{2C}!(N_1 - N_{2C})!} + \frac{q_H^{N_1} j_H^{N_{2H}} N_1!}{N_{2H}!(N_1 - N_{2H})!} \qquad (7\text{-}257)$$

and

$$Z(N_1, \mu_2, T, \psi) = \sum_{N_{2C}=0}^{N_1} Q_C \lambda_2^{N_{2C}} + \sum_{N_{2H}=0}^{N_1} Q_H \lambda_2^{N_{2H}} e^{-N_1 \psi / kT}$$

$$= [q_C(1 + j_C \lambda_2)]^{N_1} + [q_H e^{-\psi/kT}(1 + j_H \lambda_2)]^{N_1}. \qquad (7\text{-}258)$$

Then we deduce

$$\hat{\mu}_1 N_1 = -kT \ln Z \qquad (7\text{-}259)$$

$$-\frac{\mu_1^{(2)}}{kT} = \frac{1}{Z}\{[q_C(1 + j_C \lambda_2)]^{N_1} \ln[q_C(1 + j_C \lambda_2)]$$

$$+ [q_H e^{-\psi/kT}(1 + j_H \lambda_2)]^{N_1} \ln[q_H e^{-\psi/kT}(1 + j_H \lambda_2)]\} \qquad (7\text{-}260)$$

$$\frac{\bar{n}}{N_1} = \frac{[q_H e^{-\psi/kT}(1 + j_H \lambda_2)]^{N_1}}{Z} \qquad (7\text{-}261)$$

$$K' = \left[\frac{q_C(1 + j_C \lambda_2)}{q_H(1 + j_H \lambda_2)}\right]^{N_1} \quad \text{at} \quad \psi = 0. \qquad (7\text{-}262)$$

The helix-coil transition may be said to occur at $K' = 1$, that is, when

$$q_C(1 + j_C \lambda_2) = q_H(1 + j_H \lambda_2). \qquad (7\text{-}263)$$

This equation gives, for example, the molality m_1^s at which the transition takes place as a function of temperature. The transition becomes sharper, of course, as $N_1 \to \infty$ (Fig. 2-4).

Equation (7-254) for $\bar{N}_2/N_1$ is again found, but with $\bar{n}/N_1$ given by Eq. (7-261). Finally,

$$\frac{\overline{n^2} - \bar{n}^2}{\bar{n}^2} = \frac{N_1 - \bar{n}}{\bar{n}} = O(1). \tag{7-264}$$

This should be contrasted with Eq. (7-255). Fluctuations are larger here because the system is forced by the model to be all helix or all coil. The order of magnitude of the fluctuations is the same as in a first-order phase transition, as expected.

More Detailed Model. The helix-coil transition with binding (for an infinite system) is discussed in a much more detailed way than above by R. F. Steiner.[1]

Experimental. The only experimental small system effect of this sort known to the author is the work of A. Wada,[2] which shows a dependence of the titration curve of poly-L-glutamic acid on molecular weight. The observed effect is small because both molecular weights used are large.

[1] See R. F. Steiner and R. F. Beers, Jr., "Polynucleotides," pp. 277–289, Elsevier, Amsterdam, 1961.
[2] A. Wada, *Mol. Phys.*, **3**, 409 (1960).

CHAPTER 8

ENVIRONMENTAL VARIABLES N, V, T

The small system under consideration in this chapter is closed, has an assigned volume V, and is in a heat bath at temperature T. This case is unimportant experimentally. However, on the theoretical side, the pertinent partition function is the canonical ensemble partition function $Q(N, V, T)$, probably the most widely used in statistical mechanics. Hence our point of view in this chapter will be primarily theoretical.

It will be recalled that Section 3-1 was concerned with an incompressible N, T system. Such a system is a degenerate case of an N, p, T system, as was pointed out in Chapter 3. But an N, T system may of course also be regarded as a degenerate form of an N, V, T system, to be studied in the present chapter.

8-I. THERMODYNAMIC RELATIONS

An introduction to this subject is provided by Eqs. (1-43) to (1-48) and Section 1-4. The fundamental equations for a small system are

$$d\bar{E} = T\,dS - p\,dV + \mu\,dN \tag{8-1}$$

$$A = \bar{E} - TS \tag{8-2}$$

$$\mathscr{E} = \bar{E} - TS + pV - \mu N \tag{8-3}$$

$$dA = -S\,dT - p\,dV + \mu\,dN \tag{8-4}$$

$$d\mathscr{E} = -S\,dT + V\,dp - N\,d\mu \tag{8-5}$$

$$A = -kT \ln Q(N, V, T). \tag{8-6}$$

Because there are two extensive environmental variables, N and V, it is not generally advantageous to introduce either $\hat{\mu}$ or $\hat{p}$. However, there are exceptions, as will be noted below.

The reader will recall that, with the environmental variables N, p, T, the important quantity $\hat{\mu}$ is equal to the "characteristic function" [see Eq. (1-81)] divided by N. If we consider the environmental variables here to be $N, V/N, T$ (one extensive variable), then an analogue of $\hat{\mu}$ would be A/N. Similarly, if the environmental variables are regarded as N/V, V, T, then an analogue of $-\hat{p}$ is A/V.

With these facts in mind, we rewrite Eq. (8-4) in the forms

$$d\left(\frac{A}{N}\right) = -\frac{S}{N}dT - \frac{pN}{N}d\left(\frac{V}{N}\right) - \frac{\mathscr{E}}{N^2}dN \qquad (8\text{-}7)$$

and

$$d\left(\frac{A}{V}\right) = -\frac{S}{V}dT + \frac{\mu V}{V}d\left(\frac{N}{V}\right) - \frac{\mathscr{E}}{V^2}dV, \qquad (8\text{-}8)$$

which resemble Eqs. (2-13) and (6-10), respectively.

Similarly, the analogue here of $\mu = (\hat{\mu}N - \mathscr{E})/N$ in an N, p, T system is $(A - \mathscr{E})/N$. Using Maxwell relations from

$$dA = -S\,dT - pN\,d\left(\frac{V}{N}\right) + \left(\frac{A - \mathscr{E}}{N}\right)dN, \qquad (8\text{-}9)$$

we obtain

$$d\left(\frac{A - \mathscr{E}}{N}\right) = -\left(\frac{\partial S}{\partial N}\right)_{T,\,V/N} dT - \left(\frac{\partial pN}{\partial N}\right)_{T,\,V/N} d\left(\frac{V}{N}\right)$$
$$- \frac{1}{N}\left(\frac{\partial \mathscr{E}}{\partial N}\right)_{T,\,V/N} dN. \qquad (8\text{-}10)$$

This corresponds to Eq. (2-17). The expression with V is

$$d\left(\frac{A - \mathscr{E}}{V}\right) = -\left(\frac{\partial S}{\partial V}\right)_{T,\,N/V} dT + \left(\frac{\partial \mu V}{\partial V}\right)_{T,\,N/V} d\left(\frac{N}{V}\right)$$
$$- \frac{1}{V}\left(\frac{\partial \mathscr{E}}{\partial V}\right)_{T,\,N/V} dV, \qquad (8\text{-}11)$$

which should be compared with Eq. (6-11).

We also have

$$\frac{A}{N} = \frac{\bar{E}}{N} - \frac{TS}{N}, \qquad \frac{A}{V} = \frac{\bar{E}}{V} - \frac{TS}{V} \qquad (8\text{-}12)$$

$$\frac{A - \mathscr{E}}{N} = \left(\frac{\partial A}{\partial N}\right)_{T,\,V/N} = \left(\frac{\partial \bar{E}}{\partial N}\right)_{T,\,V/N} - T\left(\frac{\partial S}{\partial N}\right)_{T,\,V/N} \qquad (8\text{-}13)$$

$$\frac{A - \mathscr{E}}{V} = \left(\frac{\partial A}{\partial V}\right)_{T,\,N/V} = \left(\frac{\partial \bar{E}}{\partial V}\right)_{T,\,N/V} - T\left(\frac{\partial S}{\partial V}\right)_{T,\,N/V}. \qquad (8\text{-}14)$$

A few relations showing the effect of the size of the system on intensive properties are:

$$\left(\frac{\partial p}{\partial N}\right)_{T,\,V/N} = \frac{1}{N}\left(\frac{\partial \mathscr{E}}{\partial V}\right)_{T,\,N} \tag{8-15}$$

$$\left(\frac{\partial \mu}{\partial V}\right)_{T,\,N/V} = -\frac{1}{V}\left(\frac{\partial \mathscr{E}}{\partial N}\right)_{T,\,V} \tag{8-16}$$

$$N^2\left(\frac{\partial S/N}{\partial N}\right)_{T,\,V/N} = \left(\frac{\partial \mathscr{E}}{\partial T}\right)_{N,\,V} = V^2\left(\frac{\partial S/V}{\partial V}\right)_{T,\,N/V} \tag{8-17}$$

$$N^2\left(\frac{\partial A/N}{\partial N}\right)_{T,\,V/N} = -\mathscr{E} = V^2\left(\frac{\partial A/V}{\partial V}\right)_{T,\,N/V}. \tag{8-18}$$

Excess functions may be defined in terms of either N or V. For example, for N [compare Eq. (2-54) et seq.]:

$$G(N, V/N, T) = N_{\mathrm{G}}^{(0)}(V/N, T) + G^{(x)}(N, V/N, T) \tag{8-19}$$

$$\mu(N, V/N, T) = \mu^{(0)}(V/N, T) + \mu^{(x)}(N, V/N, T) \tag{8-20}$$

$$p(N, V/N, T) = p^{(0)}(V/N, T) + p^{(x)}(N, V/N, T). \tag{8-21}$$

Then

$$\mathscr{E} = A^{(x)} + p^{(x)}V - \mu^{(x)}N \tag{8-22}$$

$$dA^{(x)} = -S^{(x)}\,dT - p^{(x)}\,dV + \mu^{(x)}\,dN \tag{8-23}$$

$$d\mathscr{E} = -S^{(x)}\,dT + V\,dp^{(x)} - N\,d\mu^{(x)}. \tag{8-24}$$

The calorimetric equations for a small N, V, T system are uncomplicated [compare Eq. (2-29) et seq.]:

$$d\bar{E} = T\,dS = DQ \qquad (N, V \text{ constant}) \tag{8-25}$$

$$C_V = \left(\frac{DQ}{\partial T}\right)_{N,\,V} = \left(\frac{\partial \bar{E}}{\partial T}\right)_{N,\,V} = T\left(\frac{\partial S}{\partial T}\right)_{N,\,V}. \tag{8-26}$$

As a final topic, we derive the analogue of the well-known macroscopic equation

$$\left(\frac{N}{V}\right)^2\left(\frac{\partial \mu}{\partial N}\right)_{T,\,V} = -\left(\frac{\partial p}{\partial V}\right)_{T,\,N} \qquad \text{(macroscopic)}.$$

This equation is useful in relating μ versus N/V and p versus V/N curves, for example, in connection with phase transitions. From

Eq. (8-5),

$$\left(\frac{\partial \mathscr{E}}{\partial V}\right)_{T,\,N} = V\left(\frac{\partial p}{\partial V}\right)_{T,\,N} - N\left(\frac{\partial \mu}{\partial V}\right)_{T,\,N} \tag{8-27}$$

and

$$\left(\frac{\partial \mathscr{E}}{\partial N}\right)_{T,\,V} = V\left(\frac{\partial p}{\partial N}\right)_{T,\,V} - N\left(\frac{\partial \mu}{\partial N}\right)_{T,\,V}. \tag{8-28}$$

A Maxwell relation which follows from Eq. (8-4) is

$$\left(\frac{\partial \mu}{\partial V}\right)_{T,\,N} = -\left(\frac{\partial p}{\partial N}\right)_{T,\,V}. \tag{8-29}$$

Using this in Eqs. (8-27) and (8-28), we have

$$\frac{N^2}{V^2}\left(\frac{\partial \mu}{\partial N}\right)_{T,\,V} + \frac{N}{V^2}\left(\frac{\partial \mathscr{E}}{\partial N}\right)_{T,\,V} = -\left(\frac{\partial p}{\partial V}\right)_{T,\,N} + \frac{1}{V}\left(\frac{\partial \mathscr{E}}{\partial V}\right)_{T,\,N}. \tag{8-30}$$

This is the desired result. A more compact form of this equation is

$$\frac{N^2}{V^2}\left(\frac{\partial \hat{\mu}}{\partial N}\right)_{T,\,V} = -\left(\frac{\partial \hat{p}}{\partial V}\right)_{T,\,N}, \tag{8-31}$$

where, as usual,

$$\hat{\mu} = \mu + \frac{\mathscr{E}}{N}, \qquad \hat{p} = p - \frac{\mathscr{E}}{V}. \tag{8-32}$$

Equations (10-132) and (10-135) should also be noted in this connection.

8-2. PHASE TRANSITIONS

A rather detailed discussion of first-order phase transitions in finite N, V, T systems has already been given elsewhere.[1] There seems little point in repeating this material here. Instead, we shall give below a brief summary of the general situation and supplement this with a consideration of three examples.

Because of interfacial effects, an *exact* theory of a first-order phase transition in a finite system will give: (a) two peaks in the probability curve $P(V)$ for an N, p, T system (Section 5-4); (b) two peaks in the probability curve $P(N)$ for a μ, V, T system (Section 6-1); and

[1] S.M., Appendix 9; and T. L. Hill, *J. Chem. Phys.*, **23**, 812 (1955).

(c) a "loop" in the p versus V/N (N constant) and μ versus N/V (V constant) curves for an N, V, T system. These loops are *not* of the van der Waals type. They are "small" loops which disappear (leaving horizontal lines) as $N \to \infty$, whereas loops of the van der Waals type, which arise through the imposition of a restraint of uniform density, do not so disappear.

It is possible for N, p, T and μ, V, T systems at a phase transition to "avoid" an interface by existing solely as one phase or the other. But an N, V, T system cannot do this; it must have an interface.

The small loops referred to above arise in exact theories, so there is no question here (as with van der Waals loops in macroscopic systems) of finding a horizontal line which is "more exact" than a given small loop. However, if a horizontal line *is* drawn in a $p-V/N$ (N constant) or $\mu-N/V$ (V constant) diagram, based on equal areas in the conventional way, the two ends of the line *do* correspond to the same value of $\hat{\mu}$ in the former case and of $\hat{p}$ in the latter. Otherwise, however, the horizontal line has no particular interest.

The proof of the above statement about $\hat{\mu}$ and $\hat{p}$ follows. From Eq. (8-5),

$$d(\mathscr{E} + \mu N) = d(\hat{\mu}N) = -S\,dT + V\,dp + \mu\,dN \qquad (8\text{-}33)$$

$$d(\mathscr{E} - pV) = -d(\hat{p}V) = -S\,dT - p\,dV - N\,d\mu. \quad (8\text{-}34)$$

Then

$$d\hat{\mu} = \frac{V}{N}\,dp \qquad (T, N \text{ constant}) \qquad\qquad (8\text{-}35)$$

$$d\hat{p} = \frac{N}{V}\,d\mu \qquad (T, V \text{ constant}). \qquad\qquad (8\text{-}36)$$

Integration of these equations gives the desired results.

A finite system with the restraint of uniform density imposed will exhibit $p-V/N$ and $\mu-N/V$ loops of the van der Waals type which will differ from the macroscopic van der Waals loops for the same system by "small" amounts only. Presumably there is no general thermo-dynamic theorem (such as exists in the macroscopic case, i.e., the equal-area theorem) that will tell us how to pass from the van der Waals loops to the small loops when the restraint of uniform density is removed.

Consider *any* $Q(N, V, T)$, exact or approximate, which gives a loop in, say, a p versus V/N (N constant) diagram. That is,

$(\partial p/\partial V)_{T, N}$ is positive in the "middle" of the curve. Then, since the first and third terms in Eq. (8-30) are larger than the other two by a factor of order N, $(\partial \mu/\partial N)_{T, V}$ will be negative in the middle of a μ versus N/V (V constant) curve for the same N, V, T system. That is, this latter diagram will also show a loop. Furthermore, the existence of a p–V loop for an N, V, T system implies[1] two peaks in the $P(V)$ probability curve for an N, p, T system (with the same Q), and the existence of a μ–N loop for an N, V, T system implies two peaks in the $P(N)$ probability curve for a μ, V, T system (with the same Q). Thus the four properties mentioned above are all tied together and all follow from the given $Q(N, V, T)$.

Example. Twelve-Site Lattice Gas on a Sphere. Consider a lattice gas of twelve sites ($B = 12$) arranged on the surface of a sphere (cubic close packing). Each site has four nearest-neighbor sites. Let w be the nearest-neighbor pair interaction energy. Then the exact canonical ensemble partition function is

$$Q(N, T) = \sum_M \Omega(N, M)y^M, \qquad (8\text{-}37)$$

where $y = e^{-w/kT}$ and $\Omega(N, M)$ is the number of ways in which N sites can be occupied so that there are M nearest-neighbor occupied pairs of sites. Of course

$$\sum_M \Omega(N, M) = \frac{12!}{N!(12 - N)!}$$

and

$$\sum_{N, M} \Omega(N, M) = 2^{12} = 4096.$$

Then one finds[2] by actual count (first done by R. Peierls for another purpose)

$$Q(0, T) = 1, \qquad Q(1, T) = 12, \qquad Q(2, T) = 42 + 24y,$$

$$Q(3, T) = 44 + 120y + 48y^2 + 8y^3,$$

$$Q(4, T) = 9 + 96y + 240y^2 + 96y^3 + 54y^4,$$

$$Q(5, T) = 108y^2 + 264y^3 + 264y^4 + 120y^5 + 36y^6,$$

$$Q(6, T) = 216y^4 + 240y^5 + 336y^6 + 96y^7 + 36y^8,$$

$$Q(N, T) = Q(12 - N, T)y^{4(N-6)} \qquad (7 \leqslant N \leqslant 12).$$

[1] See S.M., pp. 415–416.
[2] T. L. Hill, *J. Chem. Phys.*, **23**, 812 (1955). The function $P(N)$ for an open system is discussed for this example in this reference, in Appendix 9 of S.M., and following Eq. (10-182).

We cannot vary B in this example to find p but we can vary N to find μ. However, N is a small number so we have to use differences rather than differentials. We therefore define[1]

$$\mu_N \equiv A_{N+1} - A_N = -kT \ln \frac{Q_{N+1}}{Q_N}.$$ (8-38)

Then

$$\frac{\mu_0}{kT} = -\ln 12, \qquad \frac{\mu_1}{kT} = -\ln\left(\frac{7 + 4y}{2}\right), \qquad \text{etc.}$$

The symmetry relation

$$\frac{\mu_N}{kT} + \frac{\mu_{11-N}}{kT} = -\ln y^4$$

is useful here. It is now easy to compute μ_N as a function of N and y.

Figure 8-1 shows μ_N/kT plotted against N for various values of $y = e^{-w/kT}$. The curves are not smooth because N is small. But it is clear that $y = 3$ is approximately the critical curve,[2] and for $y > 3$ one finds the equivalent of loops. That is, in the middle of the μ_N–N curves, for $y > 3$, the slope is negative, whereas at the edges the loops are not completed only because of discreteness in N. This is indicated schematically by the dashed additions to the $y = 4$ curve.

These curves[3] leave no doubt that an exact theory of a first-order phase transition in the canonical ensemble will give loops. The loops here appear "large" rather than "small" only because B is so small. The extent of the "loop" along the μ_N/kT axis in Fig. 8-1 is

$$\Delta\left(\frac{\mu_N}{kT}\right) = O(1),$$

which is consistent with the expected range[4]

$$\Delta\left(\frac{\mu_N}{kT}\right) = O(B^{-1/2}).$$

[1] See Chapter 15.
[2] The value $y = 3.1$ was guessed (loc. cit.) from the $P(N)$ curves.
[3] My colleague, Professor S. Katsura, has verified these results by the same kind of calculation for sites on a finite torus (3×3, 4×4, 6×6, 8×8). See also Z. W. Salsburg, J. D. Jacobson, W. Fickett, and W. W. Wood, *J. Chem. Phys.*, **30**, 65 (1959).
[4] T. L. Hill, loc. cit.

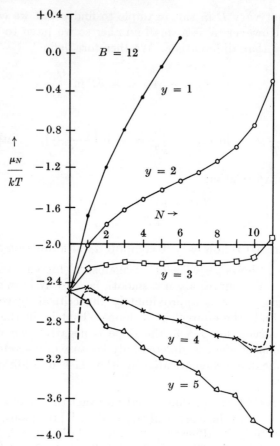

FIGURE 8-1.   Exact calculation of μ_N/kT versus N for twelve-site spherical lattice gas in canonical ensemble. $y = e^{-w/kT}$ is essentially a measure of temperature. "Loops" are obtained.

Example. Incompressible Phases. This is the same simple model as in Eqs. (5-144) and (5-145), but here we must put in an explicit interfacial term.

We consider a first-order transition between two condensed phases A and B. When only phase A is present (i.e., at one end of the transition), the number density ($\equiv N/V$) is ρ_A, assumed a function of T only. When only B is present, $\rho = \rho_B(T)$. We take

$\rho_B > \rho_A$, as before. The phase transition occurs at $p = p_0$ and $\mu = \mu_0$, both assumed functions of T only.

For values of ρ between ρ_A and ρ_B, an interface must be present and there is an interfacial contribution, A_{int}, to the Helmholtz free energy A. To a first approximation, A_{int} is simply proportional to the interfacial area. This area, in turn, is a function of ρ which is determined by the geometry of the system. The case we consider here is very simple: we assume that the interfacial area varies linearly with ρ, with a maximum area at $\rho = (\rho_A + \rho_B)/2$. We take A_{int} at this maximum to be $c(T)V^{2/3}$, where $c > 0$. Thus

$$A_{\text{int}} = \frac{2cV^{2/3}(\rho - \rho_A)}{\rho_B - \rho_A} \qquad \left(\rho_A \leqslant \rho \leqslant \frac{\rho_A + \rho_B}{2}\right)$$

$$= \frac{2cV^{2/3}(\rho_B - \rho)}{\rho_B - \rho_A} \qquad \left(\frac{\rho_A + \rho_B}{2} \leqslant \rho \leqslant \rho_B\right). \tag{8-39}$$

Then, for the complete free energy,

$$A = N\mu_0 - p_0 V + A_{\text{int}} \qquad (\rho_A \leqslant \rho \leqslant \rho_B). \tag{8-40}$$

We can now derive thermodynamic properties of interest in the two-phase region. For the chemical potential, we find

$$\mu = \left(\frac{\partial A}{\partial N}\right)_{T,\,V} = \mu_0 + \frac{2cV^{-1/3}}{\rho_B - \rho_A} \qquad (A)$$

$$= \mu_0 - \frac{2cV^{-1/3}}{\rho_B - \rho_A} \qquad (B), \tag{8-41}$$

where (A) and (B) refer to the respective intervals in Eq. (8-39). Figure 8-2a shows μ as a function of ρ, with the simplified loop that is a consequence of Eq. (8-39).

The pressure is

$$p = -\left(\frac{\partial A}{\partial V}\right)_{T,\,N} = p_0 + \frac{2cV^{-1/3}(\rho + 2\rho_A)}{3(\rho_B - \rho_A)} \qquad (A)$$

$$= p_0 - \frac{2cV^{-1/3}(2\rho_B + \rho)}{3(\rho_B - \rho_A)} \qquad (B). \tag{8-42}$$

This is shown schematically in Fig. 8-2b.

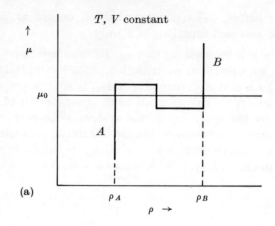

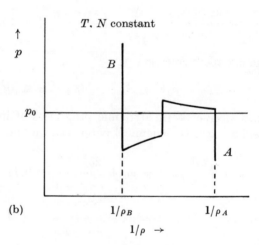

FIGURE 8-2. (a) μ as a function of ρ for simple phase transition model. (b) p as a function of $1/\rho$ for simple phase transition model.

From A, p, and μ we can easily deduce $\mathscr{E}$:

$$\mathscr{E} = \frac{2cV^{2/3}(\rho - \rho_A)}{3(\rho_B - \rho_A)} \qquad (A)$$

$$= \frac{2cV^{2/3}(\rho_B - \rho)}{3(\rho_B - \rho_A)} \qquad (B).$$

(8-43)

Thus $\mathscr{E} = A_{\text{int}}/3$. Using $\mathscr{E}$, we then have

$$\hat{\mu} = \mu_0 + \frac{2cV^{-1/3}(4\rho - \rho_A)}{3(\rho_B - \rho_A)\rho} \qquad (A)$$

$$= \mu_0 - \frac{2cV^{-1/3}(4\rho - \rho_B)}{3(\rho_B - \rho_A)\rho} \qquad (B)$$

(8-44)

and

$$\hat{p} = p_0 + \frac{2cV^{-1/3}\rho_A}{\rho_B - \rho_A} \qquad (A)$$

$$= p_0 - \frac{2cV^{-1/3}\rho_B}{\rho_B - \rho_A} \qquad (B).$$

(8-45)

Equations (8-30) and (8-31) may be used as a check on Eqs. (8-41) to (8-45).

Example. Bragg-Williams Lattice Gas. This model was discussed in Section 6-2 for an open system. The canonical ensemble partition function [Eq. (6-58)] is

$$Q(N, B, T) = \frac{B!e^{-\alpha N^2/B}}{N!(B - N)!}.$$

(8-46)

As is well known, this partition function gives a loop of the van der Waals type in a μ versus N/B plot for a macroscopic system when $-\alpha > 2$. Our object here is merely to confirm the expected: that the loop still exists for a finite system but is modified by small terms.

To obtain the first-order nonmacroscopic effect, we write

$$\ln Q = B \ln B - N \ln N - (B - N) \ln (B - N)$$

$$- \tfrac{1}{2} \ln \frac{2\pi N(B - N)}{B} - \frac{\alpha N^2}{B} + \cdots.$$

(8-47)

Then, from

$$-\frac{\mu}{kT} = \left(\frac{\partial \ln Q}{\partial N}\right)_{V,T},$$

we find

$$\lambda = e^{\mu/kT} = \frac{\rho e^{2\alpha\rho}}{1 - \rho}\left[1 + \frac{1}{B}\frac{(1 - 2\rho)}{2\rho(1 - \rho)} + \cdots\right],$$

(8-48)

where $\rho = N/B$. The leading factor on the right-hand side is the macroscopic $(B \to \infty)$ expression which exhibits the van der Waals loop referred to above. The quantity in brackets will obviously modify the loop quantitatively but not qualitatively for B large but finite.

CHAPTER 9

ENVIRONMENTAL
VARIABLES N, V, E

An isolated small system with environmental variables N, V, E is of no interest experimentally. It is also usually a difficult case to handle in statistical mechanics, because of the restraints of constant N and E. But an isolated system occupies an important position in the development of the principles of statistical mechanics and represents one extreme in the classification of environmental variables (all variables are extensive, or "closed"), hence it deserves at least passing mention for the sake of completeness.

The basic equations are [see Eqs. (1-49) to (1-54)]:

$$dE = T\,dS - p\,dV + \mu\,dN \qquad (9\text{-}1)$$

$$dS = \frac{1}{T}\,dE + \frac{p}{T}\,dV - \frac{\mu}{T}\,dN \qquad (9\text{-}2)$$

$$\mathscr{S} = -\frac{\mathscr{E}}{T} = S - \frac{E}{T} - \frac{pV}{T} + \frac{\mu N}{T} \qquad (9\text{-}3)$$

$$d\mathscr{S} = d\left(-\frac{\mathscr{E}}{T}\right) = d\left(S - \frac{E}{T} - \frac{pV}{T} + \frac{\mu N}{T}\right)$$

$$= -E\,d\left(\frac{1}{T}\right) - V\,d\left(\frac{p}{T}\right) + N\,d\left(\frac{\mu}{T}\right). \qquad (9\text{-}4)$$

The relation to statistical mechanics is

$$S = k\ln\Omega(N, V, E). \qquad (9\text{-}5)$$

Legendre transformations give equations "intermediate" between (9-2) and (9-4). For example,

$$d\left(S - \frac{E}{T}\right) = d\left(-\frac{A}{T}\right) = -E\,d\left(\frac{1}{T}\right) + \frac{p}{T}\,dV - \frac{\mu}{T}\,dN \quad (9\text{-}6)$$

$$d\left(S - \frac{E}{T} - \frac{pV}{T}\right) = d\left(-\frac{F}{T}\right) = -E\,d\left(\frac{1}{T}\right) - V\,d\left(\frac{p}{T}\right) - \frac{\mu}{T}\,dN$$
$$\qquad (9\text{-}7)$$

$$d\left(S - \frac{E}{T} + \frac{\mu N}{T}\right) = -E\,d\left(\frac{1}{T}\right) + \frac{p}{T}\,dV + N\,d\left(\frac{\mu}{T}\right). \quad (9\text{-}8)$$

Three Maxwell relations follow from each of the six differential equations above.

ENVIRONMENTAL VARIABLES N, $p = 0$, E. In a sense, a more realistic small, isolated system is one with given N and E and fluctuating V at $p = 0$. An example would be a nonvolatile colloidal particle in a vacuum. An $N, p/T, E$ system is formally identical with an N, V, T system (one intensive environmental variable). Hence, a transcription of the equations of Chapter 8 could be made to treat this case. The differential equation with environmental variables independent is

$$d\left(S - \frac{p\bar{V}}{T}\right) = \frac{1}{T}\, dE - \bar{V}\, d\left(\frac{p}{T}\right) - \frac{\mu}{T}\, dN, \qquad (9\text{-}9)$$

whereas the connection with statistical mechanics is

$$S - \frac{p\bar{V}}{T} = k \ln \sum_V \Omega(N, V, E)e^{-pV/kT}. \qquad (9\text{-}10)$$

Example. Twelve-Site Spherical Lattice Gas. An exact treatment of a twelve-site lattice gas on the surface of a sphere, using the canonical ensemble, was presented in Section 8-2. The microcanonical partition function $\Omega(N, M)$ (M is a measure of E since $E = Mw$) was included in that discussion and can now be used for comparative purposes.

Thus, for example, let us compare the dependence of the energy on temperature in the canonical (N, T) and microcanonical (N, E) ensembles. In both cases, of course, B is fixed at $B = 12$. In the canonical ensemble,

$$\bar{E} = -\left[\frac{\partial \ln Q}{\partial(1/kT)}\right]_N$$

or

$$\bar{M} = \frac{y}{Q}\left(\frac{\partial Q}{\partial y}\right)_N. \qquad (9\text{-}11)$$

Thus $\bar{M}$ is a quotient of two polynomials in y, and hence is a smooth function of y. The parameter y is related to the temperature by $y = e^{-w/kT}$. Figures 9-1a and 9-1b show $\bar{M}$ versus y for $N = 5$

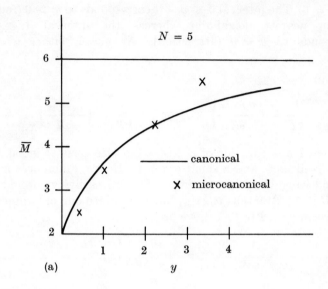

(a)

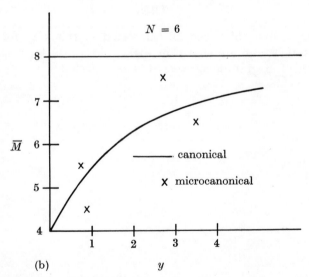

(b)

FIGURE 9-1. $\bar{M}$ (energy) against y (related to temperature) in canonical and microcanonical ensembles for twelve-site spherical lattice gas.

and $N = 6$. The interval $0 \leqslant y < 1$ corresponds to $w > 0$ (repulsion between nearest neighbors) whereas the interval $1 < y \leqslant \infty$ corresponds to $w < 0$ (attraction). At $y = 1$, either $w = 0$ or $T = \infty$.

For an N, E system,

$$\frac{1}{kT} = \left(\frac{\partial \ln \Omega}{\partial E} \right)_N \qquad \text{or} \qquad \frac{w}{kT} = \left(\frac{\partial \ln \Omega}{\partial M} \right)_N .$$

This gives T as a function of E, instead of vice versa as in Eq. (9-11). But M is discrete and a small number. Hence, differences must be used and irregular points anticipated. Ordinarily[1] we would define $\ln [\Omega(M + 1)/\Omega(M)]$ as w/kT_M, but here, since our only object is a comparison with Eq. (9-11), we use

$$\frac{w}{kT_{M+1/2}} = \ln \frac{\Omega(N, M + 1)}{\Omega(N, M)}$$

or

$$y_{M+1/2} = \frac{\Omega(N, M)}{\Omega(N, M + 1)} . \tag{9-12}$$

The four points which can be calculated in this way for each of $N = 5$ and $N = 6$ are shown in Figs. 9-1a and 9-1b, respectively. The order-of-magnitude agreement is as expected.

---

[1] See Chapter 15.

CHAPTER 10

ENVIRONMENTAL VARIABLES μ, p, T

As a convenience to the reader, we begin by repeating here a few of the comments made in the introduction to Chapter 2.

Consider an experimental one-component small system at p and T. The pressure on the system (colloidal particle, macromolecule, etc.) is that exerted on the solvent in which it is immersed. Also, the temperature of the small system is that of the solvent. The remaining environmental variable may be N or μ. If the small system is closed, we use N. A clear-cut example is a polymer molecule consisting of N monomers held together by chemical bonds. But an aggregate of molecules bound by relatively weak van der Waals forces would be open rather than closed. That is, N fluctuates. In this case, the third environmental variable is μ. The criterion distinguishing the two cases is whether the system maintains N = constant, within experimental error, during the time required to make the thermodynamic measurements of interest.

The closed-system (N, p, T) case was discussed in Chapter 2. Here we consider an open (μ, p, T) system. This encompasses an important class of colloidal particles: crystallite embryos in a liquid near the freezing point; precipitation crystallites in a dilute solution; micelles in a dilute soap solution; any kind of aggregate in solution which is in dynamic equilibrium with respect to the size of the aggregate; molecular clusters in a one-component gas; viruses which are aggregates of spherical particles; etc. In all cases, the macroscopic system must be dilute in small systems.

The equilibrium ensemble of μ, p, T systems will include small systems with various values of N. Such an ensemble is, however, not to be confused with a collection of small, closed systems with different values of N. In the latter case, which we refer to as "polydisperse," there is *not* a dynamic aggregation equilibrium. Polydisperse systems are treated in Chapter 13.

In macroscopic statistical mechanics, completely open (μ, p, T) systems are rather troublesome and require special treatment (see Section 14 of S.M., for example). Basically, this is because only two of μ, p, and T can be independent variables for a one-component macroscopic system. But we have seen throughout this book that for a *small* system, any intensive property in a one-component system may be regarded as a function of two intensive variables *and* a size variable. The dependence on the size variable vanishes as the system gets larger. There is thus one extra degree of freedom for a small system, although this extra degree is, so to speak, not so "free" as the usual degrees of freedom. That is, the dependence of thermodynamic properties on the extra variable, whatever it is, involves "small" terms only. In a μ, p, T system, the extra degree of freedom manifests itself in the independence of all three of μ, p, and T, although again, as we shall see, one of the three variables is not so "free" as the other two.[1]

As one might expect, because of the independence of μ, p, and T, there is no special difficulty in using the appropriate partition function Υ [see Eq. (1-61)] for a small, completely open system. Hence the method of choice in applying Υ to a macroscopic system would appear to be as follows: Set up Υ using values of μ, p, and T corresponding to a finite system; calculate Υ and thermodynamic functions using small system thermodynamics; finally, note the asymptotic expressions for the thermodynamic functions of interest as the size of the system approaches infinity (i.e., as the chosen values of μ, p, and T approach their macroscopic relationship). This will be illustrated in Section 10-2.

There are some completely open small systems which do not have a macroscopic limit—i.e., they are always small systems. An example is the system of bound ions or molecules on a naturally occurring protein molecule in solution. The size of the protein molecule cannot be varied. Hence the number of binding sites is constant and finite. The environmental variables are μ (chemical potential of bound species), p (pressure on solvent), and T. This is closely related to an N_1, μ_2, p, T system (Chapter 7) in which N_1 is held constant. This type of system is considered in Section 10-5.

If component 1 is in a dynamic aggregation equilibrium and component 2 is bound on the aggregating units, the environmental variables are μ_1, μ_2, p, and T. Ion binding on a soap micelle is an example. This case is treated beginning on page 135. It involves a generalization of a μ, p, T system to two components.

---

[1] See, for example, the discussion of Eq. (10-27).

10-1. BASIC EQUATIONS FOR ENSEMBLE OF DISTINGUISHABLE SYSTEMS

The reader should review the end of Section 1-3 and Section 1-4 as an introduction to the present section. We shall be concerned here (and in the following four sections) with an ensemble of equivalent, distinguishable, independent μ, p, T systems, each with fixed center of mass. Such an ensemble is of interest primarily in connection with theoretical models in statistical mechanics. Experimental μ, p, T systems, that is, those in solvent or gas, will be discussed in Section 10-6.

The fundamental thermodynamic equations, which we repeat here, are

$$d\bar{E} = T\,dS - p\,d\bar{V} + \mu\,d\bar{N} \tag{10-1}$$

$$dS = \frac{1}{T}\,d\bar{E} + \frac{p}{T}\,d\bar{V} - \frac{\mu}{T}\,d\bar{N} \tag{10-2}$$

$$\mathscr{E} = \bar{E} - TS + p\bar{V} - \mu\bar{N} \tag{10-3}$$

$$\mathscr{S} = -\frac{\mathscr{E}}{T} = S - \frac{1}{T}\bar{E} - \frac{p}{T}\bar{V} + \frac{\mu}{T}\bar{N} \tag{10-4}$$

$$d\mathscr{E} = -S\,dT + \bar{V}\,dp - \bar{N}\,d\mu \tag{10-5}$$

$$d\mathscr{S} = -\bar{E}\,d\!\left(\frac{1}{T}\right) - \bar{V}\,d\!\left(\frac{p}{T}\right) + \bar{N}\,d\!\left(\frac{\mu}{T}\right). \tag{10-6}$$

The basic statistical mechanical equations are

$$\mathscr{E} = -kT\ln\Upsilon \tag{10-7}$$

$$\Upsilon = e^{-\mathscr{E}/kT} = \sum_{N,V} Q(N, V, T)e^{-pV/kT}\,e^{N\mu/kT} \tag{10-8}$$

$$= \sum_V \Xi(\mu, V, T)e^{-pV/kT} = \sum_V e^{\hat{p}V/kT}e^{-pV/kT} = \sum_V e^{-\mathscr{E}_V/kT} \tag{10-9}$$

$$= \sum_N \Delta(N, p, T)e^{N\mu/kT} = \sum_N e^{-N\hat{\mu}/kT}e^{N\mu/kT} = \sum_N e^{-\mathscr{E}_N/kT}, \tag{10-10}$$

where the definitions of $\mathscr{E}_V$ and $\mathscr{E}_N$ are obvious from the equations.

From Eq. (10-5),

$$-S = \left(\frac{\partial\mathscr{E}}{\partial T}\right)_{p,\,\mu}, \qquad \bar{V} = \left(\frac{\partial\mathscr{E}}{\partial p}\right)_{T,\,\mu}, \qquad -\bar{N} = \left(\frac{\partial\mathscr{E}}{\partial\mu}\right)_{T,\,p}. \tag{10-11}$$

Three similar equations follow from Eq. (10-6). Since $\mathscr{E}$ is a function of μ, p, and T, Eqs. (10-11) show that these three intensive variables suffice to determine the extensive properties of the one-component small system. This is quite unlike the situation in macroscopic thermodynamics where only two intensive variables can be independent and their specification does not fix the size of the system. A completely open small system with c components will have $c + 2$ independent intensive variables, and there will be $c + 2$ relations of the type shown in Eq. (10-11).

An important special characteristic of a completely open system is that none of the thermodynamic functions occurring in Eqs. (10-1) to (10-6) is discrete because E, V, and N are all averaged. Hence, very small systems can be included in the discussion.

There are, of course, various Maxwell relations, Examples are

$$-\left(\frac{\partial S}{\partial p}\right)_{T,\,\mu} = \left(\frac{\partial \bar{V}}{\partial T}\right)_{p,\,\mu}, \qquad \left(\frac{\partial S}{\partial \mu}\right)_{p,\,T} = \left(\frac{\partial \bar{N}}{\partial T}\right)_{p,\,\mu},$$

$$\left(\frac{\partial \bar{V}}{\partial \mu}\right)_{T,\,p} = -\left(\frac{\partial \bar{N}}{\partial p}\right)_{\mu,\,T}. \qquad (10\text{-}12)$$

All these derivatives are infinite in macroscopic thermodynamics, since their reciprocals are equal to zero.

The independent variables in Eqs. (10-5) and (10-6) may be changed by Legendre transformations. An example is

$$d(\mathscr{E} + \mu\bar{N}) = -S\,dT + \bar{V}\,dp + \mu\,d\bar{N}, \qquad (10\text{-}13)$$

an equation much used in Chapter 2.

Two rather unusual equations which have no counterparts in macroscopic thermodynamics are

$$d\left(\ln \mathscr{S} + \frac{S}{\mathscr{S}}\right) = \frac{1}{T}\,d\left(\frac{\bar{E}}{\mathscr{S}}\right) + \frac{p}{T}\,d\left(\frac{\bar{V}}{\mathscr{S}}\right) - \frac{\mu}{T}\,d\left(\frac{\bar{N}}{\mathscr{S}}\right) \qquad (10\text{-}14)$$

and

$$d\left(\ln \mathscr{E} + \frac{\bar{E}}{\mathscr{E}}\right) = T\,d\left(\frac{S}{\mathscr{E}}\right) - p\,d\left(\frac{\bar{V}}{\mathscr{E}}\right) + \mu\,d\left(\frac{\bar{N}}{\mathscr{E}}\right). \qquad (10\text{-}15)$$

Excess functions may be defined in several ways. For example, let us arbitrarily select p and T as the "basic" intensive variables. Let $\mu^{(0)}(p, T)$ be the macroscopic chemical potential at p and T. For given values of the environmental variables μ, p, and T, the small system will have some definite value of $\bar{N}$. For any extensive variable G, let $G^{(0)}$ be the value of G for $\bar{N}$ molecules of a macroscopic sample at the same p and T as the small system. Then the excess quantity $G^{(x)}$ is defined by the equation

$$G(\mu, p, T) = G^{(0)}[\bar{N}(\mu, p, T), p, T] + G^{(x)}(\mu, p, T). \qquad (10\text{-}16)$$

The excess quantity $\mu^{(x)}$ is defined in terms of the assigned value of the environmental variable μ and of $\mu^{(0)}(p, T)$ by the equation

$$\mu = \mu^{(0)}(p, T) + \mu^{(x)}(\mu, p, T). \qquad (10\text{-}17)$$

In Eq. (10-1), we now use Eq. (10-16) for $\bar{E}$, S, and $\bar{V}$, and Eq. (10-17) for μ, with the result

$$d\bar{E}^{(x)} = T\,dS^{(x)} - p\,d\bar{V}^{(x)} + \mu^{(x)}\,d\bar{N}. \qquad (10\text{-}18)$$

Also, Eq. (10-3) becomes

$$\mathscr{E} = \bar{E}^{(x)} - TS^{(x)} + p\bar{V}^{(x)} - \mu^{(x)}\bar{N}. \qquad (10\text{-}19)$$

Then

$$d\mathscr{E} = -S^{(x)}\,dT + \bar{V}^{(x)}\,dp - \bar{N}\,d\mu^{(x)}. \qquad (10\text{-}20)$$

These relations are formally identical with those on page 39 of Part I for an N, p, T system (because of our arbitrary choice, at the outset, of p and T as basic intensive variables).

The next section is devoted to a discussion of four simple theoretical models of completely open systems. In all these examples we consider an ensemble of distinguishable systems without rotation or translation.

10-2. APPLICATIONS TO THEORETICAL MODELS

LINEAR AGGREGATE. This is the model on page 69 of Part I, but without rotation or translation.

In the *canonical ensemble* (environmental variables N, T), a system consists of N units in a linear sequence. Each unit has an intrinsic partition function $j(T)$. The energy of interaction between neighboring units is ϵ, a constant. The system is assumed incompressible. This model corresponds to a one-dimensional Einstein crystal. Thus $Q(N, T)$ is simply

$$Q(N, T) = j(T)^N e^{-(N-1)\epsilon/kT} \qquad (10\text{-}21)$$

for $N \geqslant 1$. But we note for future use that $Q(0, T) = 1$. Then (see page 61 of Part I)

$$N\hat{\mu} = - kT \ln Q = - NkT \ln j + (N - 1)\epsilon \qquad (N \geqslant 1).$$

$$(10\text{-}22)$$

The chemical potential $\mu^{(0)}(T)$ of the macroscopic system (i.e., an infinitely long linear aggregate of units) at T is thus

$$\mu^{(0)}(T) = - kT \ln j + \epsilon \qquad (10\text{-}23)$$

and (page 39 of part I)

$$\hat{\mu}^{(x)} = \hat{\mu} - \mu^{(0)} = - \frac{\epsilon}{N}. \qquad (10\text{-}24)$$

Equation (10-23) is of course valid for *any* ensemble, as it refers to a macroscopic system. The entropy is

$$S = - \left(\frac{\partial N\hat{\mu}}{\partial T} \right)_N = Nk \ln j + NkT \frac{d \ln j}{dT} \qquad (10\text{-}25)$$

and the energy

$$\bar{E} = TS + N\hat{\mu} = NkT^2 \frac{d \ln j}{dT} + (N - 1)\epsilon. \qquad (10\text{-}26)$$

The entropy above is just the "intrinsic" entropy per unit multiplied by the number of units.

We turn now to a *completely open system*. This is a linear aggregate of units at T and μ. The number of units N in the system fluctuates. The aggregate may be thought of as being in equilibrium with a reservoir containing units (monomers) at μ. The partition function [see Eq. (10-8)] is

$$\Upsilon = \sum_{N=0}^{\infty} Q(N, T)e^{N\mu/kT}$$

$$= 1 + e^{\epsilon/kT} \sum_{N=1}^{\infty} (je^{-\epsilon/kT}\lambda)^N$$

$$= \frac{1 - x + cx}{1 - x} \qquad (x < 1), \qquad (10\text{-}27)$$

where we have introduced the notation

$$\lambda = e^{\mu/kT}, \qquad c = e^{\epsilon/kT}, \qquad x = je^{-\epsilon/kT}\lambda, \qquad cx = j\lambda. \qquad (10\text{-}28)$$

The series above converges for $x < 1$ but not for $x \geqslant 1$. In view of Eqs. (10-17) and (10-23), we also have

$$x = \exp\left[-\frac{\mu^{(0)}(T) - \mu}{kT}\right] = \exp\left[\frac{\mu^{(x)}(\mu, T)}{kT}\right]. \qquad (10\text{-}29)$$

Thus Υ converges and a small system can exist if, for given T, μ is chosen so that $\mu < \mu^{(0)}(T)$. Because of this restriction, we do not have a completely free choice of μ (once T is assigned). Furthermore, as will be seen below, in order for the small system to be at all sizeable, μ must be rather close to $\mu^{(0)}$. On the other hand, as has already been pointed out in Section 10-1, there is no difficulty (arising from discreteness in extensive environmental variables) in treating a very small, completely open system, since *all* variables are continuous (μ, T, $\bar{N}$, S, $\bar{E}$, $\mathscr{E}$, etc., in the present example).

From Eq. (10-7),

$$\mathscr{E} = -kT \ln \frac{1 - x + cx}{1 - x}. \qquad (10\text{-}30)$$

Then, using Eq. (10-11c), we find for the mean number of units in an aggregate

$$\bar{N} = \frac{cx}{(1 - x)(1 - x + cx)}. \qquad (10\text{-}31)$$

Note that $\bar{N} \to \infty$ (macroscopic system) as $x \to 1$. Equation (10-31) is identical in form with the well-known Brunauer–Emmett–Teller adsorption isotherm. The reason for this is that the B.E.T. equation can be derived[1] from statistical mechanics using as a model an independent linear pile of adsorbed molecules on each adsorption site of the surface. Thus a B.E.T. "pile" corresponds to an open linear aggregate here, and the whole adsorbed phase ($\mathscr{N}$ sites) corresponds to the ensemble here ($\mathscr{N}$ systems). In the B.E.T. model, the first molecule on a site is "different" because of interaction with the surface. Here, the first molecule in a system is "different" because it lacks an interaction energy ϵ with a neighbor. In the B.E.T. theory, generally $c > 1$. In a typical aggregate, on the other hand, $\epsilon < 0$ and $c < 1$. Figure 10-1 shows $\bar{N}$ as a function of x for $c = 10$, 1, and $\frac{1}{10}$.

---

[1] See S.T., p. 134. It is because of the connection with B.E.T. theory that we have adopted the c, x notation, which otherwise would be a poor choice here.

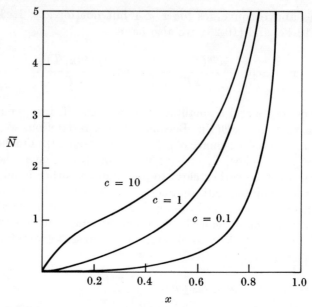

FIGURE 10-1. Size of open linear aggregate as function of norma-
lized absolute activity.

It can be seen from the bottom of page 25, Part I, that $-\mathscr{E}$ is the
equivalent of the surface pressure in the B.E.T. theory.

When $x \to 1$,

$$\bar{N} \to \frac{1}{1-x}, \qquad x \to 1 - \frac{1}{\bar{N}}$$

$$\Upsilon \to \frac{c}{1-x} = c\bar{N}, \qquad \mathscr{E} \to -kT \ln \bar{N}.$$
$$(x \to 1) \quad (10\text{-}32)$$

When $x \to 0$,

$$\bar{N} \to cx, \qquad \Upsilon \to 1 + cx = 1 + \bar{N}, \qquad \mathscr{E} \to -\bar{N}kT \qquad (x \to 0).$$
$$(10\text{-}33)$$

The probability that a system (aggregate) contains N units is

$$P(N) = \frac{Q(N, T)e^{N\mu/kT}}{\Upsilon}. \qquad (10\text{-}34)$$

Since $Q(0, T) = 1$, the probability that a system contains no units at all is $P(0) = 1/\Upsilon$. Hence

$$\mathscr{E} = kT \ln P(0), \tag{10-35}$$

where

$$P(0) = \frac{1 - x}{1 - x + cx}. \tag{10-36}$$

The relation (10-35) is valid for any μ, T system for which $Q(0, T) = 1$ [see p. xi].

We also have

$$P(N) = \frac{x^N c(1 - x)}{1 - x + cx} \qquad (N \geqslant 1). \tag{10-37}$$

Thus, since $x < 1$, $P(N)$ falls off exponentially with N, and this decrease becomes more gradual as $x \to 1$. In particular, $P(N)$ does *not* have a peak at or near $N = \bar{N}$ which becomes sharper as $\bar{N} \to \infty$, as would be the case in a *partially* open system in the absence of a phase transition (e.g., in a μ, V, T system; see page 145, Part I). The flatness of $P(N)$ exhibited in Eq. (10-37) resembles the behavior of $P(N)$ at a critical point (see Fig. 6-7). Fluctuations in N will be large, as we now verify.

From $\Upsilon = \Sigma_N Q \lambda^N$ we easily find the usual type of expression for the fluctuation in N:

$$\overline{N^2} - \bar{N}^2 = kT \left(\frac{\partial \bar{N}}{\partial \mu} \right)_T. \tag{10-38}$$

Then, with the aid of Eq. (10-31), we obtain

$$\frac{\overline{N^2} - \bar{N}^2}{\bar{N}^2} = \frac{1 - x^2 + cx^2}{cx}, \tag{10-39}$$

which is of order unity unless x is very small. For a partially open system, on the other hand, this quantity would ordinarily be of order $1/\bar{N}$.

The entropy of an aggregate is

$$S = -\left(\frac{\partial \mathscr{E}}{\partial T} \right)_\mu$$

$$= \bar{N}k \ln j + \bar{N}kT \frac{d \ln j}{dT} - \bar{N}k \ln x - k \ln P(0) - [1 - P(0)]\frac{\epsilon}{T}, \tag{10-40}$$

and the energy is

$$\bar{E} = \mathscr{E} + TS + \bar{N}\mu$$

$$= \bar{N}kT^2 \frac{d\ln j}{dT} + [\bar{N} - 1 + P(0)]\epsilon. \qquad (10\text{-}41)$$

The entropy contains the intrinsic entropy of $\bar{N}$ units, as in Eq. (10-25), and in addition the excess entropy [see Eq. (10-16)]

$$S^{(x)} = -\bar{N}k\ln x - k\ln P(0) - [1 - P(0)]\frac{\epsilon}{T}. \qquad (10\text{-}42)$$

It is easy to verify that

$$S^{(x)} = -k\sum_{N=0}^{\infty} P(N)\ln P(N), \qquad (10\text{-}43)$$

as might have been expected. Thus $S^{(x)}$ is the entropy associated with the fluctuations in N. This entropy is necessarily positive, and does not exist for a closed system [Eq. (10-25); environmental variables N, T]. Therefore, if we choose N in Eq. (10-25) equal to $\bar{N}$ in Eq. (10-40),

$$S(\mu, T \text{ system}) > S(N, T \text{ system}) \qquad (10\text{-}44)$$

because of the fact that the μ, T system is open with respect to N. In a comparison of this sort, the more open system will always have the larger entropy.[1] For large $\bar{N}$,

$$S^{(x)} \to k\ln\bar{N} \qquad (x \to 1). \qquad (10\text{-}45)$$

Despite the abnormally large fluctuations in N, this term becomes negligible compared to the first two terms $(S^{(0)})$ in Eq. (10-40) when $\bar{N}$ is very large.

The first term in $\bar{E}$, Eq. (10-41), is the "intrinsic energy." The second term is the mean potential energy:

$$\sum_{N=2}^{\infty} (N-1)\epsilon P(N) = [\bar{N} - 1 + P(0)]\epsilon. \qquad (10\text{-}46)$$

The excess energy is

$$\bar{E}^{(x)} = -[1 - P(0)]\epsilon. \qquad (10\text{-}47)$$

[1] See S.M., pp. 75–76, and E. A. Guggenheim, *Research*, **2**, 450 (1949).

It is easy to verify that the various excess quantities satisfy

$$\mathscr{E} = \bar{E}^{(x)} - TS^{(x)} - \mu^{(x)}\bar{N} \tag{10-48}$$

and also Eq. (10-20).

It should be noted that Υ can be expressed in terms of excess quantities:

$$\Upsilon = 1 + \sum_{N=1}^{\infty} \exp\left(\frac{-N\hat{\mu}}{kT}\right)\exp\left(\frac{N\mu}{kT}\right)$$

$$= 1 + \sum_{N=1}^{\infty} \exp\left[\frac{N\mu^{(x)}(\mu,\,T)}{kT}\right]\exp\left[\frac{-N\hat{\mu}^{(x)}(N,\,T)}{kT}\right], \tag{10-49}$$

where $\mu^{(x)} = \mu - \mu^{(0)}(T)$ must be negative for convergence and $\hat{\mu}^{(x)}$ is the excess chemical potential for the closed system with N and T. In the present example, $\hat{\mu}^{(x)} = -\epsilon/N$. Of course $\mu^{(x)}$ and $\hat{\mu}^{(x)}$ refer to two different environments (μ, T and N, T, respectively).

This example illustrates a point made previously: The thermodynamic properties of a completely open macroscopic system can be obtained without difficulty and without the use of special techniques if we first deduce the properties of a finite system (as we have done above) and then take the macroscopic limit of these properties. Thus, in the present problem,

$$\mu^{(0)} = -kT\ln j + \epsilon \quad \text{(from } x = 1\text{)} \tag{10-50}$$

$$S^{(0)} = \bar{N}k\ln j + \bar{N}kT\,\frac{d\ln j}{dT} \tag{10-51}$$

$$\bar{E}^{(0)} = \bar{N}kT^2\,\frac{d\ln j}{dT} + \bar{N}\epsilon. \tag{10-52}$$

SPHERICAL AGGREGATE. Various versions of this model have been mentioned on pages 41, 70, and 129 of Part I. Here we consider a spherical, incompressible liquid (or solid) aggregate without rotation or translation and take $Q(N, T)$ for an N, T system to be

$$Q(N, T) = j(T)^N \exp\left[-\frac{a(T)N^{2/3}}{kT}\right], \tag{10-53}$$

where N is the number of molecules or monomers, $aN^{2/3}$ is the surface free energy, and $j(T)$ is the macroscopic partition function per molecule ("Einstein model"). The function $j(T)$ includes the intermolecular potential energy per molecule, a partition function for vibration of a molecule about an equilibrium point, communal entropy (if any), and internal degrees of freedom (if any). The quantity $a(T)$ is positive. Its physical significance is discussed on page 132 of Part I. The main point is that a is proportional to the surface tension.

For a *closed system* (environmental variables N, T),

$$N\hat{\mu} = - kT \ln Q = - NkT \ln j + aN^{2/3}. \qquad (10\text{-}54)$$

The first term is the macroscopic term:

$$\mu^{(0)} = - kT \ln j, \qquad \hat{\mu}^{(x)} = aN^{-1/3}. \qquad (10\text{-}55)$$

Also,

$$S = - \left(\frac{\partial N\hat{\mu}}{\partial T}\right)_N = Nk \ln j + NkT \frac{d \ln j}{dT} - \frac{da}{dT} N^{2/3} \qquad (10\text{-}56)$$

$$\bar{E} = TS + N\hat{\mu} = NkT^2 \frac{d \ln j}{dT} + \left(a - T \frac{da}{dT}\right)N^{2/3}. \qquad (10\text{-}57)$$

We now turn to an *open system* (environmental variables μ, T). The surface free energy $aN^{2/3}$ is realistic only for fairly large N ($N > 20$, e.g.). Hence we should restrict ourselves to values of μ (for given T) that lead to sizeable $\bar{N}$. The partition function Υ is [see Eq. (10-49)]

$$\Upsilon = \sum_N \exp\left(\frac{N\mu^{(x)}}{kT}\right) \exp\left(- \frac{N\hat{\mu}^{(x)}}{kT}\right), \qquad (10\text{-}58)$$

where $\hat{\mu}^{(x)}$ is given in Eq. (10-55) and $\mu^{(x)} = \mu - \mu^{(0)}(T)$. If $\mu^{(x)}$ is positive, the first exponential dominates for large N, and the sum diverges. A finite system is then not possible. If $\mu^{(x)} \leqslant 0$, the sum converges, since $a(T)$ is positive.

For convenience, we introduce the notation

$$\delta(\mu, T) = \frac{\mu^{(0)}(T) - \mu}{kT} = - \frac{\mu^{(x)}}{kT} \geqslant 0$$

$$\alpha(T) = \frac{a(T)}{kT} > 0.$$

In order to obtain aggregates of reasonable size we must choose δ very small. In fact, we confine ourselves below to the case $\delta \to 0+$. This means we are examining "open" aggregates which are in equilibrium with the bulk phase. In other words, these are clusters in the saturated vapor phase in equilibrium with a liquid. But even with a saturated vapor the clusters will be sizeable only near the critical temperature where the surface tension is very small, that is, where $\alpha(T)$ is small. This requirement $(T \to T_c)$ can easily be verified by numerical substitution in the expression for $\bar{N}$ below.

Because we are interested only in $\bar{N}$ fairly large, we replace the sum in Eq. (10-58) by an integral and extend the integration to $N = 0$. Even though the model is inadequate for small N, the error introduced in this region of the integration (say $0 \leqslant N \leqslant 20$) will not be serious when $\bar{N}$ is large enough. Equation (10-58) becomes, for $\delta \to 0+$,

$$\Upsilon(\mu, T) = \int\limits_0^\infty (1 - \delta N)e^{-\alpha N^{2/3}} \, dN$$

$$= \frac{3\pi^{1/2}}{4\alpha^{3/2}} - \frac{3\delta}{\alpha^3}. \tag{10-59}$$

Then, from Eq. (10-11c),

$$\bar{N} = \left(\frac{\partial \ln \Upsilon}{\partial \mu/kT}\right)_T = \left(\frac{\partial \ln \Upsilon}{\partial \delta}\right)_\alpha \left(\frac{\partial \delta}{\partial \mu/kT}\right)_T = \frac{4}{\pi^{1/2}\alpha^{3/2}}. \tag{10-60}$$

Thus, $\Upsilon = 3\pi\bar{N}/16$.

The probability that an aggregate contains between N and $N + dN$ molecules is

$$P(N) \, dN = \frac{e^{-\alpha N^{2/3}} \, dN}{\Upsilon} = \frac{16e^{-\alpha N^{2/3}} \, dN}{3\pi\bar{N}} \qquad (\delta \to 0+). \tag{10-61}$$

Since α is small, this is again (as in the previous example) a slowly decreasing function of N, with no sign of the conventional peak at or near $N = \bar{N}$.

We can use

$$\bar{N} = \int\limits_0^\infty NP(N) \, dN \tag{10-62}$$

to verify Eq. (10-60). From Eq. (5-153),

$$\bar{N} = \frac{2}{3\pi v}\left(\frac{kT}{\gamma}\right)^{3/2}.$$ (10-63)

Hence $\bar{N} \to \infty$ as $\gamma \to 0$, as expected. We also find, in the same way,

$$\overline{N^{2/3}} = \frac{3}{2\alpha}$$ (10-64)

and

$$\frac{\overline{N^2} - \bar{N}^2}{\bar{N}^2} = \frac{105\pi}{128} - 1 = O(1).$$ (10-65)

This result also follows from Eq. (10-38) if we calculate one more term $(315\pi^{1/2}\delta^2/64\alpha^{9/2})$ in Eq. (10-59).

In general for this model, $\bar{N}$ would be a function of μ and T, but we have taken $\mu \to \mu^{(0)}(T)$ so $\bar{N}$ is a function of T only. The calculation of $\bar{N}$ illustrates again (see the previous example) the fact that a complete set of intensive variables (in this case μ and T) can determine the extensive properties of a small system. In the case of a macroscopic system, there is one less intensive variable in a complete set, and these cannot determine extensive variables (the system can have any size).

Equation (10-59) for Υ and

$$-\bar{E} = \left[\frac{\partial \ln \Upsilon}{\partial(1/kT)}\right]_{\mu/kT}$$ (10-66)

lead to

$$\bar{E} = \bar{N}kT^2\frac{d \ln j}{dT} + \left(a - T\frac{da}{dT}\right)\overline{N^{2/3}}.$$ (10-67)

This result also follows immediately from Eq. (10-57). For, if we denote the average energy in Eq. (10-57) by $\bar{E}^E$ (the super E means that averaging has been carried out over E), then

$$\bar{E}(\mu, T) \equiv \bar{E}^{E, N} = \frac{1}{\Upsilon}\sum_N e^{N\mu/kT}\sum_E E\Omega(N, E)e^{-E/kT}$$

$$= \frac{\sum_N \bar{E}^E(N, T)Q(N, T)e^{N\mu/kT}}{\Upsilon}.$$ (10-68)

Substitution of Eq. (10-57) for $\bar{E}^E$ in Eq. (10-68) gives Eq. (10-67). In this example the energy is different for closed (N, T) and open (μ, T) systems. For if in Eq. (10-57) we choose the same T as here and choose N there equal to the $\bar{N}$ here, then the two energies differ because $\bar{N}^{2/3} \neq \overline{N^{2/3}}$.

The entropy is, from Eq. (10-3),

$$S = \frac{\bar{E}}{T} - \frac{\mu^{(0)}\bar{N}}{T} + k \ln \Upsilon$$
$$= \bar{N}k \ln j + \bar{N}kT \frac{d \ln j}{dT} - \frac{da}{dT}\overline{N^{2/3}} + k \ln \frac{3\pi\bar{N}}{16} + \frac{a}{T}\overline{N^{2/3}}.$$

$$(10\text{-}69)$$

This result also follows from $S = (\partial kT \ln \Upsilon/\partial T)_\mu$, using Eq. (10-59) for Υ. Comparison with Eq. (10-56) for S in an N, T system shows that the last two terms above are the additional positive terms associated with fluctuations in N. This is verified by

$$- k \int_0^\infty P(N) \ln P(N)\, dN = k \ln \frac{3\pi\bar{N}}{16} + \frac{a}{T}\overline{N^{2/3}}. \qquad (10\text{-}70)$$

This expression approaches $k \ln \bar{N}$ for large $\bar{N}$ (the term in a is equal to $3k/2$).

In the preceding example Υ diverges at $\mu = \mu^{(0)}(T)$ because $N\hat{\mu}^{(x)}$ in Eq. (10-49) is a constant ($-\epsilon$). As a consequence, a small system of any size ($\bar{N}$) can be generated by choosing μ as close as one pleases to $\mu^{(0)}(T)$. In the present example, Υ converges at $\mu = \mu^{(0)}(T)$ because $N\hat{\mu}^{(x)}$ is a positive function of N which increases sufficiently rapidly with N. Consequently, for given T and a, $\bar{N}$ cannot be made arbitrarily large but has a maximum possible value at $\mu = \mu^{(0)}(T)$. This is the value in Eq. (10-60) or (10-63). But even in this case the macroscopic properties (i.e., $\bar{E}^{(0)}$ and $S^{(0)}$) can easily be ascertained by inspection of the expressions for $\bar{E}$ and S [Eqs. (10-67) and (10-69)] at $\mu = \mu^{(0)}(T)$. Of course Υ diverges and $\bar{N} = \infty$ for $\mu > \mu^{(0)}(T)$.

IDEAL LATTICE GAS. This is the same model as on pages 42 and 142 of Part I and 203 of Part II. The partition function is

$$\Upsilon = \sum_{B=0}^\infty \sum_{N=0}^B \frac{B!}{N!(B-N)!} e^{mN} e^{-\varphi B},$$

where for convenience we write $m = \mu/kT$ and $\varphi = p/kT$. It might be noted that this may be thought of as the partition function for an open two-component system. One component $(B, -p)$ forms an aggregate of sites [as in Eq. (10-27), but with $\epsilon = 0$, $j = 1$], whereas the other component (N, μ) can be bound on these sites, at most one per site. Note that $P(N = 0, B = 0) = 1/\Upsilon$.

It is most convenient to sum first over N:

$$\Upsilon = \sum_{B=0}^{\infty} (1 + e^m)^B e^{-\varphi B}. \tag{10-71}$$

We note that [see Eq. (6-51)ff.]

$$\Xi = e^{\hat{p}B/kT} = (1 + e^m)^B = e^{p^{(0)}B/kT} = e^{\varphi^{(0)}B} \tag{10-72}$$

and $\hat{p}^{(x)} = 0$. Therefore

$$\Upsilon(m, \varphi) = \sum_{B=0}^{\infty} e^{-(\varphi-\varphi^{(0)})B}$$

$$= \frac{1}{1 - e^{-[\varphi-\varphi^{(0)}(m)]}} \qquad [\varphi > \varphi^{(0)}(m)]. \tag{10-73}$$

That is, Υ converges and will lead to a finite $\bar{B}$ (small system) if φ is chosen so that $\varphi > \varphi^{(0)}(m)$. If $\varphi \leqslant \varphi^{(0)}$, a small system cannot exist $(\bar{B} \to \infty)$.

If we sum first over B, the second sum (over N) converges if m is chosen less than $m^{(0)}(\varphi)$, and Eq. (10-73) is again obtained. In this case [see Eq. (2-79)], $\hat{\mu}/kT$ contains an excess function: $\hat{\mu}^{(x)}/kT = N^{-1} \ln (1 - e^{-\varphi})$.

From Eq. (10-6) we find

$$\bar{B}(m, \varphi) = -\left(\frac{\partial \ln \Upsilon}{\partial \varphi}\right)_m = \frac{e^{-(\varphi-\varphi^{(0)})}}{1 - e^{-(\varphi-\varphi^{(0)})}} \tag{10-74}$$

and

$$\bar{N}(m, \varphi) = \left(\frac{\partial \ln \Upsilon}{\partial m}\right)_\varphi = \frac{\bar{B}(m, \varphi)e^m}{1 + e^m} = \bar{B}(1 - e^{-\varphi^{(0)}}). \tag{10-75}$$

Hence $\Upsilon = 1 + \bar{B}$. This result for $\bar{N}/\bar{B}$ is the same as for a macroscopic system (any ensemble). To obtain a sizeable $\bar{B}$, we need $\varphi - \varphi^{(0)} \ll 1$. Then $\bar{B} = (\varphi - \varphi^{(0)})^{-1}$.

The entropy is

$$\frac{S}{k} = \varphi \bar{B} - m\bar{N} + \ln \Upsilon$$

$$= (1 + \bar{B}) \ln (1 + \bar{B}) - \bar{N} \ln \bar{N} - (\bar{B} - \bar{N}) \ln (\bar{B} - \bar{N}). \quad (10\text{-}76)$$

This is an exact expression (no Stirling approximation, etc.). It is of interest to compare this with the entropy from other environments, all for the same N and B. Equation (2-84) gives S/k for the $N, p/T$ case; Eq. (6-57) pertains to the $\mu/T, B$ case; and Eq. (15-97) gives S/k to $O(1)$ for the variables N, B. The order of increasing entropy is: N, B; $\mu/T, B$; $N, p/T$; and $\mu/T, p/T$. This is just the expected sequence: completely closed; semiopen; semiopen; completely open.

One needs in general to use difference as well as differential relations when applying thermodynamics to very small systems with environmental variables which include one or more extensive properties (e.g., in a μ, B, T lattice gas system there is a discrete difference between, say, $B = 9$ and $B = 10$). As we have already pointed out, a special feature associated only with a completely open system is that *all* thermodynamic functions vary smoothly, even for systems which are very small on the average. As an example of this, we consider the present model when $\varphi - \varphi^{(0)} \gg 1$ so that $\bar{B} = \exp[-(\varphi - \varphi^{(0)})] \ll 1$. Equation (10-75) is unchanged and Eq. (10-76) becomes

$$\frac{S}{k} = \bar{B} - \bar{N} \ln \bar{N} - (\bar{B} - \bar{N}) \ln (\bar{B} - \bar{N}). \qquad (10\text{-}77)$$

Only the first few terms in Υ need be retained:

$$\Upsilon = 1 + e^{-\varphi} + e^m e^{-\varphi}. \qquad (10\text{-}78)$$

The probabilities P_{NB} of the various states are

$$P_{00} = \frac{1}{\Upsilon} = 1 - \bar{B}, \qquad P_{01} = \frac{e^{-\varphi}}{\Upsilon} = \bar{B} - \bar{N}, \qquad P_{11} = \frac{e^m e^{-\varphi}}{\Upsilon} = \bar{N}.$$

$$(10\text{-}79)$$

We can then verify that (see page 13 of Part I)

$$\frac{S}{k} = -(P_{00} \ln P_{00} + P_{01} \ln P_{01} + P_{11} \ln P_{11}) \qquad (10\text{-}80)$$

also gives Eq. (10-77).

Fluctuations in both N and B are large, but we leave details to the reader.

CLASSICAL IDEAL GAS. This is a hypothetical gas of noninteracting point particles which obey classical statistics for all values of N and V. Or, alternatively, this is a very dilute, real, monatomic gas for which we ignore the small errors made on using a dilute-gas model over the whole range of N and V. That is, there are negligible contributions to integrals from N and V values which do not correspond to a dilute gas if μ, p, and T are chosen so that the gas is, in fact, dilute.

For an N, V, T system [see Eq. (15-59)],

$$Q(N, V, T) = \frac{V^N}{N! \Lambda^{3N}} \tag{10-81}$$

where

$$\Lambda = \frac{h}{(2\pi m k T)^{1/2}}.$$

For a μ, V, T system,

$$\Xi(\mu, V, T) = \sum_{N=0}^{\infty} Q\lambda^N = \exp\left(\frac{V\lambda}{\Lambda^3}\right) = e^{\hat{p}V/kT}, \tag{10-82}$$

where $\lambda = e^{\mu/kT}$. Note that $\hat{p}^{(x)} = 0$.

For an N, p, T system,

$$\Delta(N, p, T) = \int_0^{\infty} Q e^{-pV/kT} \, d\left(\frac{pV}{kT}\right). \tag{10-83}$$

Integration instead of summation over V must be used because V can be varied continuously. The choice of pV/kT as the dimensionless variable of integration is simple and natural but somewhat arbitrary.[1] We find

$$\Delta = \left(\frac{kT}{p\Lambda^3}\right)^N = e^{-N\hat{\mu}/kT}. \tag{10-84}$$

Note that $\hat{\mu}^{(x)} = 0$.

[1] See S.M., p. 63.

For a μ, p, T system,

$$\Upsilon(\mu, p, T) = \sum_{N=0}^{\infty} \Delta\lambda^N = \frac{1}{1 - \dfrac{kT\lambda}{p\Lambda^3}} \qquad \left(\frac{kT\lambda}{p\Lambda^3} < 1\right). \qquad (10\text{-}85)$$

The same result follows from

$$\Upsilon = \int_0^{\infty} \Xi e^{-pV/kT} \, d\left(\frac{pV}{kT}\right). \qquad (10\text{-}86)$$

The macroscopic relationship between p, T, and $\mu^{(0)}(p, T)$ is seen from Eq. (10-84) to be $kT\lambda^{(0)}/p\Lambda^3 = 1$. Hence Υ can be written in the form

$$\Upsilon = \frac{1}{1 - e^{-(\mu^{(0)}-\mu)/kT}}. \qquad (10\text{-}87)$$

Thus Υ converges for $\mu < \mu^{(0)}$ and diverges for $\mu \geqslant \mu^{(0)}$.

From

$$\mathscr{E} = kT \ln\left(1 - \frac{kT\lambda}{p\Lambda^3}\right) \qquad (10\text{-}88)$$

we deduce

$$\bar{N} = -\left(\frac{\partial\mathscr{E}}{\partial\mu}\right)_{p,T} = \frac{(kT\lambda/p\Lambda^3)}{1 - (kT\lambda/p\Lambda^3)} \qquad (10\text{-}89)$$

$$\bar{V} = \left(\frac{\partial\mathscr{E}}{\partial p}\right)_{\mu,T} = \frac{\bar{N}kT}{p} \qquad (10\text{-}90)$$

$$S = -\left(\frac{\partial\mathscr{E}}{\partial T}\right)_{\mu,p} = -\frac{\mathscr{E}}{T} + \frac{p\bar{V}}{T} - \frac{\mu\bar{N}}{T} + \frac{3}{2}\bar{N}k. \qquad (10\text{-}91)$$

Therefore, from Eq. (10-3),

$$\bar{E} = \tfrac{3}{2}\bar{N}kT. \qquad (10\text{-}92)$$

We note that $\bar{N}$ and $\bar{V}$ become infinitely large as $\mu \to \mu^{(0)}$.

For given μ, p, and T, the probability that a system contains N molecules and has a volume such that pV/kT lies between pV/kT

and $(pV/kT) + d(pV/kT)$ is

$$P(N,\ V)\ d\!\left(\frac{pV}{kT}\right) = \frac{V^N e^{-pV/kT}\lambda^N}{\Upsilon N!\Lambda^{3N}}\ d\!\left(\frac{pV}{kT}\right). \qquad (10\text{-}93)$$

The probability that a system contains N molecules, irrespective of V, is

$$P(N) = \int_0^\infty P(N,\ V)\ d\!\left(\frac{pV}{kT}\right) = \frac{\Delta(N,\,p,\,T)\lambda^N}{\Upsilon}$$

$$= \frac{1}{\Upsilon}\!\left(\frac{kT\lambda}{p\Lambda^3}\right)^N = \frac{1}{\Upsilon}[e^{-(\mu^{(0)}-\mu)/kT}]^N. \qquad (10\text{-}94)$$

This is the same dependence on N as in Eq. (10-37) (linear aggregate). Note that $P(0) = 1/\Upsilon$ again. Similarly,

$$P(V) = \sum_{N=0}^\infty P(N,\ V) = \frac{\Xi(\mu,\ V,\ T)e^{-pV/kT}}{\Upsilon}$$

$$= \frac{1}{\Upsilon}\!\left[\exp\!\left(\frac{\lambda}{\Lambda^3} - \frac{p}{kT}\right)\right]^V = \frac{1}{\Upsilon}[e^{(p^{(0)}-p)/kT}]^V, \qquad (10\text{-}95)$$

where $p^{(0)}(\mu, T)$ is defined by $kT\lambda/p^{(0)}\Lambda^3 = 1$. This is the same dependence as that which follows from the expression preceding Eq. (10-73) (ideal lattice gas).

The function $P(N,\ V)$, for large N and V, has the form of a "Gaussian mountain range" (Fig. 10-2). This can be seen as follows. For large N,

$$\ln P = N \ln V - \frac{pV}{kT} + \frac{N\mu}{kT} - N \ln \Lambda^3$$

$$- N \ln N + N - \tfrac{1}{2} \ln 2\pi N - \ln \Upsilon. \qquad (10\text{-}96)$$

Now we take $N = \text{constant} = N'$ and investigate the dependence of $\ln P$ on V. We find

$$\frac{\partial \ln P}{\partial V} = \frac{N'}{V} - \frac{p}{kT}, \qquad \frac{\partial^2 \ln P}{\partial V^2} = -\frac{N'}{V^2},$$

Thus the maximum with respect to V occurs at $V_m = N'kT/p$ and

$$P(N',\ V) \cong P(N',\ V_m) \exp\!\left[-\tfrac{1}{2}N'\!\left(\frac{V - V_m}{V_m}\right)^2\right]. \qquad (10\text{-}97)$$

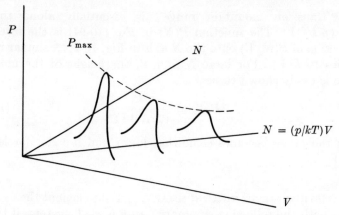

FIGURE 10-2. The probability function $P(N, V)$ for a classical ideal gas (schematic). μ, p, and T are constant.

The relative standard deviation in V is the usual $(N')^{-1/2}$. Equation (10-97) is of course also essentially the probability distribution in V for an N, p, T system.

Next, we take $V = $ constant $= V'$ and consider $\ln P$ as a function of N:

$$\frac{\partial \ln P}{\partial N} = \ln\left(\frac{V'}{N\Lambda^3}\right) + \frac{\mu}{kT} - \frac{1}{2N}, \qquad \frac{\partial^2 \ln P}{\partial N^2} = -\frac{1}{N} + \frac{1}{2N^2}.$$

If we denote by N_m the value of N at the maximum with respect to N, we find

$$P(N, V') \cong P(N_m, V') \exp\left[-\tfrac{1}{2}(N_m - \tfrac{1}{2})\left(\frac{N - N_m}{N_m}\right)^2\right], \qquad (10\text{-}98)$$

where

$$N_m + \tfrac{1}{2} = \frac{pV'}{kT} \exp\left[-\frac{(\mu^{(0)} - \mu)}{kT}\right]. \qquad (10\text{-}99)$$

As $\mu \to \mu^{(0)}$, $N_m \to pV'/kT$. The relative standard deviation in N in Eq. (10-98) is $N_m^{-1/2}$. Equation (10-98) is also applicable to a μ, V, T system.

Thus a vertical section taken parallel to either the ordinate or the abscissa in Fig. 10-2 produces a Gaussian curve. The axis of this "Gaussian mountain range" is essentially along the line $N = (p/kT)V$. The function $P(N)$ in Eq. (10-94) is the integrated projection of $P(N, V)$ onto the N axis in Fig. 10-2. A similar remark applies to $P(V)$. For large N and V, the height of the mountain range is easily shown to be

$$P_{\max} \simeq \frac{1}{(2\pi N)^{1/2}\Upsilon}. \tag{10-100}$$

Thus the range becomes somewhat lower and broader for large N and V.

STATISTICAL MECHANICAL SUMMARY. We supplement the examples above with the following summary. In a μ, p, T system, if the last sum is over, say, V, we have

$$\Upsilon = \sum_V \exp\left\{\frac{[p^{(0)}(\mu, T) - p]V}{kT}\right\} \exp\left[\frac{\hat{p}^{(x)}(\mu, V, T)V}{kT}\right]. \tag{10-101}$$

The first factor dominates for large V. A small system is therefore possible (Υ converges) if p is chosen so that $p > p^{(0)}(\mu, T)$. Such a system is not possible if $p < p^{(0)}(\bar{V} \to \infty)$. The behavior at $p = p^{(0)}$ depends on the particular case.

The choice of the last variable over which to sum is obviously arbitrary. If the last sum is over N [compare Eq. (10-49)],

$$\Upsilon = \sum_N \exp\left\{\frac{[\mu - \mu^{(0)}(p, T)]N}{kT}\right\} \exp\left[-\frac{N\hat{\mu}^{(x)}(N, p, T)}{kT}\right]. \tag{10-102}$$

The sufficient condition for convergence here is $\mu < \mu^{(0)}(p, T)$. If the last sum is over E, this condition is $T < T^{(0)}(\mu, p)$. It is easy to show that if values of μ, p, and T are chosen such that $p > p^{(0)}(\mu, T)$, then it will also be that $\mu < \mu^{(0)}(p, T)$ and $T < T^{(0)}(\mu, p)$. If the surface $\mu^{(0)}(p, T)$ is drawn in a p, T, μ coordinate system (μ increases in the upward direction), then Υ converges for points under this surface and possibly on it, but not above it.

10-3. SUBDIVISION POTENTIAL AND STABILITY CONDITIONS

The discussion here is not confined to μ, p, T systems. As in the preceding two sections, we shall be referring specifically to ensembles of distinguishable systems.

For convenience, we reproduce a few of the relations from pages 23 to 25 of Part I. The fundamental equation (for any environment) for an ensemble of $\mathcal{N}$ systems is (omitting bars)

$$dE_t = T\,dS_t - p\,dV_t + \sum_i \mu_i\,dN_{ti} + \mathscr{E}\,d\mathcal{N}, \qquad (10\text{-}103)$$

where

$$E_t = \mathcal{N}E, \qquad V_t = \mathcal{N}V, \qquad N_{ti} = \mathcal{N}N_i, \qquad S_t = \mathcal{N}S.$$

We also have

$$dA_t = -S_t\,dT - p\,dV_t + \sum_i \mu_i\,dN_{ti} + \mathscr{E}\,d\mathcal{N} \qquad (10\text{-}104)$$

$$dF_t = -S_t\,dT + V_t\,dp + \sum_i \mu_i\,dN_{ti} + \mathscr{E}\,d\mathcal{N} \qquad (10\text{-}105)$$

$$d\left(F_t - \sum_i \mu_i N_{ti}\right) = -S_t\,dT + V_t\,dp - \sum_i N_{ti}\,d\mu_i + \mathscr{E}\,d\mathcal{N}, \qquad (10\text{-}106)$$

where

$$A_t = E_t - TS_t, \qquad F_t = E_t - TS_t + pV_t.$$

Thus the subdivision potential $\mathscr{E}$ has the alternative definitions (among others):

$$\mathscr{E} = \left(\frac{\partial E_t}{\partial \mathcal{N}}\right)_{S_t, V_t, N_{ti}} = \left(\frac{\partial A_t}{\partial \mathcal{N}}\right)_{T, V_t, N_{ti}} = \left(\frac{\partial F_t}{\partial \mathcal{N}}\right)_{T, p, N_{ti}} \qquad (10\text{-}107)$$

$$= \left[\frac{\partial\left(F_t - \sum_i \mu_i N_{ti}\right)}{\partial \mathcal{N}}\right]_{T, p, \mu_i} = \frac{F_t - \sum_i \mu_i N_{ti}}{\mathcal{N}} \qquad (10\text{-}108)$$

$$= E - TS + pV - \sum_i \mu_i N_i. \qquad (10\text{-}109)$$

These are reminiscent of the alternative definitions possible for the chemical potentials μ_i. The subdivision potential is a measure of the increase in the appropriate energy or free energy function accompanying an increase in $\mathcal{N}$ (i.e., accompanying further subdivision of the ensemble). From the first definition in Eq. (10-107) it is clear that $\mathscr{E}$ is the work that must be done on the ensemble to create one more small system (since S_t, V_t, and N_{ti} are held constant).

It is apparent from Eqs. (10-107) to (10-109) that $\mathscr{E}$ is independent of any arbitrary choices of the zeros of energy or entropy.

SPONTANEOUS CHANGE IN $\mathscr{N}$. The subdivision potential has a deeper physical significance in the special case of a closed ensemble (N_{ti} constant) of systems in which it is conceivable that $\mathscr{N}$ could change spontaneously (i.e., without the intervention of any outside agency). Let us see what kind of ensemble this must be. In the first place, the ensemble must consist of open systems, each of which contains at least one molecule (monomer, etc.). That is, an empty "system" (all $N_i = 0$) is *not* counted as a system of the ensemble.[1] The point is that in this case and only this case, $\mathscr{N}$ *can* change *spontaneously*. For example (linear aggregates, N_t constant):

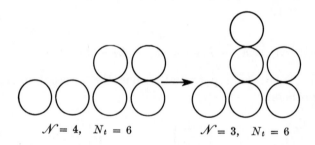

$$\mathscr{N} = 4, \quad N_t = 6 \qquad\qquad \mathscr{N} = 3, \quad N_t = 6$$

In the second place, if $\mathscr{N}$ changes spontaneously, it is not possible, without outside intervention, to hold constant the total volume of the ensemble, V_t, for this would require precise distribution of the volumes of systems that become empty (through fluctuations in the N_i) among those that are not empty. Therefore we must choose p rather than V_t as a variable to be kept constant during any spontaneous change in $\mathscr{N}$. Finally, since we cannot maintain S_t constant (in the spontaneous process under consideration, $T\, dS_t > DQ_t$), we choose $T = $ constant.

The conclusion we reach is therefore the following. A spontaneous process in which $\mathscr{N}$ changes is possible in an ensemble of open systems (each of which contains at least one molecule) held at

[1] This is the natural, realistic, and necessary point of view which we will take in discussing experimental μ, p, T systems (aggregates) in a solvent or gas. See Section 10-6.

constant N_{ti}, p, and T. The ensemble is as usual assumed to be very large ($\mathscr{N} \to \infty$). The environmental variables for each system of the ensemble are μ_i, p, T.

If the spontaneous process occurs, it takes place in a closed ensemble at constant p and T. Therefore, in the process, $dF_t < 0$. From Eq. (10-105), it then follows that $\mathscr{E}\, d\bar{\mathscr{N}} < 0$, where $\bar{\mathscr{N}}$ is the average number of systems in the ensemble (this is a time average for one ensemble, or an ensemble average if we consider an ensemble of ensembles). Consequently, in such a spontaneous change, $\bar{\mathscr{N}}$ will decrease (larger systems are formed) if $\mathscr{E}$ is positive, and $\bar{\mathscr{N}}$ will increase (smaller systems are formed) if $\mathscr{E}$ is negative.

We also have, for the above ensemble, the stability condition

$$\left(\frac{\partial^2 F_t}{\partial \bar{\mathscr{N}}^2}\right)_{T, p, N_{ti}} = \left(\frac{\partial \mathscr{E}}{\partial \bar{\mathscr{N}}}\right)_{T, p, N_{ti}} > 0. \tag{10-110}$$

This follows immediately from statistical mechanics, as we now show. The ensemble partition function appropriate to the independent variables in Eq. (10-105) is

$$e^{-F_t/kT} = \Delta_t(N_{ti}, \mathscr{N}, p, T). \tag{10-111}$$

Similarly, associated with the thermodynamic equation

$$d(F_t - \mathscr{E}\bar{\mathscr{N}}) = -S_t\, dT + V_t\, dp + \sum_i \mu_i\, dN_{ti} - \bar{\mathscr{N}}\, d\mathscr{E}, \tag{10-112}$$

we have the partition function

$$\exp\left[-\left(\frac{F_t - \mathscr{E}\bar{\mathscr{N}}}{kT}\right)\right] = \sum_{\mathscr{N}} \Delta_t(N_{ti}, \mathscr{N}, p, T)e^{\mathscr{N}\mathscr{E}/kT}. \tag{10-113}$$

On differentiating twice with respect to $\mathscr{E}$, we find the usual kind of result,

$$\overline{\mathscr{N}^2} - \bar{\mathscr{N}}^2 = kT\left(\frac{\partial \bar{\mathscr{N}}}{\partial \mathscr{E}}\right)_{p, T, N_{ti}} > 0. \tag{10-114}$$

This is a quite general situation in statistical thermodynamics: Whenever the mean value of an extensive, mechanical[1] quantity ($\mathscr{N}$ in this case) is free to vary in a spontaneous process, the quantity

[1] See p. 13 of Part I.

will also be free to fluctuate, and there will consequently be an inequality (stability condition) of the type (10-114).

The resemblance between the above paragraph and Eqs. (5-76) to (5-78), which pertain to a chemical reaction, should be noted. This similarity is not surprising because we are concerned here with a change in the degree of subdivision of small systems which, in a very general sense, is itself a special case of a "chemical reaction" (on the system rather than molecular level).

Thus we have

$$\mathscr{E} \, d\bar{\mathscr{N}} < 0 \quad \text{and} \quad \frac{\partial \mathscr{E}}{\partial \bar{\mathscr{N}}} > 0$$

in the spontaneous process under consideration. Since $\mathscr{E}$ and $d\bar{\mathscr{N}}$ have opposite signs, whereas $d\bar{\mathscr{N}}$ and $d\mathscr{E}$ have the same sign, it follows that $\mathscr{E}$ and $d\mathscr{E}$ have opposite signs:

$$\mathscr{E} \, d\mathscr{E} < 0, \qquad d(\mathscr{E}^2) < 0, \qquad d|\mathscr{E}| < 0. \qquad (10\text{-}115)$$

That is, regardless of its sign, $\mathscr{E}$ changes spontaneously in the direction of its final equilibrium value,

$$\left(\frac{\partial F_t}{\partial \bar{\mathscr{N}}} \right)_{T, \, p, \, N_{ti}} = \mathscr{E} = 0. \qquad (10\text{-}116)$$

Just as ΔT determines the direction of heat transfer, Δp the direction of volume transfer, and $\Delta \mu$ the direction of transfer of matter, so $\mathscr{E}$ determines the tendency toward more or less subdivision in an ensemble of nonempty, small μ_i, p, T systems.

A complete set of independent variables for the ensemble is N_{ti}, p, T, $\mathscr{E}$, when $\mathscr{E}$ has an arbitrary value [see Eq. (10-112)]. In the special case of subdivision equilibrium ($\mathscr{E} = 0$), a complete set is N_{ti}, p, T. For a single system, a complete set is ordinarily μ_i, p, T (or $\bar{N}_i$, p, T). In the special case of subdivision equilibrium, the condition

$$\mathscr{E}(\mu_i, p, T) = 0 \quad \text{or} \quad \mathscr{E}(\bar{N}_i, p, T) = 0 \qquad (10\text{-}117)$$

furnishes one relation between independent variables which reduces their number by one.

In a closed ensemble of $\mathscr{N}$ one-component μ, p, T systems, $\bar{N} = N_t/\mathscr{N}$. If $\mathscr{N}$ itself fluctuates ($N \geqslant 1$), as we have been considering above, we include averaging over $\mathcal{N}$ as well as N: $\bar{N} = N_t \overline{\mathcal{N}^{-1}}$. But we are interested, as always, in the limit $\mathcal{N} \to \infty$, so that the probability distribution in $\mathcal{N}$ is essentially a Dirac δ-function. Thus $\overline{\mathcal{N}^{-1}} = 1/\bar{\mathcal{N}}$ and

$$N_t = \bar{N}\bar{\mathcal{N}} = \text{constant}, \qquad d\bar{\mathcal{N}} = -\frac{\bar{\mathcal{N}}}{\bar{N}} d\bar{N}.$$

Equation (10-114) becomes, then,

$$
\begin{aligned}
\overline{\mathcal{N}^2} - \bar{\mathcal{N}}^2 &= kT\left(\frac{\partial \bar{\mathcal{N}}}{\partial \mathscr{E}}\right)_{T,p,N_t} = -\frac{kT\bar{\mathcal{N}}}{\bar{N}}\left(\frac{\partial \bar{N}}{\partial \mathscr{E}}\right)_{T,p} \\
&= -\frac{kT\bar{\mathcal{N}}}{\bar{N}}\left(\frac{\partial \mu}{\partial \mathscr{E}}\right)_{T,p}\left(\frac{\partial \bar{N}}{\partial \mu}\right)_{T,p} \\
&= \frac{\bar{\mathcal{N}}(\overline{N^2} - \bar{N}^2)}{\bar{N}^2} = \bar{\mathcal{N}} O(1),
\end{aligned}
\tag{10-118}
$$

where we have used Eqs. (10-11c) and (10-38). The fluctuations in N are unusually large in a completely open system, as noted in the examples of Section 10-2. The fluctuations in $\mathcal{N}$ are of the normal order of magnitude for an extensive property of a macroscopic system.

If the systems above are multicomponent,

$$d\bar{N}_i = -\frac{\bar{N}_i}{\bar{\mathcal{N}}} d\bar{\mathcal{N}} \qquad (N_{ti} \text{ constant})$$

$$d\mathscr{E} = \sum_i \left(\frac{\partial \mathscr{E}}{\partial \bar{N}_i}\right)_{p,T,\bar{N}} d\bar{N}_i \qquad (p, T \text{ constant}),$$

and therefore

$$
\begin{aligned}
\left(\frac{\partial \mathscr{E}}{\partial \bar{\mathcal{N}}}\right)_{p,T,N_{ti}} &= -\frac{1}{\bar{\mathcal{N}}}\sum_i \bar{N}_i\left(\frac{\partial \mathscr{E}}{\partial \bar{N}_i}\right)_{p,T,\bar{N}_j} \\
&= \frac{1}{\bar{\mathcal{N}}}\sum_{i,k} \bar{N}_i \bar{N}_k \left(\frac{\partial \mu_k}{\partial \bar{N}_i}\right)_{p,T,\bar{N}_j} > 0,
\end{aligned}
\tag{10-119}
$$

where we have used Eq. (4-4). The inequality $\Sigma_{i,k} > 0$ is applicable to any nonempty μ_i, p, T system.

EXAMPLE OF SPONTANEOUS CHANGE IN $\mathcal{N}$. Let us consider a closed ensemble of open linear aggregates as an illustration. The model we use is exactly the same as that treated at the beginning of Section 10-2, but here we impose the requirement (or definition) that a system must contain at least one molecule ($N \geqslant 1$). We therefore subtract the $N = 0$ term from Υ in Eq. (10-27) and obtain

$$\Upsilon = \frac{1 - x + cx}{1 - x} - 1 = \frac{cx}{1 - x} \qquad (x < 1). \qquad (10\text{-}120)$$

Then

$$\mathscr{E} = - kT \ln \frac{cx}{1 - x} = - kT \ln c(\bar{N} - 1) \qquad (10\text{-}121)$$

and

$$\bar{N} = - \left(\frac{\partial \mathscr{E}}{\partial \mu}\right)_T = \frac{1}{1 - x} = 1 + e^{-\epsilon/kT} e^{-\mathscr{E}/kT}. \qquad (10\text{-}122)$$

Equation (10-121) gives $\mathscr{E}$ as a function of μ and T or as a function of $\bar{N}$ and T. $\mathscr{E}$ may be positive, negative, or zero. Equation (10-122) provides $\bar{N}$ as a function of μ and T or as a function of $\mathscr{E}$ and T.

Other properties are easy to derive in the ordinary way:

$$\bar{E} = \bar{N}kT^2 \frac{d \ln j}{dT} + (\bar{N} - 1)\epsilon \qquad (10\text{-}123)$$

$$S = \bar{N}k \ln j + \bar{N}kT \frac{d \ln j}{dT} + S^{(x)} \qquad (10\text{-}124)$$

$$S^{(x)} = - k \sum_{N=1}^{\infty} P(N) \ln P(N)$$

$$= k \ln \bar{N} + (\bar{N} - 1)k \ln \frac{\bar{N}}{\bar{N} - 1}, \qquad (10\text{-}125)$$

where

$$P(N) = (1 - x)x^{N-1} \qquad (N \geqslant 1). \qquad (10\text{-}126)$$

Now we imagine that $\mathcal{N}$ is allowed to change spontaneously to a final equilibrium value, in a closed ensemble held at constant T. When this equilibrium is reached,

$$\mathscr{E} = 0, \qquad \Upsilon = 1, \qquad \lambda = \frac{1}{j(1 + e^{-\epsilon/kT})}$$

$$\bar{N} = 1 + e^{-\epsilon/kT}, \qquad \mathcal{N} = N_t/\bar{N}. \qquad (10\text{-}127)$$

If $\epsilon < 0$, $\bar{N} > 2$. There is, of course, one less degree of freedom in this equilibrium state (for a single system, only T is independent).

It might be recalled, for comparison, that when we considered this model in Section 10-2, beginning with Eq. (10-27), and allowed empty systems in the ensemble, we had

$$Q(0, T) = 1, \qquad \Upsilon \geqslant 1, \qquad \text{and} \qquad \mathscr{E} \leqslant 0. \qquad (10\text{-}128)$$

The value $\mathscr{E} = 0$ is achievable in this case only in the limit $\lambda \to 0$, $\bar{N} \to 0$ (and it does not have the physical significance of an equilibrium value).

Returning to Eq. (10-121), we observe that as $x \to 1$, $\bar{N} \to \infty$ and

$$\mathscr{E} \to - kT \ln \bar{N},$$

as in Eq. (10-32). Although $\mathscr{E}$ is negligible for a macroscopic system (it has to be compared with terms of order $\bar{N}kT$), it is *not* equal to zero in the strict sense that we are using $\mathscr{E} = 0$ above as an equilibrium condition. The macroscopic state is therefore not to be confused with the equilibrium state.

COMPILATION OF $\mathscr{E}$ VALUES. For the convenience of the reader, we collect here some of the expressions for $\mathscr{E}$ found elsewhere for a few simple models and several choices of environmental variables.

Ideal Lattice Gas

N, B: $\qquad \mathscr{E} = - kT \left[\dfrac{1}{2} \ln \dfrac{2\pi N(B - N)}{B} - \dfrac{B}{B - N} + \cdots \right]$ (15-94)

$\dfrac{\mu}{T}, B$: $\qquad \mathscr{E} = 0$ (6-54)

$N, \dfrac{p}{T}$: $\qquad \mathscr{E} = kT \ln (1 - e^{-p/kT})$ (2-81)

$\dfrac{\mu}{T}, \dfrac{p}{T}$: $\qquad \mathscr{E} = - kT \ln (1 + \bar{B}) \qquad (N \geqslant 0).$ (10-73)

Classical Ideal Gas

N, V, T: $\mathscr{E} = \dfrac{kT}{2} \ln \dfrac{2\pi N}{e^2} + \cdots$ (15-64)

μ, V, T: $\mathscr{E} = 0$ (10-82)

N, p, T: $\mathscr{E} = 0$ (10-84)

μ, p, T: $\mathscr{E} = -kT \ln (1 + \bar{N})$ $(N \geqslant 0)$.   (10-88)

Spherical Aggregate

N, T: $\mathscr{E} = \tfrac{1}{3} a N^{2/3}$ (10-54)

μ, T: $\mathscr{E} = -kT \ln \dfrac{3\pi \bar{N}}{16}$ $[\mu = \mu^{(0)}(T)]$.   (10-59)

Linear Aggregate

N, T: $\mathscr{E} = -\epsilon$ (10-22)

μ, T: $\mathscr{E} = -kT \ln \dfrac{1 - x + cx}{1 - x}$ $(N \geqslant 0)$ (10-30)

μ, T: $\mathscr{E} = -kT \ln c(\bar{N} - 1)$ $(N \geqslant 1)$.   (10-121)

Positive, negative, and zero values of $\mathscr{E}$ are included above. Also, positive, negative, and zero values of the derivative $(\partial \mathscr{E} / \partial N)_{T,\, p}$ may be noted. Equation (10-139), below, requires that this derivative be negative for a completely open system.

STABILITY CONDITIONS. We shall not attempt an exhaustive discussion here but rather shall confine ourselves to deductions which follow directly from standard statistical mechanical fluctuation formulas for one-component systems.

We have pointed out a number of times in this book that thermodynamic equations for small systems are the same for all environments, although thermodynamic functions differ (see the expressions for $\mathscr{E}$, above, for example). Stability conditions (inequalities) also prove to be different for different environments. For example,

$(\partial \mu/\partial N)_{V, T}$ can never be negative for a μ, V, T system (see below), but this derivative may be negative for an N, V, T system (as in Fig. 8-1).

We first recall two stability conditions already encountered. Equation (5-78) states that $\partial \bar{n}/\partial \psi < 0$ for a chemical reaction in an N_i, p, T system [see also Eq. (5-9)]. The second case is $\partial \mathcal{N}/\partial \mathcal{E} > 0$ in Eq. (10-114).

In an N, V, T system, the energy E fluctuates. From

$$Q(N, V, T) = \sum_E \Omega(N, V, E)e^{-E/kT}$$

we deduce

$$\frac{\overline{E^2} - \bar{E}^2}{kT^2} = \left(\frac{\partial \bar{E}}{\partial T}\right)_{N, V} = C_V = T\left(\frac{\partial S}{\partial T}\right)_{N, V} > 0. \quad (10\text{-}129)$$

We can say nothing in general about $(\partial p/\partial V)_{N, T}$ and $(\partial \mu/\partial N)_{V, T}$ for a small N, V, T system. Both signs are possible for both derivatives, even in exact theories (see Fig. 8-1), although of course $\partial p/\partial V$ is usually negative and $\partial \mu/\partial N$ is usually positive.

In a μ, V, T system, N and E fluctuate. Equations (1-19) and (6-16) lead to

$$\frac{\overline{N^2} - \bar{N}^2}{kT} = \left(\frac{\partial \bar{N}}{\partial \mu}\right)_{V, T} > 0 \quad\quad (10\text{-}130)$$

$$\frac{\overline{L^2} - \bar{L}^2}{kT^2} = \left(\frac{\partial \bar{L}}{\partial T}\right)_{\mu, V} = T\left(\frac{\partial S}{\partial T}\right)_{\mu, V} > 0, \quad\quad (10\text{-}131)$$

where

$$L = E - \mu N = TS - \hat{p}V.$$

In view of Eq. (10-130), and because the first and third terms dominate in Eq. (8-30), in general $(\partial p/\partial V)_{\bar{N}, T} < 0$. But a more precise statement[1] follows from Eq. (6-8):

$$\left(\frac{\partial \hat{p}}{\partial V/\bar{N}}\right)_{V, T} = -\frac{\bar{N}^3}{V^2}\left(\frac{\partial \mu}{\partial \bar{N}}\right)_{V, T} < 0. \quad\quad (10\text{-}132)$$

[1] This is the same as Eq. (28.10) in S.M. and Eq. (12) in T. L. Hill, *J. Phys. Chem.* **57**, 324 (1953).

In an N, p, T system, we derive from $\Delta(N, p, T)$

$$-\frac{\overline{V^2} - \bar{V}^2}{kT} = \left(\frac{\partial \bar{V}}{\partial p}\right)_{N, T} < 0 \tag{10-133}$$

$$\frac{\overline{H^2} - \bar{H}^2}{kT^2} = \left(\frac{\partial \bar{H}}{\partial T}\right)_{N, p} = T\left(\frac{\partial S}{\partial T}\right)_{N, p} > 0, \tag{10-134}$$

where $H = E + pV$. From Eqs. (8-30) and (10-133), $(\partial \mu / \partial N)_{\bar{V}, T} > 0$, in general. More precisely, from Eq. (2-3),

$$\left(\frac{\partial \hat{\mu}}{\partial N/\bar{V}}\right)_{N, T} = -\frac{\bar{V}^3}{N^2}\left(\frac{\partial p}{\partial \bar{V}}\right)_{N, T} > 0. \tag{10-135}$$

In a μ, p, T system, $\Upsilon(\mu, p, T)$ leads to

$$\frac{\overline{N^2} - \bar{N}^2}{kT} = \left(\frac{\partial \bar{N}}{\partial \mu}\right)_{p, T} > 0 \tag{10-136}$$

$$-\frac{\overline{V^2} - \bar{V}^2}{kT} = \left(\frac{\partial \bar{V}}{\partial p}\right)_{\mu, T} < 0 \tag{10-137}$$

$$\frac{\overline{Y^2} - \bar{Y}^2}{kT^2} = \left(\frac{\partial \bar{Y}}{\partial T}\right)_{\mu, p} = T\left(\frac{\partial S}{\partial T}\right)_{\mu, p} > 0, \tag{10-138}$$

where

$$Y = \mathscr{E} + TS = E + pV - \mu N.$$

Equations (10-5), (10-136), and (10-137) then give the further relations

$$\left(\frac{\partial \mathscr{E}}{\partial \bar{N}}\right)_{p, T} = -\bar{N}\left(\frac{\partial \mu}{\partial \bar{N}}\right)_{p, T} < 0 \tag{10-139}$$

$$\left(\frac{\partial \mathscr{E}}{\partial \bar{V}}\right)_{\mu, T} = \bar{V}\left(\frac{\partial p}{\partial \bar{V}}\right)_{\mu, T} < 0. \tag{10-140}$$

10-4. PHASE TRANSITIONS IN μ, p, T SYSTEMS

Again, as in Sections 10-1 to 10-3, we consider an ensemble of distinguishable systems. The discussion here is a continuation of that in Sections 5-4 and 6-1. It can be brief because this subject proves to be less interesting for a μ, p, T system than for N, p, T

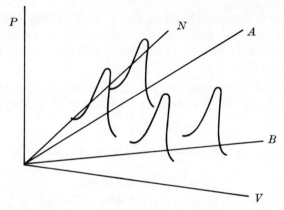

FIGURE 10-3. The probability function $P(N, V)$ in a two-phase region (schematic). μ, p, and T are constant.

or μ, V, T systems. For variety, following the suggestion in the footnote on page 149 of Part I, we employ a statistical mechanical (rather than thermodynamic) approach here.

As we have pointed out on page 62, an exact or approximate $Q(N, V, T)$ which leads to the two-state approximation for an N, p, T system also leads to this approximation for a μ, V, T system. The essential point to be made here is that, still referring to the same $Q(N, V, T)$, the two-state approximation carries over to the next level in the hierarchy of ensembles—that is, to a μ, p, T system. This can be seen, for example, by considering a series of neighboring values of the volume, V', V'', V''', etc., for a μ, V, T system in a phase-transition region. The probability curve $P(N)$ will have two peaks (A and B) for each of these values of V (μ and T held constant). If we put these curves together to form a $P(N, V)$ probability surface[1] for a μ, p, T system, as in Fig. 10-2, the surface will have the form of two separated Gaussian mountain ranges, each range corresponding to one of the two states A and B (Fig. 10-3). Thus a vertical section through this surface, parallel to the V axis ($N = N' = $ constant), will give a $P(N', V)$ curve as in Fig. 5-1c, whereas a vertical section parallel to the N axis ($V = V' = $ constant) will produce a two-peaked $P(N, V')$ curve, as already mentioned.

[1] $P(N, V)$ is defined as $Q(N, V, T)e^{N\mu/kT}e^{-pV/kT}/\Upsilon$.

Figure 7-2 is closely related to the $P(N, V)$ surface in Fig. 10-3, but the former figure exhibits two Gaussian peaks rather than two Gaussian mountain ranges. This point will be referred to further in the next section.

We turn now to a more analytical discussion and begin with the equation on page 149 of Part I for a two-state N, p, T system:

$$\Delta = \Delta_A + \Delta_B. \tag{10-141}$$

We multiply by $e^{N\mu/kT}$ and sum over N to obtain

$$\Upsilon = \Upsilon_A + \Upsilon_B. \tag{10-142}$$

Alternatively, we could have started with Ξ instead of Δ.

Incidentally, although the additive form of Δ or Ξ is retained on passing to the "higher" (more open) partition function Υ, this form does not obtain in the lower partition function Q. The physical reason why Δ, Ξ, and Υ are essentially additive at a phase transition is that density fluctuations are possible in all these cases and hence the system can *alternate* between states A and B. On the other hand, in an exact theory, an N, V, T system must have phases A and B present *simultaneously*, which leads to a Q in the form of a product rather than a sum.[1] In an approximate, uniform-density theory of a phase transition, there is just one expression (neither sum nor product) for $Q(N, V, T)$, but still Δ, Ξ, and Υ are in general additive.

Returning now to Eq. (10-142), the probability of observing a given system in state A, or the fraction of systems of an ensemble which are in state A, is

$$P_A = \frac{\mathcal{N}_A}{\mathcal{N}} = \frac{\Upsilon_A}{\Upsilon}. \tag{10-143}$$

Therefore

$$\frac{\mathcal{N}_A}{\mathcal{N}_B} = \frac{e^{-\mathcal{E}_A/kT}}{e^{-\mathcal{E}_B/kT}}, \tag{10-144}$$

which is the analogue of Eqs. (5-118) and (6-35).

Equation (10-142) can be rewritten in the forms

$$e^{-\mathcal{E}/kT} = e^{-\mathcal{E}_A/kT} + e^{-\mathcal{E}_B/kT}, \tag{10-145}$$

or

$$\mathcal{E} = P_A\mathcal{E}_A + P_B\mathcal{E}_B + kT(P_A \ln P_A + P_B \ln P_B). \tag{10-146}$$

[1] See, for example, Eqs. (A9.21) to (A9.24) of S.M.

We find easily from Eq. (10-145) that

$$\bar{V} = \left(\frac{\partial \mathscr{E}}{\partial p}\right)_{T,\,\mu} = P_A \bar{V}_A + P_B \bar{V}_B \qquad (10\text{-}147)$$

and

$$\bar{N} = -\left(\frac{\partial \mathscr{E}}{\partial \mu}\right)_{T,\,p} = P_A \bar{N}_A + P_B \bar{N}_B. \qquad (10\text{-}148)$$

Although Eqs. (10-144) to (10-148) have the same formal appearance as the corresponding equations in Sections 5-4 and 6-1, they have less interesting implications here. This comes about as follows. Consider first an N, p, T system which exhibits a phase transition. If we hold the environmental variables N and T constant, and vary p over a suitable range (see Figs. 5-2 and 5-4), the system will pass through the transition—that is, it will start in one state, say A, and end in the other, say B. This is a consequence of the fact that the macroscopic system has two degrees of freedom; therefore, if we hold one intensive variable (T) constant we can still span the transition region by varying a second intensive variable (p). Similar comments can be made about a μ, V, T system and Figs. 6-1 and 6-2.

But now consider a μ, p, T system. If we hold any two environmental variables[1] constant, say p and T, then we can still vary μ, but this variation will not cause the system to pass from one state to another; that is, nothing very interesting happens. This follows because specification of any two of μ, p, and T fixes the macroscopic stable state as either A or B (except in the very special case where the values of the two specified variables correspond to the two macroscopic phases in equilibrium with each other; but even in this case the system does not pass from one state to the other as the third environmental variable is varied).

Figure 10-4 illustrates the above comments. The curves shown are the macroscopic chemical potentials $\mu_A^{(0)}(p)$ and $\mu_B^{(0)}(p)$ (T is held constant). The partition function Υ_A converges for $\mu < \mu_A^{(0)}$, whereas Υ_B converges for $\mu < \mu_B^{(0)}$. Hence Υ in Eq. (10-142) converges in the crosshatched region (and possibly on the curves bordering this region). The vertical arrows indicate possible variation in

---

[1] Environmental variables are, essentially by definition, always the "natural" variables to hold constant.

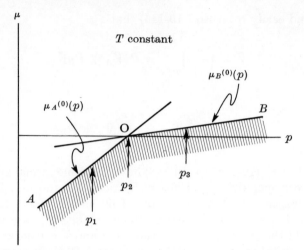

FIGURE 10-4.   Phase transition in μ, p, T system. See text for explanation.

the value of μ at constant p. From Eq. (10-102),

$$\Upsilon = \Upsilon_A + \Upsilon_B$$
$$= \sum_N \exp\left[\frac{(\mu - \mu_A^{(0)})N}{kT}\right] \exp\left(-\frac{N\hat{\mu}_A^{(x)}}{kT}\right)$$
$$+ \sum_N \exp\left[\frac{(\mu - \mu_B^{(0)})N}{kT}\right] \exp\left(-\frac{N\hat{\mu}_B^{(x)}}{kT}\right). \qquad (10\text{-}149)$$

At $p = p_1$, Υ_A and $\bar{N}_A$ become significant in size only as μ approaches the value $\mu_A^{(0)}(p_1)$. But for this value of μ, Υ_B and $\bar{N}_B$ are very small. Thus $P_A \cong 1$ and, in the appropriate version of Fig. 10-3, "mountain range" B is very small compared to range A. For no value of μ will $\mathscr{E}_A = \mathscr{E}_B$. For practical purposes, at $p = p_1$ and μ near $\mu_A^{(0)}(p_1)$, the system is confined to state A and has the properties of this state. Of course, the macroscopic stable state at p_1, T is A. The situation described above is exactly reversed with respect to A and B at $p = p_3$.

At $p = p_2(T)$, $\mu_A^{(0)} = \mu_B^{(0)}$ in Eq. (10-149). Thus Υ_A and Υ_B differ only by virtue of the relatively small quantities $\hat{\mu}_A^{(x)}$ and $\hat{\mu}_B^{(x)}$. Hence

Υ_A and Υ_B will be of the same order of magnitude, although P_A will in general vary somewhat with μ. Mountain ranges A and B (Fig. 10-3) will be of similar size. A value of μ may or may not exist at which $\mathscr{E}_A = \mathscr{E}_B$. Because of the limited opportunities for occurrence of this equality, Clausius–Clapeyron equations derived from $d\mathscr{E}_A = d\mathscr{E}_B$ [compare Eq. (5-135)] are not very important.

For cases in which Υ_A and Υ_B converge at $\mu = \mu_A^{(0)}$ and $\mu = \mu_B^{(0)}$, respectively, it would be possible to follow a transition from one state to another in a μ, p, T system in this way: Hold only T constant, vary p, and choose μ equal to the lesser of $\mu_A^{(0)}(p)$ and $\mu_B^{(0)}(p)$ for each p (curve AOB in Fig. 10-4). But this procedure seems too contrived to be worth pursuing in any detail.

Another procedure of the same sort is the following: Hold T constant, vary p, and adjust μ for each p to give a constant $\bar{N}$ (or $\bar{V}$).

Example. The extension of Eqs. (6-72)ff. to a μ, p, T system provides a simple example. For a μ, B, T system, we assume

$$
\begin{aligned}
\hat{p}_1(\mu, T) &= \hat{p}_0(T) + \rho_1(T)[\mu - \mu_0(T)] \\
\hat{p}_2(\mu, T) &= \hat{p}_0(T) + \rho_2(T)[\mu - \mu_0(T)],
\end{aligned}
\tag{10-150}
$$

where ρ_1 and ρ_2 are densities ($\rho_1 > \rho_2$). Ordinarily $\hat{p}_1$ and $\hat{p}_2$ would be functions of B, but not in this simple model. Then

$$
\begin{aligned}
\Upsilon(\mu, p, T) &= \Upsilon_1 + \Upsilon_2 \\
&= \sum_{B=0}^{\infty} e^{\hat{p}_1 B/kT}\, e^{-pB/kT} + \sum_{B=0}^{\infty} e^{\hat{p}_2 B/kT}\, e^{-pB/kT} \\
&= \frac{1}{1 - e^{(\hat{p}_1 - p)/kT}} + \frac{1}{1 - e^{(\hat{p}_2 - p)/kT}}.
\end{aligned}
\tag{10-151}
$$

Thus

$$
\frac{P_1}{P_2} = \frac{\mathscr{N}_1}{\mathscr{N}_2} = \frac{\Upsilon_1}{\Upsilon_2} = \frac{e^{-\mathscr{E}_1/kT}}{e^{-\mathscr{E}_2/kT}} = \frac{1 - e^{(\hat{p}_2 - p)/kT}}{1 - e^{(\hat{p}_1 - p)/kT}}.
\tag{10-152}
$$

Figure 10-5 is the analogue of Fig. 10-4. Convergence of Υ occurs in the crosshatched region. That is, Υ_1 converges for $p > \hat{p}_1$ and Υ_2 converges for $p > \hat{p}_2$.

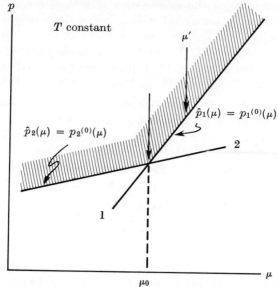

FIGURE 10-5. Example of phase transition in μ, p, T system [see Eqs. (10–150) to (10–158)].

We find easily that

$$\bar{N}_1 = -\left(\frac{\partial \mathscr{E}_1}{\partial \mu}\right)_{p,\,T} = \frac{e^{(\hat{p}_1 - p)/kT}\rho_1}{1 - e^{(\hat{p}_1 - p)/kT}} \qquad (10\text{-}153)$$

$$\bar{B}_1 = \left(\frac{\partial \mathscr{E}_1}{\partial p}\right)_{\mu,\,T} = \frac{\bar{N}_1}{\rho_1}, \qquad \Upsilon_1 = 1 + \bar{B}_1, \qquad (10\text{-}154)$$

with similar expressions for $\bar{N}_2$, $\bar{B}_2$, and Υ_2.

Let us consider a particular value of μ, say $\mu = \mu'$, in Fig. 10-5. Then we have to choose $p > \hat{p}_1(\mu')$. In order that the small systems have a reasonable size, with $\bar{N}_1 \gg 1$, $(p - \hat{p}_1)/kT$ must be very small. Let us call this quantity α. Now $0 < \alpha \ll 1$ and

$$\Upsilon_1 = \frac{1}{\alpha}, \qquad \bar{N}_1 = \frac{\rho_1}{\alpha}. \qquad (10\text{-}155)$$

As $\alpha \to 0$, $\bar{N}_1 \to \infty$.

The quantity

$$\beta \equiv e^{(\hat{p}_1 - \hat{p}_2)/kT} = e^{(\rho_1 - \rho_2)(\mu' - \mu_0)/kT}$$

might be of order, say, 2 to 10. Then $(\alpha \to 0)$

$$\Upsilon_2 = \frac{\beta}{\beta - 1} = O(1), \qquad \bar{N}_2 = \frac{\rho_2}{\beta - 1} = O(1), \qquad (10\text{-}156)$$

and

$$\frac{P_1}{P_2} = \frac{\beta - 1}{\alpha\beta} = O\left(\frac{1}{\alpha}\right) \qquad\qquad (10\text{-}157)$$

$$\to \infty \text{ as } \alpha \to 0.$$

If we choose μ equal to μ_0,

$$\hat{p}_1 = \hat{p}_2, \qquad \Upsilon_1 = \Upsilon_2, \qquad P_1 = P_2 = \tfrac{1}{2}. \qquad (10\text{-}158)$$

The two states are equally probable in this case. The systems become large, as before, as $p \to \hat{p}_1 = \hat{p}_2$.

10-5. N_1, μ_2, p, T SYSTEMS WITH N_1 CONSTANT

In Section 7-1 we considered an ensemble of distinguishable N_1, μ_2, p, T systems. If N_1 is always held constant, the remaining environmental variables are μ_2, p, and T. This is formally equivalent to a μ, p, T system. An example is the adsorption of component 2 at μ_2 onto an aggregate of N_1 molecules (or sites) of component 1, where $N_1 = $ constant. Essentially the same kind of system is obtained if we start with a μ, V, T system (or μ, B, T system, where $B = $ number of sites) and hold V (or B) constant.

When we put $N_1 = $ constant, Eqs. (7-2), (7-4), and (7-5) become

$$\hat{\mu}_1 N_1 = \bar{E} - TS + p\bar{V} - \mu_2 \bar{N}_2 \qquad\qquad (10\text{-}159)$$

$$d\bar{E} = T\, dS - p\, d\bar{V} + \mu_2\, d\bar{N}_2 \qquad\qquad (10\text{-}160)$$

$$d(\hat{\mu}_1 N_1) = -S\, dT + \bar{V}\, dp - \bar{N}_2\, d\mu_2. \qquad (10\text{-}161)$$

These are the analogues of Eqs. (10-3), (10-1), and (10-5), respectively, for a μ, p, T system:

$$\mathscr{E} = \bar{E} - TS + p\bar{V} - \mu\bar{N} \qquad\qquad (10\text{-}162)$$

$$d\bar{E} = T\, dS - p\, d\bar{V} + \mu\, d\bar{N} \qquad\qquad (10\text{-}163)$$

$$d\mathscr{E} = -S\, dT + \bar{V}\, dp - \bar{N}\, d\mu. \qquad\qquad (10\text{-}164)$$

Thus $\hat{\mu}_1 N_1$ plays the role of $\mathscr{E}$. The functions $\bar{E}$, S, and $\bar{V}$ in Eqs.

(10-159) to (10-161) include contributions from both components 1 and 2. The function $\hat{\mu}_1 N_1$ will be small (like $\mathscr{E}$) compared with the other terms in Eq. (10-159) only if $\bar{N}_2 \gg N_1$. This can occur in cases where there is no limit on the value of $\bar{N}_2$ ($\bar{N}_2 \to \infty$)—for example, in multilayer adsorption of component 2 onto N_1 sites (but not in the case of monolayer adsorption onto N_1 sites).

Perhaps a more natural procedure is to subtract out of the functions in Eqs. (10-159) to (10-161) the properties of pure component 1. If we put $\bar{N}_2 = 0$ ($\mu_2 \to -\infty$) in these equations, we have (for the same constant value of N_1)

$$\hat{\mu}_{10} N_1 = \bar{E}_0 - TS_0 + p\bar{V}_0$$

$$d\bar{E}_0 = T\,dS_0 - p\,d\bar{V}_0$$

$$d(\hat{\mu}_{10} N_1) = -S_0\,dT + \bar{V}_0\,dp.$$

These relations are now subtracted from Eqs. (10-159) to (10-161) to give

$$(\hat{\mu}_1 - \hat{\mu}_{10})N_1 = (\bar{E} - \bar{E}_0) - T(S - S_0) + p(\bar{V} - \bar{V}_0) - \mu_2 \bar{N}_2$$

$$(10\text{-}165)$$

$$d(\bar{E} - \bar{E}_0) = T\,d(S - S_0) - p\,d(\bar{V} - \bar{V}_0) + \mu_2\,d\bar{N}_2 \quad (10\text{-}166)$$

$$d[(\hat{\mu}_1 - \hat{\mu}_{10})N_1] = -(S - S_0)\,dT + (\bar{V} - \bar{V}_0)\,dp - \bar{N}_2\,d\mu_2.$$

$$(10\text{-}167)$$

These expressions involve, essentially, one-component thermodynamic functions and hence they are closer analogues of Eqs. (10-162) to (10-164) than are Eqs. (10-159) to (10-161). Again, however, the analogue of $\mathscr{E}$, namely, $(\hat{\mu}_1 - \hat{\mu}_{10})N_1$ will be "small" in Eq. (10-165) only when $\bar{N}_2 \gg N_1$.

Equations (10-165) to (10-167) resemble the relations of adsorption thermodynamics,[1] except that here N_1 can be arbitrarily small. The quantity $\hat{\mu}_{10} - \hat{\mu}_1$ is the analogue of the surface pressure.[2]

The connection with statistical mechanics is through the partition functions Δ and Γ [see Eqs. (1-32) and (7-7)]:

$$-kT \ln \Delta(N_1, p, T) = \hat{\mu}_{10} N_1 \qquad (10\text{-}168)$$

$$-kT \ln \Gamma(N_1, \mu_2, p, T) = \hat{\mu}_1 N_1. \qquad (10\text{-}169)$$

[1] T. L. Hill, *J. Chem. Phys.*, **18**, 246 (1950).
[2] Loc. cit., Appendix III.

Therefore

$$(\hat{\mu}_1 - \hat{\mu}_{10})N_1 = - kT \ln \frac{\Gamma(N_1, \mu_2, p, T)}{\Delta(N_1, p, T)}. \qquad (10\text{-}170)$$

Example. As an extremely simple example consider an ideal lattice gas of $\bar{N}_2$ molecules adsorbed on a group of N_1 independent and equivalent sites.[1] The partition function for the sites alone is taken to be $Q(N_1, T) = j_1(T)^{N_1}$ (Q replaces Δ). For the binary system, we have

$$Q(N_1, N_2, T) = \frac{j_1(T)^{N_1} j_2(T)^{N_2} N_1!}{N_2!(N_1 - N_2)!} \qquad (10\text{-}171)$$

and

$$\Gamma(N_1, \mu_2, T) = \sum_{N_2=0}^{N_1} Q(N_1, N_2, T)\lambda_2^{N_2} = j_1^{N_1}(1 + j_2\lambda_2)^{N_1}. \qquad (10\text{-}172)$$

The energy of adsorption of a component 2 molecule on a site is included in j_2. Then

$$\hat{\mu}_{10}N_1 = - N_1 kT \ln j_1 \qquad (10\text{-}173)$$

$$\hat{\mu}_1 N_1 = - N_1 kT[\ln j_1 + \ln(1 + j_2\lambda_2)] \qquad (10\text{-}174)$$

and

$$(\hat{\mu}_1 - \hat{\mu}_{10})N_1 = - N_1 kT \ln(1 + j_2\lambda_2). \qquad (10\text{-}175)$$

From Eqs. (10-167) and (10-175),

$$\bar{N}_2 = - \frac{\partial[(\hat{\mu}_1 - \hat{\mu}_{10})N_1]}{\partial \mu_2} = \frac{N_1 j_2\lambda_2}{1 + j_2\lambda_2}. \qquad (10\text{-}176)$$

In this model $\bar{N}_2$ cannot exceed N_1. All terms in Eq. (10-165) are of order $N_1 kT$. The usual fluctuation formula

$$\overline{N_2^2} - \bar{N}_2^2 = kT\left(\frac{\partial \bar{N}_2}{\partial \mu_2}\right)_{N_1, T},$$

gives

$$\frac{\overline{N_2^2} - \bar{N}_2^2}{\bar{N}_2^2} = \frac{1}{N_1 j_2\lambda_2} = O\left(\frac{1}{N_1}\right) = O\left(\frac{1}{\bar{N}_2}\right). \qquad (10\text{-}177)$$

Unlike the examples of μ, p, T systems in Section 10-2, the fluctuations here are "normal." The basic reason for this is that in a μ, p, T system, no extensive variable is specified and hence the

---

[1] See also the discussion preceding Eq. (10-71).

size of the system can fluctuate widely. Here, although N_1 is constant, it does serve to fix the size of the system (the system is "partially open" rather than "completely open").

We mentioned, in connection with Eq. (10-31), that the B.E.T. multilayer adsorption model amounts to having a "linear aggregate" of adsorbed molecules on each site. Thus, in the example above, if we allow B.E.T. multilayer adsorption of component 2 on each of the N_1 sites (instead of a maximum of only one adsorbed molecule per site), we will have

$$\bar{N}_2 = \frac{N_1 c x}{(1 - x)(1 - x + cx)} \tag{10-178}$$

and

$$(\hat{\mu}_1 - \hat{\mu}_{10})N_1 = - N_1 kT \ln \frac{1 - x + cx}{1 - x}. \tag{10-179}$$

In this case $\bar{N}_2 \to \infty$ as $x \to 1$. Thus we may have $\bar{N}_2 \gg N_1$. In Eq. (10-165), the terms on the right-hand side are of order $\bar{N}_2 kT$ whereas the left-hand side is of order $N_1 kT$. The fluctuation in N_2 is given by [see Eq. (10-39)]

$$\frac{\overline{N_2^2} - \bar{N}_2^2}{\bar{N}_2^2} = \frac{1}{N_1}\left(\frac{1 - x^2 + cx^2}{cx}\right) = O\left(\frac{1}{N_1}\right). \tag{10-180}$$

This relative fluctuation is "normal" (small) if N_1 is large, say, 50 to 100 or more, and of order unity if N_1 is very small [in Eq. (10-39), $N_1 = 1$]. This is because each linear aggregate has large fluctuations but the total relative fluctuation in a large number of aggregates is considerably reduced by cancellation.

Hence, in this case, as well as in others where $\bar{N}_2 \to \infty$ is possible, the extreme fluctuations characteristic of μ, p, T systems are found when N_1 is very small but not when $N_1 \gg 1$. When the maximum possible value of $\bar{N}_2$ is of order N_1, normal fluctuations are always encountered.

BINDING ON PROTEINLIKE MOLECULES. Suppose component 2 is bound on a macromolecule of fixed composition and molecular weight which, however, is not simply an aggregate or polymer of N_1 identical monomers. A protein molecule is an example. It has a definite composition and may contain many different amino acids. Hence N_1 and $\hat{\mu}_1$ lose their separate meaning.

To take care of this situation, it is necessary only to make a trivial change in notation. We start with Eq. (7-1):

$$dE_t = T\,dS_t - p\,dV_t + \mu_2\,dN_{t2} + X\,d\mathcal{N}.$$

From this we deduce Eqs. (10-159) to (10-161), but we retain the symbol X instead of using $\hat{\mu}_1 N_1$. Similarly, in the $\bar{N}_2 = 0$ equations ("bare protein"), we replace $\hat{\mu}_{10} N_1$ by X_0. Then Eqs. (10-165) to (10-167) are obtained, except that $(\hat{\mu}_1 - \hat{\mu}_{10})N_1$ is replaced by $X - X_0$.

TWO-STATE APPROXIMATION FOR PHASE TRANSITION. There are two possibilities here, both of which have already been discussed. The $P(N_2, V)$ probability function may appear as in Fig. 7-2 (fluctuations in N_2 and V normal) or as in Fig. 10-3 (large fluctuations in N_2 and V). The latter behavior will obtain only when N_1 is very small and $\bar{N}_2 \to \infty$ is possible. Intermediate behavior may occur when N_1 is, say, of order 10 to 20 and when $\bar{N}_2 \to \infty$ is possible.

Example of Phase Transition. In Section 8-2, we discussed the exact canonical ensemble partition function for a lattice gas of N molecules, with nearest-neighbor interaction energy w, on $B = 12$ sites arranged on the surface of a sphere. If this system is open, it becomes an example of a μ_2, T ($N_1 = $ constant) system. The notational correspondences are $N_1 = B = 12 = $ constant, $N_2 = N$, $\mu_2 = \mu$.

The partition function $Q(N, T)$ for a closed system is given in Eq. (8-37). For an open system, the partition function is

$$\Gamma(\mu, T) = \sum_{N=0}^{12} Q(N, T)\lambda^N. \tag{10-181}$$

The probability that the open system contains N molecules is

$$P(N) = \frac{Q(N, T)\lambda^N}{\Gamma(\mu, T)}. \tag{10-182}$$

Figures 10-6 and 10-7 show examples of the function $P(N)$. In all these curves, w is negative. If we regard w as constant, $y = e^{-w/kT}$ is a measure of the temperature. In Fig. 10-6, we have chosen $\lambda = y^{-2}$ for each curve. This value of λ leads to symmetrical $P(N)$ curves and hence corresponds to $\bar{N}/B = \frac{1}{2}$ (i.e., $\bar{N} = 6$). Four temperatures are shown in Fig. 10-6: $y = 5.00$ is well below the

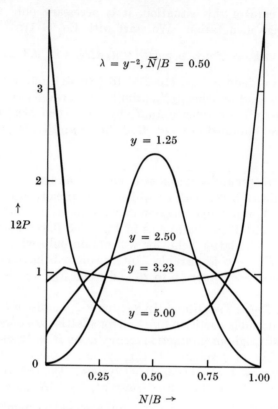

FIGURE 10-6. Probability function $P(N)$ for open 12-site spherical lattice gas at $\overline{N}/B = 0.50$.

critical temperature; $y = 3.23$ appears to be slightly below the critical temperature; on the other hand, $y = 2.50$ and $y = 1.25$ are above the critical temperature. The two peaks in $P(N)$ at $y = 5.00$ correspond to the two phases in a phase equilibrium. The peaks are not well separated or Gaussian in shape because B is so small ($B = 12$). At the two highest temperatures, there is only one "phase" present and one peak.

In Fig. 10-7, the temperature is again $y = 5.00$ but λ is smaller than in Fig. 10-6: $\lambda = 0.90y^{-2}$. There are still two peaks ("phases") in $P(N)$, but the curve is unsymmetrical. The dilute "phase" has a higher probability of occurrence than the concentrated phase.

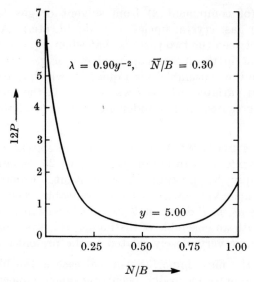

FIGURE 10-7. Probability function $P(N)$ for open 12-site spherical lattice gas at $\bar{N}/B = 0.30$.

We calculate $\bar{N}/B = 0.30$ from the $P(N)$ curve. Thus we have three points on a λ-$\bar{N}/B$ plot for $y = 5.00$: $\lambda = y^{-2}$, $\bar{N}/B = 0.50$; $\lambda = 0.90y^{-2}$, $\bar{N}/B = 0.30$; and, by symmetry, $\lambda = 1.11y^{-2}$, $\bar{N}/B = 0.70$. The derivative $(\partial \bar{N}/\partial \mu)_T$ is therefore positive, as required by the fluctuation formula following (10-176); i.e., there is no "loop."

The above results should be compared with[1] Figs. 6-6 and 6-7. These figures, it will be recalled, are based on the Bragg–Williams approximation and on a B that can be varied.

10-6. SMALL SYSTEMS IN SOLVENT OR GAS

Section 7-2 provides the foundation for much of the present section. We consider here a small system which is closed with respect to component 1 (moreover, N_1 is invariable) and open with respect to component 2. There are two cases: $N_1 \neq 0$ and $N_1 = 0$. The former case has essentially been covered in Chapter 7. The latter case is new and more interesting. It is concerned with the formation of

[1] See also D. A. Chesnut and Z. W. Salsburg, *J. Chem. Phys.*, **38**, 2861 (1963).

aggregates (of component 2) from solvent or gas (soap micelles, clusters in a gas, crystal nuclei in a liquid, etc.). A fundamental difference between the two cases is that when $N_1 \neq 0$ the number of small systems in the macroscopic solvent or gas (i.e., the number of systems in the "ensemble") is a quantity which is an independent, experimental variable, whereas when $N_1 = 0$, the number of small systems (aggregates) is not independently controllable.

SMALL SYSTEMS WITH $N_1 \neq 0$. When the *solvent contains two or more components*, we can adopt pages 15 to 25, essentially without change, simply by putting $N_1 = $ constant. Equations such as (7-103), in which N_1 is varied, are not applicable. The environmental variables are μ_2, p, T or m_1^s, p, T, with sc' constant. Section 10-5 is concerned with an ensemble of distinguishable systems of this type, and is of course very closely related to the present subsection.

Probably the most important special case is the binding of ions or molecules onto naturally occurring macromolecules, such as proteins, in solution. In this kind of system the macromolecule is not simply an aggregate of N_1 identical monomers (see page 114). Hence, N_1 and $\hat{\mu}_1$ are not separately defined. However, the product $X = N_1\hat{\mu}_1$ is well defined. Thus, for example, we have [Eqs. (7-69) and (7-90)]

$$X = \bar{E} - TS + p\bar{V} - \bar{N}_2\mu_2 \qquad (10\text{-}183)$$

and

$$dX = -(S - \bar{N}_2\tilde{s}_1^{\square})\,dT + (\bar{V} - \bar{N}_2\tilde{v}_1^{\square})\,dp - \bar{N}_2kT\,d\ln m_1^s$$
$$(m_1^s \to 0,\, sc'). \qquad (10\text{-}184)$$

When $\bar{N}_2 = 0$, as in Eq. (7-108),

$$dX_0 = -S_0\,dT + \bar{V}_0\,dp \qquad (m_1^s \to 0,\, sc')$$
$$X_0 = \bar{E}_0 - TS_0 + p\bar{V}_0. \qquad (10\text{-}185)$$

Thus, on subtraction,

$$d(X - X_0) = -(S - S_0 - \bar{N}_2\tilde{s}_1^{\square})\,dT + (\bar{V} - \bar{V}_0 - \bar{N}_2\tilde{v}_1^{\square})\,dp$$
$$- \bar{N}_2kT\,d\ln m_1^s \qquad (m_1^s \to 0,\, sc') \qquad (10\text{-}186)$$
$$X - X_0 = (\bar{E} - \bar{E}_0) - T(S - S_0) + p(\bar{V} - \bar{V}_0) - \bar{N}_2\mu_2.$$
$$(10\text{-}187)$$

Usually all these terms have the same order of magnitude.

From Eq. (10-186) we can find $X - X_0$ by integration over m_1^s at constant T, p, and sc', as in Eq. (7-113). If $X - X_0$ is calculated in this way at several temperatures and pressures, we can then use [see Eq. (7-110)]

$$\left(\frac{\partial \ln m_1^s}{\partial T}\right)_{p,\,sc',\,X-X_0} = \frac{1}{kT}\left(\tilde{s}_1^\square - \frac{S - S_0}{\bar{N}_2}\right) \qquad (m_1^s \to 0) \qquad (10\text{-}188)$$

and

$$\left(\frac{\partial \ln m_1^s}{\partial p}\right)_{T,\,sc',\,X-X_0} = \frac{1}{kT}\left(\frac{\bar{V} - \bar{V}_0}{\bar{N}_2} - \tilde{v}_1^\square\right) \qquad (m_1^s \to 0) \qquad (10\text{-}189)$$

to obtain information about S and $\bar{V}$. Equations (10-188) and (10-189) follow from (10-186).

Equation (7-107) provides an analogous expression for $(\partial S/\partial \bar{N}_2)_{T,p,sc'}$ which can be combined with Eqs. (10-186) and (10-188) to give

$$\left[\frac{\partial(X - X_0)}{\partial T}\right]_{p,\,\bar{N}_2,\,sc'} = \left[\frac{\partial(X - X_0)}{\partial T}\right]_{p,\,sc} - \bar{N}_2 kT\left(\frac{\partial \ln m_1^s}{\partial T}\right)_{p,\,\bar{N}_2,\,sc'}$$

$$= \bar{N}_2\left(\frac{\partial S}{\partial \bar{N}_2}\right)_{T,\,p,\,sc'} - (S - S_0).$$

Equation (10-229), below, may be consulted for further details.

If we put

$$\mu_2 = \mu_1^* = \tilde{\mathrm{E}}_1^\square + p\tilde{v}_1^\square - T\tilde{s}_1^\square \qquad (m_1^s \to 0)$$

in Eq. (10-187), there results

$$X - X_0 = (\bar{E} - \bar{E}_0 - \bar{N}_2\tilde{\mathrm{E}}_1^\square) - T(S - S_0 - \bar{N}_2\tilde{s}_1^\square)$$

$$+ p(\bar{V} - \bar{V}_0 - \bar{N}_2\tilde{v}_1^\square) \qquad (m_1^s \to 0). \qquad (10\text{-}190)$$

Since we can find the terms in X, S, and $\bar{V}$ from Eqs. (7-113), (10-188), and (10-189), respectively, the term in $\bar{E}$ may be calculated from Eq. (10-190).

The above are practical equations applicable to adsorption or binding of a dilute solute from solution onto a macromolecule or colloidal particle. Very similar methods have been used in gas adsorption work (see page 25).

If a phase transition occurs in the small systems and the two-state approximation is used, pages 34 to 38 of Chapter 7 apply, provided that we take $N_1 =$ constant. The notation $X_A = N_1\hat{\mu}_{1A}$ and $X_B = N_1\hat{\mu}_{1B}$ may be introduced, if necessary. What appear to be experimental examples of phase transitions involving protein molecules have been encountered by Colvin[1] and Foster.[2] In the former case, the adsorbate (component 2) undergoes a transition, whereas in the latter case the protein itself (component 1) does.

When the *solvent contains only one component*, we put $N_1 =$ constant in pages 27 to 30, and introduce $X = N_1\hat{\mu}_1$ whenever N_1 and $\hat{\mu}_1$ are not separately defined. Examples are the hydration of a protein molecule in water and the adsorption of a gas onto gaseous colloidal particles with invariable N_1.

Most applications of this subsection will probably be of the type $\bar{N}_2$ (maximum) $= O(N_1)$ or $O(N_1^{2/3})$. But $\bar{N}_2 \to \infty$ is also a possibility, as, for example, in heterogeneous nucleation (the small system serves as a nucleus to start a new phase). These two types of behavior are referred to in Section 10-5.

The remainder of this section is concerned with cases in which $N_1 = 0$.

SMALL SYSTEMS, WITH $N_1 = 0$, IN SOLUTION. We now turn to the important situation in which aggregates are formed in a solution ($c \geqslant 2$). We consider one-component aggregates first, for simplicity. Two-component aggregates (open with respect to both components) are of considerable interest, but the necessary generalization of the present treatment is straightforward. Hence, we present a separate and brief discussion of this topic later.

First, we re-emphasize (see Section 7-2) that if one of the components of a solution, say 1^s, produces aggregates or clusters in the solution, the only completely rigorous procedure is to ignore this fact in the thermodynamics. But if the aggregates are well enough defined to be measured (in, say, size and number) by some extra-thermodynamic method, then it is profitable and informative to treat the aggregates as a separate component of the macroscopic solution. The precise definition of an aggregate is arbitrary in so far as pure thermodynamics is concerned. All that is required is that the definition be unambiguous and self-consistent.[3] From an operational point of view, the experimental method used to detect and

[1] J. R. Colvin, *Can. J. Chem.*, **30**, 320 (1952).
[2] See, for example, J. F. Foster and P. Clark, *J. Biol. Chem.*, **237**, 3163 (1962).
[3] See S.M., p. 156.

measure the aggregates imposes the "definition" of an aggregate.

An extreme theoretical definition would be that any cluster (suitably defined) of two or more molecules of 1^s is an "aggregate." There is no objection to this in principle but it does limit the small system thermodynamics (small system = aggregate) to solutions dilute in 1^s. This follows because the macroscopic solution must be dilute enough in aggregates that interactions between them are negligible. A pair–pair interaction is fourth-order in 1^s and would affect, for example, the fourth osmotic pressure virial coefficient. Hence only third-order terms in m_1^s would be allowable if a cluster of two molecules is considered an "aggregate."

Let us pursue this point a little further. Small system thermodynamics cannot be applied to a macroscopic collection of aggregates which interact significantly with each other. The aggregates must be defined in such a way (made large enough) that the macroscopic system is dilute in aggregates. Consider an example. Suppose that in a moderately dilute soap solution (with added electrolyte) the fraction of soap molecules involved in clusters of size N is plotted against N, as in Fig. 10-8 (strictly schematic). Small clusters of

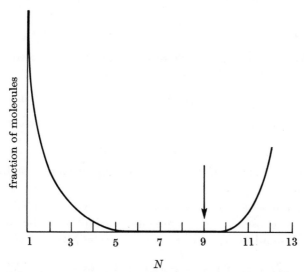

FIGURE 10-8. Fraction of soap molecules involved in clusters of size N (schematic). Clusters with $N \geqslant 9$ are defined as aggregates or small systems.

size $N = 2$ to 6 are considered to contribute to the nonideality of the solution, but large clusters (micelles; $N \geqslant 9$) are treated as a new component (aggregates or small systems). The solution represented in the figure may be dilute in micelles or aggregates ($N \geqslant 9$), but it is certainly not dilute in clusters ($N \geqslant 2$).

We assume from this point on that aggregates in the macroscopic solution are suitably defined and very dilute. We can adopt the equations of Chapter 7, starting with Eq. (7-62), without a great deal of modification. In the notation of Eq. (7-62), $N_1 = $ constant $= 0$ (i.e., we are concerned here with homogeneous rather than heterogeneous nucleation). The number of aggregates (small systems) is $\mathcal{N}$ and the mean number of molecules of component 2 (that same as 1^s), per aggregate, is $\bar{N}_2$. However, since the aggregate contains only one component, we now drop the subscript 2 from μ_2 and $\bar{N}_2$.

Consider a macroscopic solution containing $\mathcal{N}$ small systems with mean size $\bar{N}$ [see Eq. (7-62)]:

$$dF_T = - S_T \, dT + V_T \, dp + \sum_{i=1}^{c} \mu_i^s \, dN_i^s + \mu^\square \, d\mathcal{N} + \mu \mathcal{N} \, d\bar{N}.$$

$$(10\text{-}191)$$

It is useful to rewrite this in the form

$$dF_T = - S_T \, dT + V_T \, dp + \sum_{j=2}^{c} \mu_j^s \, dN_j^s + \mu_1^s \, d(N_1^s + N_t)$$

$$+ (\mu - \mu_1^s) \, dN_t + (\mu^\square - \mu \bar{N}) \, d\mathcal{N}, \qquad (10\text{-}192)$$

where $N_t = \mathcal{N} \bar{N}$. If the macroscopic solution is closed (N_j^s, $N_1^s + N_t$ constant) and held at constant T and p,

$$dF_T = (\mu - \mu_1^s) \, dN_t + (\mu^\square - \mu \bar{N}) \, d\mathcal{N} \leqslant 0. \qquad (10\text{-}193)$$

The conditions for aggregation equilibrium are therefore

$$\mu = \mu_1^s, \qquad \mu^\square = \mu \bar{N}. \qquad (10\text{-}194)$$

These are "phase" and "chemical" equilibrium conditions, respectively.

For convenience, write $\mu - \mu_1^s = \alpha_p$ and $\mu^\square - \mu \bar{N} = \alpha_c$. If α_p and α_c are chosen as environmental variables of the macroscopic solution instead of N_t and $\mathcal{N}$, we have [compare Eq. (10-112)]

$$d(F_T - \alpha_p \bar{N}_t - \alpha_c \mathcal{N}) = - S_T \, dT + V_T \, dp + \sum_{j=2}^{c} \mu_j^s \, dN_j^s$$

$$+ \mu_1^s \, d(\bar{N}_1^s + \bar{N}_t) - \bar{N}_t \, d\alpha_p - \mathcal{N} \, d\alpha_c. \qquad (10\text{-}195)$$

We have put bars over the macroscopic quantities N_t, $\mathcal{N}$, and N_1^s here just to emphasize that these variables fluctuate under the conditions of actual interest ($\alpha_p = \alpha_c = 0$):

$$\overline{N_t^2} - \bar{N}_t^2 = kT\left(\frac{\partial \bar{N}_t}{\partial \alpha_p}\right)_{T, p, N_j^s, \bar{N}_1^s + \bar{N}_t, \alpha_c} > 0, \qquad (10\text{-}196)$$

$$\overline{\mathcal{N}^2} - \bar{\mathcal{N}}^2 = kT\left(\frac{\partial \bar{\mathcal{N}}}{\partial \alpha_c}\right)_{T, p, N_j^s, \bar{N}_1 + \bar{N}_t, \alpha_p} > 0. \qquad (10\text{-}197)$$

The relative fluctuations are normal (small). Stability conditions may be discussed[1] as in Eq. (10-114)ff.

At equilibrium ($\alpha_p = \alpha_c = 0$), all the properties of the macroscopic solution are determined by T, p, $\bar{N}_1^s$, N_j^s. Thus, for example, $\mathcal{N}$, $\bar{N}$, μ, and $\mu^\square$ are functions of these variables. In fact, $\bar{N}$, μ, and $\mu^\square$ are functions of p, T, sc, or p, T, m_1^s, sc', only. Note especially that $\mathcal{N}$ is a dependent and not an independent variable.

We now return to Eq. (10-191) and proceed much as we did in Chapter 7, although many of the applicable equations in Chapter 7 will not be repeated here. At the outset, the equilibrium conditions ($\alpha_p = \alpha_c = 0$) are not used and the aggregates are treated as an independent, dilute component of the macroscopic solution. That is, we consider temporarily that there are an assigned number $\mathcal{N}$ of open systems with environmental variables μ, p, T immersed in the solvent. Each of the $\mathcal{N}$ small systems is, of course, in "internal" equilibrium with respect to fluctuations in N at the chemical potential μ. We shall see that introduction of the condition $\mu^\square = \mu\bar{N}$ determines the equilibrium value of $\mathcal{N}$ and hence removes $\mathcal{N}$ as an independent variable, whereas the condition $\mu = \mu_1^s$ serves to bring the solvent, as a reservoir for 1^s molecules, into the picture explicitly.

The basic expressions for $\mu^\square$ are

$$\mu^\square = \tilde{\mathrm{E}}^\square - T\tilde{\mathrm{s}}^\square + p\tilde{\mathrm{v}}^\square \qquad (10\text{-}198)$$

$$= F(\bar{N}, p, T, sc) + kT \ln x', \qquad (10\text{-}199)$$

where

$$F = \mathcal{E}(\bar{N}, p, T, sc) + \bar{N}\mu(\bar{N}, p, T, sc) = \bar{N}\hat{\mu}(\bar{N}, p, T, sc) \qquad (10\text{-}200)$$

---

[1] We shall see below that the coefficient of $d\mathcal{N}$ in Eq. (10-193) is equal to $\mathcal{E} + kT \ln x'$, [instead of $\mathcal{E}$, as in Eq. (10-105)].

and

$$x' = \frac{\mathcal{N}}{\Sigma_i N_i^s} \quad \left(\text{or } \frac{\bar{\mathcal{N}}}{\bar{N}_1^s + \Sigma_j N_j^s}\right).$$

At equilibrium, as already pointed out, $\bar{N}$ in $F(\bar{N}, p, T, sc)$, etc., is itself a function of p, T, sc.

We also have

$$d\mu^\square = -\tilde{s}^\square dT + \tilde{v}^\square dp + kT \, d \ln x' + \beta \, dm_1^s + \mu \, d\bar{N} \quad (sc'),$$
$$(10\text{-}201)$$

where $\beta = (\partial F/\partial m_1^s)_{T, \, p, \, \bar{N}, \, sc'}$.

We define

$$S = \tilde{s}^\square + k \ln x', \qquad \bar{E} = \tilde{\text{E}}^\square, \qquad \bar{V} = \tilde{v}^\square.$$

Equations (10-198) and (10-201) become, then,

$$F = \mathscr{E} + \bar{N}\mu = \bar{N}\hat{\mu} = \bar{E} - TS + p\bar{V} \qquad (10\text{-}202)$$

$$dF = -S \, dT + \bar{V} \, dp + \mu \, d\bar{N} + \beta \, dm_1^s \qquad (sc'). \qquad (10\text{-}203)$$

Also,

$$d\mathscr{E} = -S \, dT + \bar{V} \, dp - \bar{N} \, d\mu + \beta \, dm_1^s \qquad (sc'). \qquad (10\text{-}204)$$

The environmental variables appear in this last equation. At equilibrium, of course, μ and m_1^s are not independent. Unlike the $N_1 \neq 0$ case (where $X - X_0$ is the corresponding quantity), $\mathscr{E}$ is a small term here.

At this point, we introduce the equilibrium conditions. We first note that, at equilibrium,

$$\mu^\square = \bar{N}\mu = \mathscr{E} + \bar{N}\mu + kT \ln x'$$

or

$$\mathscr{E} = \bar{N}(\hat{\mu} - \mu) = -kT \ln x', \qquad \mathscr{S} = k \ln x'. \qquad (10\text{-}205)$$

The number of small systems $\mathcal{N}$, at equilibrium, is determined by this equation if we regard $\mathscr{E}$ (and other properties of the individual small systems) as a function of p, T, m_1^s, sc'. Conversely, if x' is measured experimentally, $\mathscr{E}$ can be calculated directly from the equation. We observe that $\mathscr{E}$ is positive and of order kT. The other terms in Eq. (10-202) are of order $\bar{N}kT$. Comparison with Eq. (10-7) shows that x' plays the formal role of a partition function. This point becomes important in the next subsection.

The second condition, $\mu = \mu_1^s$, can be introduced in different ways, as in Chapter 7. For example, if we eliminate $d\mu$ from Eq. (10-204), we find

$$
\begin{aligned}
d\mathscr{E} &= - d(kT \ln x') \\
&= - (S - \bar{N}\tilde{s}_1^*)\, dT + (\bar{V} - \bar{N}\tilde{v}_1^*)\, dp \\
&\quad + \left[\beta - \bar{N}\left(\frac{\partial \mu_1^*}{\partial m_1^s}\right)_{T,\,p,\,sc'} \right] dm_1^s \qquad (sc'), \qquad (10\text{-}206)
\end{aligned}
$$

which is the analogue of Eq. (7-81).

Equation (10-206), and others below that apply to a single small system, are unchanged from Chapter 7, except that here we are dealing with a special case ($N_1 = $ constant $= 0$). The equilibrium condition $\mu = \mu_1^s$ has been used in both places. The other condition, $\mu^\square = \mu\bar{N}$, does not affect the small system equations *per se*; rather, it provides a subsidiary relation which determines x' in terms of small system properties. That is, as already mentioned above, the condition $\mu^\square = \mu\bar{N}$ eliminates $\mathscr{N}$ as an independent variable; in effect, the macroscopic solution selects that value of $\mathscr{N}$ which minimizes F_T. When $N_1 \neq 0$, $\mathscr{N}$ is not adjustable in this way. The present situation resembles that described on page 96ff., of course.

Another form of Eq. (10-206) is

$$
- kT\, d\ln x' = \left(\frac{\bar{N}\tilde{\mathrm{H}}_1^* - \bar{H}}{T} \right) dT + (\bar{V} - \bar{N}\tilde{v}_1^*)\, dp \\
+ \left(\beta - \bar{N}\frac{\partial \mu_1^*}{\partial m_1^s} \right) dm_1^s \qquad (sc'), \qquad (10\text{-}207)
$$

where

$$
\bar{N}\tilde{\mathrm{H}}_1^* - \bar{H} = T(\bar{N}\tilde{s}_1^* - S) - \mathscr{E}. \qquad (10\text{-}208)
$$

From Eq. (10-206), one can immediately obtain expressions for $\partial\mathscr{E}/\partial T$, $\partial\mathscr{E}/\partial p$, and $\partial\mathscr{E}/\partial m_1^s$. Similarly, Eq. (10-207) provides equations for $\partial \ln x'/\partial T$, $\partial \ln x'/\partial p$, and $\partial \ln x'/\partial m_1^s$. Also, Eqs. (10-206) and (10-207) give $\partial m_1^s/\partial T$, $\partial m_1^s/\partial p$, and $\partial p/\partial T$, all at constant $\mathscr{E}$, or x', respectively. The reader may wish to write out all these relations.

When the solvent is dilute in 1^s, we have the more practical equation

$$- kT \, d \ln x' = \left(\frac{\bar{N}\tilde{H}_1^{\square} - \bar{H}}{T} \right) dT + (\bar{V} - \bar{N}\tilde{v}_1^{\square}) \, dp$$
$$- \bar{N}kT \, d \ln m_1^s \qquad (m_1^s \to 0, sc').$$
(10-209)

Then, for example,

$$\bar{N} = \left(\frac{\partial \ln x'}{\partial \ln m_1^s} \right)_{T, p, sc'}, \qquad \left(\frac{\partial \ln x'}{\partial T} \right)_{p, sc} = \frac{\bar{H} - \bar{N}\tilde{H}_1^{\square}}{kT^2} \qquad (m_1^s \to 0)$$
(10-210)

$$\left(\frac{\partial \ln m_1^s}{\partial T} \right)_{p, x', sc'} = \frac{1}{kT^2} \left(\tilde{H}_1^{\square} - \frac{\bar{H}}{\bar{N}} \right) \qquad (m_1^s \to 0).$$
(10-211)

Equation (10-211) resembles Eq. (7-110).

If $x'(m_1^s)$ is easier to measure than $\bar{N}$, Eq. (10-210a) provides a method for obtaining $\bar{N}$. On the other hand, if $\bar{N}(m_1^s)$ is easy to measure, Eq. (10-210) may be integrated to give x'. The procedure is the following. In the limit $m_1^s \to 0$, suppose $\bar{N} \to N_0(T, p, sc')$. N_0 is the minimum possible value of N; it is a quantity independent of m_1^s but dependent on our definition of an "aggregate." On integrating Eq. (10-210a), we find that the limiting law for x' is

$$x_0'(m_1^s) = C(T, p, sc')(m_1^s)^{N_0}.$$

The constant of integration C remains undetermined unless some information is at hand which allows us to evaluate it. Next, we note that

$$\bar{N} - N_0 = \left(\frac{\partial \ln x'/x_0'}{\partial \ln m_1^s} \right)_{T, p, sc'} \qquad (m_1^s \to 0).$$
(10-212)

If we integrate this equation from $m_1^s = 0$ to $m_1^s = m'$, the desired result is

$$\ln x'(m') = \ln Cm'^{N_0} + \int_0^{m'} \frac{[\bar{N}(m_1^s) - N_0]}{m_1^s} \, dm_1^s \qquad (m_1^s \to 0).$$
(10-213)

Incidentally, the generalization of Henry's law is

$$\bar{N} - N_0 = k_1^s(T, p, sc')m^s.$$
(10-214)

Let us digress to consider an example. Suppose we are given (the notation is simplified in an obvious way)

$$\bar{N} = N_0 + am + bm^2 + \cdots \qquad (10\text{-}215)$$

and the "constant" C. Then Eq. (10-213) leads to

$$\ln x'(m) = \ln Cm^{N_0} + am + \frac{b}{2}m^2 + \cdots = -\frac{\mathscr{E}}{kT} \qquad (10\text{-}216)$$

and

$$x'(m) = Cm^{N_0} + aCm^{N_0+1} + \left(\frac{b + a^2}{2}\right)Cm^{N_0+2} + \cdots \qquad (10\text{-}217)$$

$$= x'_{N_0} + x'_{N_0+1} + x'_{N_0+2} + \cdots, \qquad (10\text{-}218)$$

where $x'_N = \mathscr{N}_N/\Sigma_i N_i^s$ and $\mathscr{N}_N$ is the mean number of aggregates of size N. An alternative expression for $\bar{N}$ is

$$\bar{N} = \frac{N_0 x'_{N_0} + (N_0 + 1)x'_{N_0+1} + (N_0 + 2)x'_{N_0+2} + \cdots}{x'}. \qquad (10\text{-}219)$$

This follows from

$$\bar{N} = \frac{m}{x'}\frac{\partial x'}{\partial m}.$$

We have mentioned that x' resembles a partition function. This is confirmed in Eq. (10-219) where x' is a sum of weights (a standard property of a partition function).

If N_0 is large, say, $N_0 \geqslant 10\text{--}20$, $x'(m)$ in Eq. (10-217) will be practically zero as m increases from zero until m reaches a fairly sharp critical value (the "critical micelle concentration"), at which point x' will increase rapidly. This follows because of the assumed high power of m in Cm^{N_0}. This "sharp" behavior is reminiscent of that in a phase transition (condensation), the more so as N_0 increases. In fact, this discussion is closely related to the Frenkel–Band approximate theory of condensation.[1]

The conventional approach to this kind of example is in terms of aggregation equilibrium constants:

$$K_{N_0} = \frac{x'_{N_0}}{m^{N_0}}, \qquad K_{N_0+1} = \frac{x'_{N_0+1}}{m^{N_0+1}}, \qquad \text{etc.} \qquad (10\text{-}220)$$

[1] See S.M., p. 147.

Then

$$x'_{N_0} = Cm^{N_0} = K_{N_0}m^{N_0}, \qquad x'_{N_0+1} = aCm^{N_0+1} = K_{N_0+1}m^{N_0+1}, \quad \text{etc.}$$

Thus the correspondences in notation are

$$C = K_{N_0}, \qquad aC = K_{N_0+1}, \qquad \left(\frac{b+a^2}{2}\right)C = K_{N_0+2}, \qquad \text{etc.}$$

$$(10\text{-}221)$$

The advantage of the present treatment is that considerations of the above sort are tied into a complete discussion of the thermodynamic properties of the aggregates. For example, use of Eqs. (10-209) to (10-211) permits evaluation of the separate terms in

$$\mathscr{E} = -\,kT \ln x' = (\bar{E} - \bar{N}\tilde{\mathtt{E}}_1^{\square}) - T(S - \bar{N}\tilde{\mathtt{s}}_1^{\square}) + p(\bar{V} - \bar{N}\tilde{\mathtt{v}}_1^{\square}).$$

$$(10\text{-}222)$$

Instead of putting $d\mu = d\mu_1^s$ in Eq. (10-204), we can use this relation directly. We start with

$$d\mu = \frac{\partial \mu}{\partial T}\, dT + \frac{\partial \mu}{\partial p}\, dp + \frac{\partial \mu}{\partial \bar{N}}\, d\bar{N} + \frac{\partial \mu}{\partial m_1^s}\, dm_1^s \qquad (sc').$$

From Eq. (10-203),

$$\frac{\partial \mu}{\partial T} = -\left(\frac{\partial S}{\partial \bar{N}}\right)_{T,p,sc}, \qquad \frac{\partial \mu}{\partial p} = \left(\frac{\partial \bar{V}}{\partial \bar{N}}\right)_{T,p,sc}, \qquad \frac{\partial \mu}{\partial m_1^s} = \left(\frac{\partial \beta}{\partial \bar{N}}\right)_{T,p,sc}.$$

Therefore,

$$d\mu = -\left(\frac{\partial S}{\partial \bar{N}}\right)_{T,p,sc} dT + \left(\frac{\partial \bar{V}}{\partial \bar{N}}\right)_{T,p,sc} dp + \left(\frac{\partial \mu}{\partial \bar{N}}\right)_{T,p,sc} d\bar{N}$$

$$+ \left(\frac{\partial \beta}{\partial \bar{N}}\right)_{T,p,sc} dm_1^s \qquad (sc'). \quad (10\text{-}223)$$

We set this equal to $d\mu_1^s$, as given by Eq. (7-80). We can select six pairs from dT, dp, $d\bar{N}$, and dm_1^s, and hence there are six equations of the Clausius–Clapeyron type. Only three of these are independent, however. The most important set is probably

$$\left(\frac{\partial \bar{N}}{\partial T}\right)_{p,sc} = \left[\left(\frac{\partial S}{\partial \bar{N}}\right)_{T,p,sc} - \tilde{\mathtt{s}}_1^*\right]\Big/\left(\frac{\partial \mu}{\partial \bar{N}}\right)_{T,p,sc} \quad (10\text{-}224)$$

$$\left(\frac{\partial \bar{N}}{\partial p}\right)_{T,sc} = \left[\tilde{\mathtt{v}}_1^* - \left(\frac{\partial \bar{V}}{\partial \bar{N}}\right)_{T,p,sc}\right]\Big/\left(\frac{\partial \mu}{\partial \bar{N}}\right)_{T,p,sc} \quad (10\text{-}225)$$

$$\left(\frac{\partial \bar{N}}{\partial m_1^s}\right)_{T, p, sc'} = \left[\left(\frac{\partial \mu_1^*}{\partial m_1^s}\right)_{T, p, sc'} - \left(\frac{\partial \beta}{\partial \bar{N}}\right)_{T, p, sc}\right] / \left(\frac{\partial \mu}{\partial \bar{N}}\right)_{T, p, sc}.$$

(10-226)

When m_1^s is small,

$$\left(\frac{\partial \bar{N}}{\partial m_1^s}\right)_{T, p, sc'} = \frac{kT/m_1^s}{(\partial \mu/\partial \bar{N})_{T, p, sc'}} \qquad (m_1^s \to 0). \qquad (10\text{-}227)$$

In the example in Eq. (10-215)ff.,

$$kT\left(\frac{\partial \bar{N}}{\partial \mu}\right)_{T, p, sc'} = m\left(\frac{\partial \bar{N}}{\partial m}\right)_{T, p, sc'} = m(a + 2bm + \cdots).$$

If we use the inverse of Eq. (10-215), that is,

$$m = \frac{1}{a}(\bar{N} - N_0) - \frac{b}{a^3}(\bar{N} - N_0)^2 + \cdots,$$

to eliminate m, we obtain

$$kT\left(\frac{\partial \bar{N}}{\partial \mu}\right)_{T, p, sc'} = (\bar{N} - N_0) + \frac{b}{a^2}(\bar{N} - N_0)^2 + \cdots.$$

Integration shows that $\mu(\bar{N})$ has the form

$$\frac{\mu}{kT} = f(T, p, sc') + \ln(\bar{N} - N_0) - \frac{b}{a^2}(\bar{N} - N_0) + \cdots, \qquad (10\text{-}228)$$

where f is an integration constant. The same result follows directly from Eq. (7-88). The notational correspondence is

$$f = \frac{\mu^\Delta}{kT} - \ln a.$$

If we eliminate $\partial \mu/\partial \bar{N}$ from Eqs. (10-224) and (10-225) using (10-227), we see that measurement of $\partial \bar{N}/\partial T$ and $\partial \bar{N}/\partial m_1^s$ will provide $(\partial S/\partial \bar{N}) - \tilde{s}_1^\square$, whereas measurement of $\partial \bar{N}/\partial p$ and $\partial \bar{N}/\partial m_1^s$ will give $\tilde{v}_1^\square - (\partial \bar{V}/\partial \bar{N})$.

We can change independent variables in Eq. (10-206) from T, p, m_1^s, to T, p, $\bar{N}$, as in Eq. (2-23), by substituting

$$dm_1^s = \left(\frac{\partial m_1^s}{\partial T}\right)_{p, \bar{N}, sc'} dT + \left(\frac{\partial m_1^s}{\partial p}\right)_{T, \bar{N}, sc'} dp$$

$$+ \left(\frac{\partial m_1^s}{\partial \bar{N}}\right)_{T, p, sc'} d\bar{N} \qquad (sc').$$

Expressions for the coefficients appearing here follow from Eqs. (10-224) to (10-226). The resultant equation for $d\mathscr{E}$ is rather complicated because of terms in β. But when m_1^s is small,

$$d\mathscr{E} = -\left[S - \bar{N}\left(\frac{\partial S}{\partial \bar{N}}\right)_{T,\,p,\,sc'}\right] dT + \left[\bar{V} - \bar{N}\left(\frac{\partial \bar{V}}{\partial \bar{N}}\right)_{T,\,p,\,sc'}\right] dp$$

$$-\bar{N}\left(\frac{\partial \mu}{\partial \bar{N}}\right)_{T,\,p,\,sc'} d\bar{N} \qquad (m_1^s \to 0,\, sc'), \qquad (10\text{-}229)$$

as in Eq. (2-23). In the derivatives $\partial\mathscr{E}/\partial T$ and $\partial\mathscr{E}/\partial p$, m_1^s is varied, along with T or p, respectively, in such a way that $\bar{N}$ remains constant.

There is a final topic that should be mentioned, one which is also of interest in Chapters 2 and 7. In Eq. (10-199) we introduced the convenient composition variable x'. But this choice is somewhat arbitrary. Suppose we use a new variable x'/ϵ instead of x', where ϵ is a constant or any function[1] of the N_i^s. That is,

$$\mu^\square = F_\epsilon + kT \ln \frac{x'}{\epsilon}$$

$$F_\epsilon = \mathscr{E}_\epsilon + \bar{N}\mu = \bar{N}\hat{\mu}_\epsilon$$

$$= F + kT \ln \epsilon = \bar{N}\hat{\mu} + kT \ln \epsilon$$

$$= \mathscr{E} + \bar{N}\mu + kT \ln \epsilon$$

$$\mathscr{E}_\epsilon = \mathscr{E} + kT \ln \epsilon.$$

The chemical potential μ is defined in Eq. (10-191) and is unaffected. Also, $\bar{E}$ and $\bar{V}$ are unchanged. The definition of S_ϵ is

$$S_\epsilon = \tilde{s}^\square + k \ln \frac{x'}{\epsilon} = S - k \ln \epsilon.$$

Equations (10-202) to (10-204) become

$$F_\epsilon = \bar{E} - TS_\epsilon + p\bar{V}$$

$$dF_\epsilon = -S_\epsilon\, dT + \bar{V}\, dp + \mu\, d\bar{N} + \beta_\epsilon\, dm_1^s \qquad (sc')$$

$$d\mathscr{E}_\epsilon = -S_\epsilon\, dT + \bar{V}\, dp - \bar{N}\, d\mu + \beta_\epsilon\, dm_1^s \qquad (sc'),$$

---

[1] We do not allow ϵ to be a function of p or T because this would introduce complications. For example, we could no longer replace $\partial\mu^\square/\partial T$ by $-\tilde{s}^\square$ in Eq. (10-201). If ϵ *does* depend on p or T (e.g., x'/ϵ is $\mathscr{N}/V_T$), this dependence can be ignored—as a good approximation.

where

$$\beta_\epsilon = \left(\frac{\partial F_\epsilon}{\partial m_1^s}\right)_{T,\,p,\,\bar{N},\,sc'} = \beta + kT\left(\frac{\partial \ln \epsilon}{\partial m_1^s}\right)_{sc'}.$$

The equilibrium condition $\mu = \mu_1^s$ is not involved. But the other equilibrium condition becomes

$$\mu^\square = \bar{N}\mu = \mathscr{E}_\epsilon + \bar{N}\mu + kT \ln \frac{x'}{\epsilon},$$

or

$$\mathscr{E}_\epsilon = - kT \ln \frac{x'}{\epsilon}.$$

We see, in conclusion, that although some of the functions have different definitions, the formal appearance of all the basic equations is unchanged if x' is replaced by a different composition variable x'/ϵ.

DETAILED ANALYSIS OF EQUILIBRIUM. It is instructive to investigate the alternative but equivalent approach in which we keep explicit account of each subspecies of aggregate: $N = N_0$, $N_0 + 1$, ... This is an essentially nonoperational or quasi statistical mechanical method as it presumes the knowledge or measurability of the properties of each of the separate subspecies. The same is true, of course, when we use K_{N_0}, K_{N_0+1}, etc., in Eq. (10-220). This type of discussion could also be applied to Section 7-2.

We start with [compare Eq. (10-191)]

$$dF_T = - S_T\,dT + V_T\,dp + \sum_{i=1}^{c} \mu_i^s\,dN_i^s + \sum_{N \geqslant N_0} \mu_N^\square\,d\mathscr{N}_N, \tag{10-230}$$

where subscript N refers to the subspecies of size N. The macroscopic solution is dilute with respect to all subspecies. The small systems interact with each other only through the aggregation equilibrium. At equilibrium, with

$$T, p, N_j^s, \text{ and } N_1^s + \sum_N N\mathscr{N}_N \text{ constant,}$$

$$dF_T = 0 = \sum_N (\mu_N^\square - \mu_1^s N)\,d\mathscr{N}_N.$$

That is,

$$\mu_N^{\square} = \mu_1^s N \qquad (N = N_0, N_0 + 1, \cdots). \qquad (10\text{-}231)$$

This set of conditions corresponds to the establishment of equilibrium with respect to fluctuations in N for each small system and also determines the equilibrium number of small systems of size N, $\bar{\mathscr{N}}_N$.

Equations (10-191) and (10-230) are equivalent (i.e., refer to the same macroscopic system) at and only at equilibrium, when they both become

$$dF_T = - S_T \, dT + V_T \, dp + \sum_{j=2}^{c} \mu_j^s \, dN_j^s + \mu_1^s \, d(\bar{N}_1^s + \bar{\mathscr{N}}\bar{N}),$$

since

$$\sum_N N \, d\bar{\mathscr{N}}_N = d(\sum_N N\bar{\mathscr{N}}_N) = d(\bar{\mathscr{N}}\bar{N}).$$

We have put bars over the quantities which fluctuate at equilibrium. Also at equilibrium, from Eqs. (10-194) and (10-231),

$$\sum_N P_N \mu_N^{\square} = \mu_1^s \sum_N P_N N = \mu_1^s \bar{N} = \mu^{\square}, \qquad (10\text{-}232)$$

where $P_N = \bar{\mathscr{N}}_N/\bar{\mathscr{N}}$, the fraction of aggregates of size N.

For subspecies N, we write [see Eq. (2-119)]

$$\mu_N^{\square} = N\hat{\mu}_N(p, T, sc) + kT \ln x_N', \qquad (10\text{-}233)$$

where $x_N' = \bar{\mathscr{N}}_N/\Sigma_i N_i^s$. At equilibrium,

$$\mu_N^{\square} = \mu_1^s N = N\hat{\mu}_N + kT \ln x_N', \qquad (10\text{-}234)$$

or

$$x_N' = \exp\left[\frac{N(\mu_1^s - \hat{\mu}_N)}{kT}\right] = e^{-N\hat{\mu}_N/kT}\lambda^N \qquad (N = N_0, N_0 + 1, \cdots),$$
$$(10\text{-}235)$$

with $\lambda = e^{\mu_1^s/kT}$. This equation determines the equilibrium number of aggregates of size N, $\bar{\mathscr{N}}_N$, if $\hat{\mu}_N(p, T, sc)$ and $\mu_1^s(p, T, sc)$ are known. It should be compared with Eqs. (10-218) and (10-220). Since $\lambda = e^{\mu^\Delta/kT}m$ in this example, the correspondence in notation is

$$K_N = e^{-N\hat{\mu}_N/kT}e^{N\mu^\Delta/kT} \qquad (N = N_0, N_0 + 1, \cdots). \qquad (10\text{-}236)$$

Let us sum Eq. (10-235) over N:

$$x' = \sum_{N \geqslant N_0} e^{-N\hat{\mu}_N/kT}\lambda^N = \sum_N \Delta_N(p, T, sc)\lambda(p, T, sc)^N, \qquad (10\text{-}237)$$

where

$$\Delta_N \equiv e^{-N\hat{\mu}_N/kT}.$$

We see that x' has the formal appearance of a partition function[1] for a completely open system [see Eq. (10-10)]. Note that

$$P_N = \frac{\bar{\mathscr{N}}_N}{\bar{\mathscr{N}}} = \frac{x_N'}{x'} = \frac{\Delta_N \lambda^N}{\Sigma_N \Delta_N \lambda^N}. \qquad (10\text{-}238)$$

If we multiply Eq. (10-234) by P_N, sum over N, and use Eq. (10-232), there results

$$\sum_N P_N \mu_N^\square = \mu_1^s \bar{N} = \mu^\square = \sum_N P_N N \hat{\mu}_N + kT \sum_N P_N \ln P_N + kT \ln x'. \qquad (10\text{-}239)$$

The correspondence with the notation in Eqs. (10-199) and (10-200) is seen to be

$$\bar{N}\hat{\mu} = \sum_N P_N N \hat{\mu}_N + kT \sum_N P_N \ln P_N \qquad (10\text{-}240)$$

and

$$\begin{aligned} \mathscr{E} &= \bar{N}(\hat{\mu} - \mu_1^s) \\ &= -kT \ln x' = -kT \ln \sum_N \Delta_N \lambda^N, \qquad (10\text{-}241) \end{aligned}$$

as in Eq. (10-7). If we define $\mathscr{E}_N$ by $N(\hat{\mu}_N - \mu_1^s)$, then

$$\mathscr{E} = \sum_N P_N \mathscr{E}_N + kT \sum_N P_N \ln P_N \qquad (10\text{-}242)$$

and

$$x' = e^{-\mathscr{E}/kT} = \sum_N e^{-\mathscr{E}_N/kT}, \qquad (10\text{-}243)$$

as in Eq. (10-10).

Now we turn to the relation

$$\mu_N^\square = \tilde{\mathrm{E}}_N^\square - T\tilde{s}_N^\square + p\tilde{v}_N^\square$$

for each subspecies (at equilibrium), multiply by P_N, and sum over N:

$$\begin{aligned} \sum_N P_N \mu_N^\square = \mu^\square &= \sum_N P_N \tilde{\mathrm{E}}_N^\square - T \sum_N P_N \tilde{s}_N^\square + p \sum_N P_N \tilde{v}_N^\square \\ &= \tilde{\mathrm{E}}^\square - T\tilde{s}^\square + p\tilde{v}^\square. \qquad (10\text{-}244) \end{aligned}$$

---

[1] This is not surprising in view of the quasi statistical mechanical nature of the discussion.

Thus, $\tilde{s}^\square = \Sigma_N P_N \tilde{s}_N^\square$. Similarly, starting with the subspecies equation

$$d\mu_N^\square = - \tilde{s}_N^\square \, dT + \tilde{v}_N^\square \, dp + kT \, d\ln x_N' + \beta_N \, dm_1^s \quad (sc'),$$

we find on summing,

$$\sum_N P_N \, d\mu_N^\square = - \tilde{s}^\square \, dT + \tilde{v}^\square \, dp + kT \sum_N P_N \, d\ln x_N' + \beta \, dm_1^s \quad (sc'),$$

$$(10\text{-}245)$$

where $\beta = \Sigma_N P_N \beta_N$. If we use

$$d\mu^\square = \sum_N \mu_N^\square \, dP_N + \sum_N P_N \, d\mu_N^\square$$

$$\sum_N \mu_N^\square \, dP_N = \mu_1^s \sum_N N \, dP_N = \mu_1^s \, d\bar{N}$$

and

$$\sum_N P_N \, d\ln x_N' = \frac{1}{x'} \sum_N dx_N' = d\ln x',$$

Eq. (10-245) becomes

$$d\mu^\square = - \tilde{s}^\square \, dT + \tilde{v}^\square \, dp + kT \, d\ln x' + \beta \, dm_1^s + \mu_1^s \, d\bar{N} \quad (sc'),$$

$$(10\text{-}246)$$

which is the same as Eq. (10-201), at equilibrium. Incidentally, since

$$S_N = \tilde{s}_N^\square + k \ln x_N' \quad \text{and} \quad S = \tilde{s}^\square + k \ln x',$$

it follows that

$$S = \sum_N P_N S_N - k \sum_N P_N \ln P_N. \quad (10\text{-}247)$$

The last term has the same physical significance as, for example, in Eqs. (10-43) and (10-70). Equation (10-247) also follows from

$$\mathscr{E}_N = \bar{E}_N - TS_N + p\bar{V}_N + \mu_1^s N,$$

$$\mathscr{E} = \bar{E} - TS + p\bar{V} + \mu_1^s \bar{N},$$

$$(10\text{-}248)$$

and Eq. (10-242).

In all these equations the point of view would generally be that $\mu_1^s(p, T, sc)$ and the $\hat{\mu}_N(p, T, sc)$ are known, and from these we can calculate the equilibrium aggregation properties: x_N', x', P_N, $\bar{N}$, $\hat{\mu}$, $\mathscr{E}$, etc.

An exact equilibrium "constant" can be defined if we replace m_1^s

by the molality activity $a_1^s(p, T, sc)$ in Eq. (7-88):

$$\frac{x_N'}{(a_1^s)^N} = e^{-N\hat{\mu}_N/kT}e^{N\mu_1^\Delta/kT} = K_N. \tag{10-249}$$

The quotient on the left does not have quite the usual significance, however, because the right-hand side is not "constant" in the conventional sense: $\hat{\mu}_N$ is a function of m_1^s as well as of p, T, sc' (the interaction of the N-aggregate with the solvent depends on the solvent composition, which depends, in turn, on m_1^s). But when m_1^s is small, the quotient $x_N'/(m_1^s)^N$ is equal to a true equilibrium constant: the right-hand side of Eq. (10-249) becomes a function of p, T, and sc' only. In this case it is easy to show that

$$\left(\frac{\partial \ln K_N}{\partial p}\right)_{T,\,sc'} = \frac{N\tilde{v}_1^\square - \bar{V}_N}{kT} \qquad (m_1^s \to 0) \tag{10-250}$$

$$\left(\frac{\partial \ln K_N}{\partial T}\right)_{p,\,sc'} = \frac{\bar{H}_N - N\tilde{H}_1^\square}{kT^2} \qquad (m_1^s \to 0). \tag{10-251}$$

The fluctuation in N, $\overline{N^2} - \bar{N}^2$, at equilibrium, follows from

$$\bar{N} = \frac{1}{x'}\sum_N N\Delta_N \lambda^N \qquad \text{and} \qquad \overline{N^2} = \frac{1}{x'}\sum_N N^2\Delta_N \lambda^N. \tag{10-252}$$

There is also the formal relation

$$\lambda\left(\frac{\partial \bar{N}}{\partial \lambda}\right)_{\Delta_N} = \overline{N^2} - \bar{N}^2. \tag{10-253}$$

The differential coefficients in Eqs. (10-204) and (10-206) may be verified by differentiating the "partition function" in Eq. (10-237). In the former case, the derivatives are "formal," as in Eq. (10-253).

TWO-COMPONENT AGGREGATES IN A SOLVENT. Suppose an aggregate in solution can bind another species from the solution. An example is the binding of hydrogen ions by a soap micelle. The aggregate is then a two-component small system, open with respect to both components. There may also be cases in which such an aggregate contains two components of similar size.

We give a rather condensed treatment of two-component aggregates here. The reader may wish to employ the basic equations given below to pursue the analysis further.

For simplicity, we use a special notation to designate components in this subsection. The notation is not quite the same as in the remainder of the section. The species 1^s and 2^s in the solvent form aggregates with components designated 1 and 2, respectively ($1^s \rightleftharpoons 1$; $2^s \rightleftharpoons 2$). The other solvent species are $3^s,..., c^s$. The molality of 1^s is $m_1^s = 1000N_1^s/(N_3^s + \cdots + N_c^s)M$ (see page 15), with a similar expression for 2^s. We still denote $\mathcal{N}/\Sigma_i N_i^s$ by x'. The solvent composition (sc) depends on m_1^s, m_2^s, and the relative composition of components $3^s,..., c^s$ (sc').

Again, some criterion must be selected as the definition of an aggregate. This criterion may depend on one or both components (e.g., an aggregate might be defined by $N_1 \geqslant N_0$, $N_2 \geqslant 0$).

We write, for the macroscopic solution,

$$dF_T = - S_T \, dT + V_T \, dp + \sum_{i=1}^{c} \mu_i^s \, dN_i^s + \mu^\square \, d\mathcal{N}$$
$$+ \mu_1 \mathcal{N} \, d\bar{N}_1 + \mu_2 \mathcal{N} \, d\bar{N}_2 \qquad (10\text{-}254)$$

$$= - S_T \, dT + V_T \, dp + \sum_{j=3}^{c} \mu_j^s \, dN_j^s + \mu_1^s \, d(N_1^s + N_{t1})$$
$$+ (\mu_1 - \mu_1^s) \, dN_{t1} + \mu_2^s \, d(N_2^s + N_{t2}) + (\mu_2 - \mu_2^s) \, dN_{t2}$$
$$+ (\mu^\square - \mu_1 \bar{N}_1 - \mu_2 \bar{N}_2) \, d\mathcal{N}, \qquad (10\text{-}255)$$

where $N_{t1} = \mathcal{N} \bar{N}_1$ and $N_{t2} = \mathcal{N} \bar{N}_2$. The equilibrium conditions are

$$\mu_1 = \mu_1^s, \qquad \mu_2 = \mu_2^s, \qquad \mu^\square = \mu_1 \bar{N}_1 + \mu_2 \bar{N}_2. \qquad (10\text{-}256)$$

Equation (10-198) is unchanged but

$$\mu^\square = F(\bar{N}_1, \bar{N}_2, p, T, sc) + kT \ln x' \qquad (10\text{-}257)$$

$$F = \mathscr{E} + \bar{N}_1 \mu_1 + \bar{N}_2 \mu_2 \qquad (10\text{-}258)$$

$$d\mu^\square = - \tilde{\mathrm{s}}^\square \, dT + \tilde{\mathrm{v}}^\square \, dp + kT \, d \ln x' + \beta_1 \, dm_1^s + \beta_2 \, dm_2^s$$
$$+ \mu_1 \, d\bar{N}_1 + \mu_2 \, d\bar{N}_2 \qquad (sc'), \qquad (10\text{-}259)$$

with

$$\beta_1 = \left(\frac{\partial F}{\partial m_1^s} \right)_{T, p, m_2^s, \bar{N}_1, \bar{N}_2, sc'}, \qquad \text{etc.}$$

Note that $\partial \beta_1/\partial m_2^s = \partial \beta_2/\partial m_1^s$ and $\partial \mu_1/\partial \bar{N}_2 = \partial \mu_2/\partial \bar{N}_1$.

The definitions of S, $\bar{E}$, and $\bar{V}$ are the same as before. Therefore Eqs. (10-198) and (10-259) lead to

$$F = \mathscr{E} + \bar{N}_1\mu_1 + \bar{N}_2\mu_2 = \bar{E} - TS + p\bar{V} \qquad (10\text{-}260)$$

$$dF = -S\,dT + \bar{V}\,dp + \mu_1\,d\bar{N}_1 + \mu_2\,d\bar{N}_2 + \beta_1\,dm_1^s + \beta_2\,dm_2^s \quad (sc') \tag{10-261}$$

$$d\mathscr{E} = -S\,dT + \bar{V}\,dp - \bar{N}_1\,d\mu_1 - \bar{N}_2\,d\mu_2 + \beta_1\,dm_1^s + \beta_2\,dm_2^s \quad (sc'). \tag{10-262}$$

On combining Eqs. (10-256) to (10-258), we find that, at equilibrium, we still have the relation

$$\mathscr{E} = -kT\ln x'. \qquad (10\text{-}263)$$

We now substitute

$$d\mu_1 = d\mu_1^s = d\mu_1^* = -\tilde{s}_1^*\,dT + \tilde{v}_1^*\,dp + \left(\frac{\partial \mu_1^*}{\partial m_1^s}\right)_{T,\,p,\,m_2^s,\,sc'} dm_1^s$$

$$+ \left(\frac{\partial \mu_1^*}{\partial m_2^s}\right)_{T,\,p,\,m_1^s,\,sc'} dm_2^s \qquad (sc'), \qquad (10\text{-}264)$$

and a similar expression for $d\mu_2$, in place of $d\mu_1$ and $d\mu_2$ in Eq. (10-262). The result is the equilibrium relation

$$d\mathscr{E} = (-S + \bar{N}_1\tilde{s}_1^* + \bar{N}_2\tilde{s}_2^*)\,dT + (\bar{V} - \bar{N}_1\tilde{v}_1^* - \bar{N}_2\tilde{v}_2^*)\,dp$$

$$+ \left(\beta_1 - \bar{N}_1\frac{\partial \mu_1^*}{\partial m_1^s} - \bar{N}_2\frac{\partial \mu_2^*}{\partial m_1^s}\right) dm_1^s$$

$$+ \left(\beta_2 - \bar{N}_1\frac{\partial \mu_1^*}{\partial m_2^s} - \bar{N}_2\frac{\partial \mu_2^*}{\partial m_2^s}\right) dm_2^s \qquad (sc'). \qquad (10\text{-}265)$$

It is easy to verify that $\partial \mu_1^*/\partial m_2^s = \partial \mu_2^*/\partial m_1^s$. Equation (10-263) may be used to introduce $d\ln x'$ in place of $d\mathscr{E}$. Equations for $\partial\mathscr{E}/\partial T$, $\partial\mathscr{E}/\partial m_1^s$, $\partial m_1^s/\partial m_2^s$, etc. (there are ten of these), may now be derived.

The equilibrium relation

$$\bar{N}_1\tilde{h}_2^* + \bar{N}_2\tilde{h}_2^* - \bar{H} = T(\bar{N}_1\tilde{s}_1^* + \bar{N}_2\tilde{s}_2^* - S) - \mathscr{E} \qquad (10\text{-}266)$$

may be useful above.

When the solvent is dilute in both 1^s and 2^s,

$$\mu_\alpha^* = \mu_\alpha^\Delta(p, T, sc') + kT \ln m_\alpha^s \qquad (\alpha = 1, 2). \qquad (10\text{-}267)$$

Then

$$- kT \, d \ln x' = \left(\frac{\bar{N}_1 \tilde{\mathrm{H}}_1^\square + \bar{N}_2 \tilde{\mathrm{H}}_2^\square - \bar{H}}{T} \right) dT$$

$$+ (\bar{V} - \bar{N}_1 \tilde{\mathrm{v}}_1^\square - \bar{N}_2 \tilde{\mathrm{v}}_2^\square) \, dp - \bar{N}_1 kT \, d \ln m_1^s$$

$$- \bar{N}_2 kT \, d \ln m_2^s \qquad (m_\alpha^s \to 0, sc'). \qquad (10\text{-}268)$$

Measurement of the dependence of x' on m_1^s and m_2^s gives $\bar{N}_1$ and $\bar{N}_2$:

$$\bar{N}_1 = \left(\frac{\partial \ln x'}{\partial \ln m_1^s} \right)_{T, p, m_2^s, sc'}, \qquad \bar{N}_2 = \left(\frac{\partial \ln x'}{\partial \ln m_2^s} \right)_{T, p, m_1^s, sc'} \qquad (m_\alpha^s \to 0).$$

$$(10\text{-}269)$$

Also,

$$\left(\frac{\partial \bar{N}_1}{\partial \ln m_2^s} \right)_{T, p, m_1^s, sc'} = \left(\frac{\partial \bar{N}_2}{\partial \ln m_1^s} \right)_{T, p, m_2^s, sc'} \qquad (m_\alpha^s \to 0). \qquad (10\text{-}270)$$

Many other relations follow from Eq. (10-268), but we leave these to the reader.

Equations involving $\bar{N}_1$ and $\bar{N}_2$ as independent variables follow from

$$d\mu_1 = - \frac{\partial S}{\partial \bar{N}_1} dT + \frac{\partial \bar{V}}{\partial \bar{N}_1} dp + \frac{\partial \mu_1}{\partial \bar{N}_1} d\bar{N}_1 + \frac{\partial \mu_2}{\partial \bar{N}_1} d\bar{N}_2$$

$$+ \frac{\partial \beta_1}{\partial \bar{N}_1} dm_1^s + \frac{\partial \beta_2}{\partial \bar{N}_1} dm_2^s$$

$$= d\mu_1^* = - \tilde{\mathrm{s}}_1^* \, dT + \tilde{\mathrm{v}}_1^* \, dp + \frac{\partial \mu_1^*}{\partial m_1^s} dm_1^s + \frac{\partial \mu_1^*}{\partial m_2^s} dm_2^s \qquad (sc')$$

$$(10\text{-}271)$$

and $d\mu_2 = d\mu_2^*$. All the derivatives in the first line are at constant T, p, $\bar{N}_2$, and sc. Equation (10-271) and the corresponding equation for component 2 involve six differentials (dT, dp, etc.), but provide two relations between them. Thus four variables are independent. When the solvent is dilute in both 1^s and 2^s, we have the simpler pair of equations

$$-\frac{\partial S}{\partial \bar{N}_1}dT + \frac{\partial \bar{V}}{\partial \bar{N}_1}dp + \frac{\partial \mu_1}{\partial \bar{N}_1}d\bar{N}_1 + \frac{\partial \mu_2}{\partial \bar{N}_1}d\bar{N}_2 = -\tilde{s}_1^{\square}dT$$
$$+ \tilde{v}_1^{\square}dp + kT\, d\ln m_1^s \quad (m_\alpha^s \to 0, sc')$$

$$-\frac{\partial S}{\partial \bar{N}_2}dT + \frac{\partial \bar{V}}{\partial \bar{N}_2}dp + \frac{\partial \mu_1}{\partial \bar{N}_2}d\bar{N}_1 + \frac{\partial \mu_2}{\partial \bar{N}_2}d\bar{N}_2 = -\tilde{s}_2^{\square}dT$$
$$+ \tilde{v}_2^{\square}dp + kT\, d\ln m_2^s. \tag{10-272}$$

Examples of deductions from Eqs. (10-272) are

$$\left(\frac{\partial \ln m_1^s}{\partial T}\right)_{p,\,\bar{N}_1,\,\bar{N}_2,\,sc'} = \frac{1}{kT}\left[\tilde{s}_1^{\square} - \left(\frac{\partial S}{\partial \bar{N}_1}\right)_{T,\,p,\,\bar{N}_2,\,sc'}\right] \quad (m_\alpha^s \to 0) \tag{10-273}$$

$$\left(\frac{\partial \bar{N}_1}{\partial \ln m_1^s}\right)_{T,\,p,\,\bar{N}_2,\,sc'} = \frac{kT}{(\partial \mu_1/\partial \bar{N}_1)_{T,\,p,\,\bar{N}_2,\,sc'}} \quad (m_\alpha^s \to 0) \tag{10-274}$$

$$\left(\frac{\partial \bar{N}_2}{\partial \ln m_1^s}\right)_{T,\,p,\,\bar{N}_1,\,sc'} = \frac{kT}{(\partial \mu_2/\partial \bar{N}_1)_{T,\,p,\,\bar{N}_2,\,sc'}} = \left(\frac{\partial \bar{N}_1}{\partial \ln m_2^s}\right)_{T,\,p,\,\bar{N}_2,\,sc'}$$
$$(m_\alpha^s \to 0) \tag{10-275}$$

$$\left(\frac{\partial \ln m_1^s}{\partial \bar{N}_1}\right)_{T,\,p,\,m_2^s,\,sc'} = \frac{\dfrac{\partial \mu_1}{\partial \bar{N}_1}\dfrac{\partial \mu_2}{\partial \bar{N}_2} - \left(\dfrac{\partial \mu_2}{\partial \bar{N}_1}\right)^2}{kT\,\dfrac{\partial \mu_2}{\partial \bar{N}_2}} \quad (m_\alpha^s \to 0) \tag{10-276}$$

$$\left(\frac{\partial \ln m_1^s}{\partial \bar{N}_2}\right)_{T,\,p,\,m_2^s,\,sc'} = \frac{\left(\dfrac{\partial \mu_2}{\partial \bar{N}_1}\right)^2 - \dfrac{\partial \mu_1}{\partial \bar{N}_1}\dfrac{\partial \mu_2}{\partial \bar{N}_2}}{kT\,\dfrac{\partial \mu_1}{\partial \bar{N}_2}} \quad (m_\alpha^s \to 0) \tag{10-277}$$

$$\left(\frac{\partial \bar{N}_2}{\partial \bar{N}_1}\right)_{T,\,p,\,m_2^s,\,sc'} = -\left(\frac{\partial \mu_1}{\partial \mu_2}\right)_{T,\,p,\,\bar{N}_1,\,sc'} \quad (m_\alpha^s \to 0). \tag{10-278}$$

If the solvent is dilute in 1^s and 2^s, and if we regard m_1^s and m_2^s in Eq. (10-265) as functions of T, p, $\bar{N}_1$, and $\bar{N}_2$, we can derive the generalization of Eq. (10-229):

$$d\mathscr{E} = -\left(S - \bar{N}_1\frac{\partial S}{\partial \bar{N}_1} - \bar{N}_2\frac{\partial S}{\partial \bar{N}_2}\right)dT + \left(\bar{V} - \bar{N}_1\frac{\partial \bar{V}}{\partial \bar{N}_1} - \bar{N}_2\frac{\partial \bar{V}}{\partial \bar{N}_2}\right)dp$$

$$-\left(\bar{N}_1\frac{\partial \mu_1}{\partial \bar{N}_1} + \bar{N}_2\frac{\partial \mu_2}{\partial \bar{N}_1}\right)d\bar{N}_1 - \left(\bar{N}_1\frac{\partial \mu_1}{\partial \bar{N}_2} + \bar{N}_2\frac{\partial \mu_2}{\partial \bar{N}_2}\right)d\bar{N}_2$$

$$(m_\alpha^s \to 0,\, sc'). \qquad (10\text{-}279)$$

This has the same formal appearance as Eq. (4-15).

ONE-COMPONENT SOLVENT. Aggregates (nuclei of a new phase) may form in a one-component gas, liquid, or solid, and these may be treated as small systems so long as they are dilute enough not to interact with each other. Up to a point [Eq. (10-206)], this is just a special case of our discussion beginning on page 120. Reference should also be made to pages 27 to 30 in Chapter 7. The solvent here has only one component, 1^s. The variables $N_2^s,\cdots, N_c^s, m_1^s$, and sc' are now all missing from the analysis. The definition of x' is $\mathscr{N}/N_1^s$. The fundamental equations are thus

$$dF_T = -S_T\, dT + V_T\, dp + \mu_1^s\, dN_1^s + \mu^\square\, d\mathscr{N} + \mu\mathscr{N}\, d\bar{N} \qquad (10\text{-}280)$$

$$\mu = \mu_1^s, \qquad \mu^\square = \mu\bar{N} \qquad \text{(equilibrium)} \qquad (10\text{-}281)$$

$$\mu^\square = F(\bar{N}, p, T) + kT\ln x' $$

$$F = \mathscr{E} + \bar{N}\mu = \bar{N}\hat{\mu} = \bar{E} - TS + p\bar{V} \qquad (10\text{-}282)$$

$$dF = -S\, dT + \bar{V}\, dp + \mu\, d\bar{N} \qquad (10\text{-}283)$$

$$d\mathscr{E} = -S\, dT + \bar{V}\, dp - \bar{N}\, d\mu \qquad (10\text{-}284)$$

$$\mathscr{E} = -kT\ln x' \qquad \text{(equilibrium).} \qquad (10\text{-}285)$$

At equilibrium $\mu = \mu_1^s = \mu_1^*$, where μ_1^* is a function of p and T only. We put

$$d\mu_1^* = -s_1^*\, dT + v_1^*\, dp$$

in place of $d\mu$ in Eq. (10-284) with the result

$$d\mathscr{E} = -(S - \bar{N}s_1^*)\, dT + (\bar{V} - \bar{N}v_1^*)\, dp, \qquad (10\text{-}286)$$

or

$$-kT\, d\ln x' = \left(\frac{\bar{N}_{H_1^*} - \bar{H}}{T}\right)dT + (\bar{V} - \bar{N}v_1^*)\, dp. \qquad (10\text{-}287)$$

If the solvent is a very dilute gas [see Eq. (7-126)],

$$d\mathscr{E} = - (S - \bar{N}s_1^{\square})\, dT - (\bar{N} - 1)kT\, d\ln p \qquad (p \to 0). \qquad (10\text{-}288)$$

These equations give expressions for $(\partial\mathscr{E}/\partial T)_p$, $(\partial\mathscr{E}/\partial p)_T$, $(\partial p/\partial T)_{\mathscr{E}}$, etc.

We can use

$$d\mu = - \left(\frac{\partial S}{\partial \bar{N}}\right)_{T,p} dT + \left(\frac{\partial \bar{V}}{\partial \bar{N}}\right)_{T,p} dp + \left(\frac{\partial \mu}{\partial \bar{N}}\right)_{T,p} d\bar{N}$$

$$= d\mu_1^* = - s_1^*\, dT + v_1^*\, dp \qquad (10\text{-}289)$$

to obtain formulas for $(\partial\bar{N}/\partial T)_p$, $(\partial\bar{N}/\partial p)_T$, and $(\partial p/\partial T)_{\bar{N}}$ at equilibrium. Also, Eq. (10-289) may be employed to eliminate dp from Eq. (10-286) in favor of dT and $d\bar{N}$, thus giving $(\partial\mathscr{E}/\partial\bar{N})_T$, etc. If the solvent is a very dilute gas,

$$d\mathscr{E} = - \left[S - (\bar{N} - 1)\left(\frac{\partial S}{\partial \bar{N}}\right)_{T,p} - s_1^{\square} \right] dT - (\bar{N} - 1)\left(\frac{\partial \mu}{\partial \bar{N}}\right)_T d\bar{N}$$

$$(p \to 0). \qquad (10\text{-}290)$$

In the *dilute gas* case, it is advantageous to introduce the definitions employed in Eqs. (7-127) to (7-131). That is, we define $S^{(3)}$ and $\mathscr{E}^{(3)}$ by

$$S = S^{(3)} + k + k \ln \frac{\mathscr{N}^{\dagger}}{N_1^s} \quad \text{and} \quad \mathscr{E} = \mathscr{E}^{(3)} + kT \ln \frac{N_1^s}{\mathscr{N}^{\dagger}}, \qquad (10\text{-}291)$$

and then $F^{(3)}$, $\hat{\mu}^{(3)}$, and $x^{(3)}$ by

$$F^{(3)} = \mathscr{E}^{(3)} + \bar{N}\mu = \bar{N}\hat{\mu}^{(3)}$$
$$\mu^{\square} = F^{(3)} + kT \ln x^{(3)}. \qquad (10\text{-}292)$$

Thus $x^{(3)} = \mathscr{N}/\mathscr{N}^{\dagger}$. Equations (10-283) to (10-285) become

$$dF^{(3)} = - S^{(3)}\, dT + \mu\, d\bar{N} \qquad (10\text{-}293)$$

$$d\mathscr{E}^{(3)} = - S^{(3)}\, dT - \bar{N}\, d\mu \qquad (10\text{-}294)$$

$$\mathscr{E}^{(3)} = - kT \ln \frac{\mathscr{N}}{\mathscr{N}^{\dagger}} \qquad \text{(equilibrium)}. \qquad (10\text{-}295)$$

We have used here, as in Chapter 7, $pV_T = N_1^s kT$ ($V_T = $ constant,

$N_1^s \gg \mathcal{N}$). Then,

$$d\mathscr{E}^{(3)} = -\left[S^{(3)} - \bar{N}\left(\frac{\partial S^{(3)}}{\partial \bar{N}}\right)_T\right] dT - \bar{N}\left(\frac{\partial \mu}{\partial \bar{N}}\right)_T d\bar{N} \qquad (10\text{-}296)$$

and, at equilibrium,

$$d\mathscr{E}^{(3)} = -(S^{(3)} - \bar{N}s_1^\square)\, dT - \bar{N}kT\, d\ln p. \qquad (10\text{-}297)$$

Example. Dilute Gas. Consider a very dilute gas in which aggregates are formed (e.g., in the Frenkel–Band theory). We shall not characterize the aggregates explicitly (see pages 69 to 72 of Part I for two special cases), but simply write, for aggregates of size N,

$$Q_N = \frac{1}{\mathcal{N}_N!}\, q_N{}^{\mathcal{N}_N}, \qquad (10\text{-}298)$$

with $q_N = V_T \psi_N(T)$. The pressure in the gas mixture is given by $pV_T = N_1^s kT$ since $N_1^s \gg \mathcal{N}_N$ for all N. The chemical potential of aggregates of size N is then

$$\mu_N^\square = kT \ln \frac{\mathcal{N}_N}{\psi_N V_T} = kT \ln \frac{p}{\psi_N kT} + kT \ln x_N', \qquad (10\text{-}299)$$

with $x_N' = \mathcal{N}_N/N_1^s$. When the aggregates of various sizes are in equilibrium with each other (i.e., when the aggregates are open small systems), $\mu_N^\square/N = \mu$ for all N. This, combined with Eq. (10-299), gives

$$x_N'(\mu, p, T) = \frac{kT\psi_N}{p} e^{N\mu/kT} \qquad (10\text{-}300)$$

$$e^{-\mathscr{E}(\mu,\, p,\, T)/kT} = x'(\mu, p, T) = \frac{kT}{p} \sum_N \psi_N e^{N\mu/kT} \qquad (10\text{-}301)$$

and

$$P_N(\mu, T) = \frac{\psi_N e^{N\mu/kT}}{\sum_N \psi_N e^{N\mu/kT}}. \qquad (10\text{-}302)$$

The coefficients in Eq. (10-284) are found to be

$$-\bar{N}(\mu, T) = \left(\frac{\partial \mathscr{E}}{\partial \mu}\right)_{p,\, T} = -\sum_N P_N N \qquad (10\text{-}303)$$

$$\bar{V}(p, T) = \left(\frac{\partial \mathscr{E}}{\partial p}\right)_{\mu, T} = \frac{kT}{p} \qquad (= \tilde{v}^\square = v_1^*) \qquad (10\text{-}304)$$

$$- S(\mu, p, T) = k \ln \frac{p}{kT} - k + k \sum_N P_N \left(\ln P_N - T\frac{d \ln \psi_N}{dT} - \ln \psi_N\right)$$
$$(10\text{-}305)$$

$$= \frac{\mathscr{E}}{T} - k + \frac{\bar{N}\mu}{T} - \frac{\bar{E}}{T},$$

where

$$\bar{E} = kT^2 \sum_N P_N \frac{d \ln \psi_N}{dT}$$

and $k = p\bar{V}/T$.

To introduce the equilibrium condition $\mu = \mu_1^*$ explicitly, we need [as in Eq. (3-32)]

$$\mu_1^*(p, T) = \mu_1^0(T) + kT \ln \frac{p}{p^\dagger}, \qquad (10\text{-}306)$$

from which we derive

$$- s_1^\square = \left(\frac{\partial \mu_1^*}{\partial T}\right)_p = \frac{d\mu_1^0}{dT} + k \ln \frac{p}{p^\dagger}.$$

We now replace μ by μ_1^* in Eq. (10-301) and have

$$x'(p, T) = \frac{kT}{p} \sum_N \psi_N e^{N\mu_1^0/kT} \left(\frac{p}{p^\dagger}\right)^N. \qquad (10\text{-}307)$$

This gives $\mathscr{E}$ for use in Eq. (10-288). Differentiation of $\mathscr{E}$ to obtain $\bar{N} - 1$ and $S - \bar{N}s_1^\square$ verifies Eqs. (10-303) and (10-305).

The dependence of x', S [Eqs. (10-301) and (10-305)], etc., on p, in this dilute gas case, is a rather artificial consequence of our definition of x' as $\mathscr{N}/N_1^s$. This dependence can be eliminated by use of

$$x^{(3)}(\mu, T) = \frac{1}{c^\dagger} \sum_N \psi_N e^{N\mu/kT}, \qquad (10\text{-}308)$$

$$- S^{(3)}(\mu, T) = k \ln c^\dagger + k \sum_N P_N \left(\ln P_N - T\frac{d \ln \psi_N}{dT} - \ln \psi_N\right),$$
$$(10\text{-}309)$$

etc., where $c^\dagger = \mathcal{N}^\dagger/V_T = $ constant. In other words, $\mathcal{N}/N_1^s$ is a natural choice for a concentration variable when the solvent is a dense phase, but it is an unnatural, though quite proper, choice for a dilute gas.

Example. Incompressible Solution. This is essentially the same example as above but here we consider that molecules of component 1^s in a liquid solution form aggregates. To achieve maximum simplicity, the solution is assumed incompressible, its volume is assumed additive, and $m_1^s \to 0$:

$$V_T = V^* + \mathrm{v} \sum_N \mathcal{N}_N N, \qquad (10\text{-}310)$$

where $V^* = $ volume of solvent $= $ constant and $\mathrm{v} = $ volume per molecule of aggregate $= $ constant. From Eqs. (10-230) and (10-310),

$$dA_T = -S_T\,dT - p\,dV_T + \sum_N \mu_N^\square\,d\mathcal{N}_N \qquad (N_i^s \text{ constant})$$

$$= -S_T\,dT + \sum_N (\mu_N^\square - p\mathrm{v}N)\,d\mathcal{N}_N \qquad (N_i^s \text{ constant}).$$
$$(10\text{-}311)$$

For the partition function Q_T, we write

$$Q_T = Q_{\text{solvent}} \prod_N Q_N, \qquad (10\text{-}312)$$

where

$$Q_N = \frac{1}{\mathcal{N}_N!}[V_T \psi_N(T)]^{\mathcal{N}_N},$$

as in Eq. (10-298). Explicit examples of $\psi_N(T)$ are provided by the function q/V in Eqs. (3-55) (rigid linear aggregate) and (3-61) (spherical aggregate).

From

$$\mu_N^\square - p\mathrm{v}N = -kT\frac{\partial \ln Q_T}{\partial \mathcal{N}_N}$$

and the equilibrium condition $\mu_N^\square/N = \mu$, we find (in the limit $\mathcal{N}_N \to 0$, as usual)

$$\mu_N^\square = kT \ln \frac{\mathcal{N}_N}{V^*\psi_N} + p\mathrm{v}N = \mu N.$$

Therefore
$$x'_N(\mu, p, T) = \frac{V^* \psi_N}{\sum_j N_j^s} e^{(\mu - pv)N/kT} \tag{10-313}$$

$$e^{-\mathscr{E}(\mu, p, T)/kT} = x'(\mu, p, T) = \frac{V^*}{\sum_j N_j^s} \sum_N \psi_N e^{(\mu - pv)N/kT} \tag{10-314}$$

and

$$P_N(\mu, p, T) = \frac{\psi_N e^{(\mu - pv)N/kT}}{\sum_N \psi_N e^{(\mu - pv)N/kT}}. \tag{10-315}$$

Equations (10-204) and (10-314) lead to

$$\bar{N}(\mu, p, T) = -\left(\frac{\partial \mathscr{E}}{\partial \mu}\right)_{T, p} = \sum_N P_N N \tag{10-316}$$

$$\bar{V}(\mu, p, T) = \left(\frac{\partial \mathscr{E}}{\partial p}\right)_{T, \mu} = \bar{N}v \tag{10-317}$$

$$- S(\mu, p, T) = \frac{\mathscr{E}}{T} - \frac{p\bar{N}v}{T} + \frac{\bar{N}\mu}{T} - \frac{\bar{E}}{T}, \tag{10-318}$$

where again, as in Eq. (10-305),

$$\bar{E} = kT^2 \sum_N P_N \frac{d \ln \psi_N}{dT}.$$

When we introduce the equilibrium condition

$$\mu = \mu_1^s = \mu_1^{\Delta}(p, T, sc') + kT \ln m_1^s,$$

we have

$$e^{-\mathscr{E}/kT} = x'(p, T, m_1^s) = \frac{V^*}{\sum_j N_j^s} \sum_N \psi_N e^{\mu_1^{\Delta} N/kT} e^{-pvN/kT} (m_1^s)^N. \tag{10-319}$$

We can then verify [see Eqs. (10-206) and (10-209)] that

$$\left(\frac{\partial \mathscr{E}}{\partial T}\right)_{p, m_1^s} = -(S - \bar{N}\tilde{s}_1^{\square}) \tag{10-320}$$

$$\left(\frac{\partial \mathscr{E}}{\partial p}\right)_{T, m_1^s} = \bar{V} - \bar{N}\tilde{v}_1^{\square} \tag{10-321}$$

$$\left(\frac{\partial \mathscr{E}}{\partial \ln m_1^s}\right)_{T, p} = -\bar{N}kT, \tag{10-322}$$

where S, $\bar{V}$, and $\bar{N}$ are given by Eqs. (10-316) to (10-318).

10-7. INTERACTING SMALL SYSTEMS IN SOLUTION

In parts of Chapters 2, 4, 5, 7, and the present one, we have considered small systems in solution. We have taken pains to emphasize that, in all cases, the solution must be infinitely dilute in small systems in order to define and measure thermodynamic functions that "belong" to a single small system.

The present section is essentially an appendix to all the chapters referred to above in which we discuss, for completeness, one example of a solution that is *not* infinitely dilute in small systems.

We choose, as our example, an N, p, T small system in a mixed solvent (see pages 56ff. of Part I). We use conventional solution thermodynamics, but we add N, the size of the small system, as a variable parameter. We employed the same kind of starting point in our treatment of an infinitely dilute solution.

The fundamental equations we need are

$$dF_T = - S_T\, dT + V_T\, dp + \sum_{i=1}^{c} \mu_i^s\, dN_i^s + \mu'\, d\mathcal{N} + \mu''\mathcal{N}\, dN \tag{10-323}$$

$$d\mu' = - \tilde{s}\, dT + \tilde{v}\, dp + \frac{\partial \mu'}{\partial x'}\, dx' + \frac{\partial \mu'}{\partial N}\, dN \qquad (sc) \tag{10-324}$$

$$\mu' = \tilde{E} - T\tilde{s} + p\tilde{v} \tag{10-325}$$

$$= N\hat{\mu}(N, p, T, sc) + kT \ln x' + B(N, p, T, sc)x'$$
$$+ C(N, p, T, sc)x'^2 + \cdots, \tag{10-326}$$

where μ' is the chemical potential of the small systems and μ'' is defined by $\mu''\mathcal{N} \equiv \partial F_T/\partial N$. In the limit $x' \to 0$, $\mu' \to \mu^\square$, $\tilde{s} \to \tilde{s}^\square$, $\mu'' \to \mu$, etc., in our previous notation. The new feature here is the inclusion of the terms in B, C, etc., in Eq. (10-326). These involve binary, ternary, etc., interactions, respectively, between small systems.

From Eq. (10-326), the derivative $\partial\mu'/\partial x'$ in Eq. (10-324) is

$$\left(\frac{\partial \mu'}{\partial x'}\right)_{T, p, N, sc} = \frac{kT}{x'} + B + 2Cx' + \cdots. \tag{10-327}$$

Similarly,

$$\left(\frac{\partial \mu'}{\partial N}\right)_{T, p, x', sc} = \mu + \left(\frac{\partial B}{\partial N}\right)_{p, T, sc} x' + \left(\frac{\partial C}{\partial N}\right)_{p, T, sc} x'^2 + \cdots. \tag{10-328}$$

The quantity μ'' will also have an expansion of the form

$$\mu'' = \mu + bx' + cx'^2 + \cdots.$$

To find b and c, we use

$$\left(\frac{\partial\mu'}{\partial N}\right)_{T,p,x',sc} = \left(\frac{\partial\mu'}{\partial N}\right)_{T,p,N_i^s,\mathcal{N}} = \left(\frac{\partial\mu''\mathcal{N}}{\partial\mathcal{N}}\right)_{T,p,N_i^s,N}$$

$$= \mu'' + x'\left(\frac{\partial\mu''}{\partial x'}\right)_{T,p,N,sc} \qquad (10\text{-}329)$$

and Eq. (10-328). By equating coefficients of like powers of x' we obtain

$$\mu'' = \mu + \frac{1}{2}\frac{\partial B}{\partial N}x' + \frac{1}{3}\frac{\partial C}{\partial N}x'^2 + \cdots. \qquad (10\text{-}330)$$

We also have the series

$$\tilde{s} = -\left(\frac{\partial\mu'}{\partial T}\right)_{p,N,x',sc} = S - k\ln x' - \frac{\partial B}{\partial T}x' - \frac{\partial C}{\partial T}x'^2 - \cdots \qquad (10\text{-}331)$$

$$\tilde{v} = \left(\frac{\partial\mu'}{\partial p}\right)_{T,N,x',sc} = \bar{V} + \frac{\partial B}{\partial p}x' + \frac{\partial C}{\partial p}x'^2 + \cdots. \qquad (10\text{-}332)$$

At this point, let us introduce the notation

$$\mu' = F + kT\ln x' + F_B x' + F_C x'^2 + \cdots$$

$$\tilde{s} = S - k\ln x' + S_B x' + S_C x'^2 + \cdots$$

$$\tilde{v} = \bar{V} + V_B x' + V_C x'^2 + \cdots, \qquad (10\text{-}333)$$

where

$$F \equiv N\hat{\mu}, \qquad F_B \equiv B, \qquad F_C \equiv C$$

$$S_B \equiv -\frac{\partial B}{\partial T} = -\frac{\partial F_B}{\partial T}, \qquad S_C \equiv -\frac{\partial C}{\partial T} = -\frac{\partial F_C}{\partial T}$$

$$V_B \equiv \frac{\partial B}{\partial p} = \frac{\partial F_B}{\partial p}, \qquad V_C \equiv \frac{\partial C}{\partial p} = \frac{\partial F_C}{\partial p}, \qquad \text{etc.}$$

Then

$$\tilde{E} = \mu' + T\tilde{s} - p\tilde{v}$$

$$= \bar{E} + E_B x' + E_C x'^2 + \cdots, \qquad (10\text{-}334)$$

where

$$\bar{E} \equiv F + TS - p\bar{V}$$
$$E_B \equiv F_B + TS_B - pV_B$$
$$E_C \equiv F_C + TS_C - pV_C, \qquad \text{etc.} \qquad (10\text{-}335)$$

The functions F, S, etc., are intrinsic properties of a single small system; the functions F_B, S_B, etc., are concerned with binary interactions between small systems; etc.

By the rules of calculus, we can of course always write

$$dF = \frac{\partial F}{\partial T} dT + \frac{\partial F}{\partial p} dp + \frac{\partial F}{\partial N} dN \qquad (sc)$$

$$dF_B = \frac{\partial F_B}{\partial T} dT + \frac{\partial F_B}{\partial p} dp + \frac{\partial F_B}{\partial N} dN \qquad (sc)$$

$$dF_C = \frac{\partial F_C}{\partial T} dT + \frac{\partial F_C}{\partial p} dp + \frac{\partial F_C}{\partial N} dN \qquad (sc)$$

etc., or

$$dF = -S\,dT + \bar{V}\,dp + \mu\,dN \qquad (sc)$$
$$dF_B = -S_B\,dT + V_B\,dp + \mu_B\,dN \qquad (sc)$$
$$dF_C = -S_C\,dT + V_C\,dp + \mu_C\,dN \qquad (sc), \qquad (10\text{-}336)$$

etc., where

$$\mu = \frac{\partial F}{\partial N}, \qquad \mu_B \equiv \frac{\partial F_B}{\partial N} = \frac{\partial B}{\partial N}, \qquad \mu_C \equiv \frac{\partial F_C}{\partial N} = \frac{\partial C}{\partial N}, \qquad \text{etc.}$$

All equations in the sets (10-335) and (10-336) have the same form, but there is nothing remarkable about this. Only definitions and the rules of partial differentiation are involved. Also, in general,

$$\frac{F}{N} \neq \frac{\partial F}{\partial N} = \mu, \qquad \frac{F_B}{N} \neq \frac{\partial F_B}{\partial N} = \mu_B, \qquad \frac{F_C}{N} \neq \frac{\partial F_C}{\partial N} = \mu_C, \qquad \text{etc.}$$

Again, this is nothing remarkable. These relations simply state that arbitrary functions $F(N, p, T)$, $F_B(N, p, T)$, etc., are not usually linear homogeneous functions of N (p and T constant). The linear homogeneous relation $F/N = (\partial F/\partial N)_{p,\,T}$ in macroscopic thermodynamics is the exception rather than the rule.

The basic reasons why Eqs. (10-335a) and (10-336a), out of the sets (10-335) and (10-336), are worth the special attention they have been paid in this book are: (a) they refer to the intrinsic properties of a *single* small system; and (b) these equations and properties go over into conventional macroscopic results in the limit $N \to \infty$.

Finally, as a check on self-consistency, we substitute Eqs. (10-327), (10-328), and (10-333) into Eq. (10-324). After cancellation of various terms and comparison of coefficients of like powers of x', we recover Eqs. (10-336).

CHAPTER 11

ELECTRIC AND
MAGNETIC FIELDS

Since the extension of the thermodynamics presented in earlier chapters to small systems in electric or magnetic fields is quite straightforward, we limit the present chapter to a rather brief analysis and a few examples.

For a complete discussion, as background material, of the *macroscopic* thermodynamics of electric and magnetic fields, the reader is referred to the papers of Koenig and Guggenheim.[1]

The statistical mechanics of finite systems in a magnetic field is a well-known subject, especially the statistical mechanics of the so-called Ising model.[2] Among other things, the present chapter should furnish the appropriate thermodynamics to apply to this type of system. On the experimental side, so-called superparamagnetic particles serve as an example of small, magnetic systems.

There have been several recent treatments of the statistical mechanics of macroscopic systems in an electric field[3] which provide some of the point of view and notation to be used below.

11-1. ELECTRIC FIELD

As a simple case, let us consider first an ensemble of closed, small N, T dielectric systems (see Chapter 3) in a uniform external electric field D (the dielectric displacement). The small systems are distinguishable, equivalent, independent, and with fixed centers of mass. The field D is imposed from outside the ensemble. The systems of the ensemble are sufficiently far apart (dilute) that each system is subject to the external field D but not to any additional contribution to the field, owing to polarization of neighboring systems of the ensemble. Thus, in this case, we could just as well write E as D ($\mathsf{E} = D$), where E is the electric field strength.

---

[1] F. O. Koenig, *J. Phys. Chem.*, **41**, 597 (1937); E. A. Guggenheim, *Proc. Roy. Soc.* (*London*), **155A**, 49, 70 (1936).

[2] For a recent review, see C. Domb, *Advan. Phys.* **9**, 149, 245 (1960).

[3] S.T., Chapter 12; T. L. Hill, *J. Chem. Phys.*, **28**, 61 (1958); **30**, 1114 (1959); *J. Am. Chem. Soc.*, **80**, 2142 (1958).

For the basic ensemble equation we then have [compare Eq. (1–24)]

$$dE_t = T \, dS_t - M_t \, dD + \mu \mathcal{N} \, dN + X \, d\mathcal{N}, \qquad (11\text{-}1)$$

where $M_t = \bar{M} \mathcal{N}$ is the total dipole moment of the ensemble ($\bar{M}$ is the mean moment per small system). M_t is an extensive property; D is intensive. As Koenig[1] has emphasized, there are a number of alternative choices of electric-field thermodynamic variables. The particular choice[2] in Eq. (11-1) is most convenient for present (but not all) purposes. In particular, E_t above includes the molecular kinetic energy of the molecules within each system, the potential energy of interaction of the molecules with the field D, and the potential energy of interaction between the molecules within each system. E_t does *not* include the energy of the field D in a vacuum ($\mathcal{N} = 0$).

Integration of the macroscopic relation (11-1) yields

$$E_t = TS_t + X\mathcal{N},$$

or

$$X = \bar{E} - TS = A. \qquad (11\text{-}2)$$

When this is used to eliminate X in Eq. (11-1), we obtain the following fundamental equations for a single system:

$$d\bar{E} = T \, dS - \bar{M} \, dD + \mu \, dN \qquad (11\text{-}3)$$

$$dA = d(\hat{\mu}N) = - S \, dT - \bar{M} \, dD + \mu \, dN \qquad (11\text{-}4)$$

$$d\mathscr{E} = - S \, dT - \bar{M} \, dD + \mu \, dN, \qquad (11\text{-}5)$$

where $A = \hat{\mu}N$ and

$$\mathscr{E} = N(\hat{\mu} - \mu) \qquad (11\text{-}6)$$

$$= \bar{E} - TS - \mu N. \qquad (11\text{-}7)$$

The connection with statistical mechanics is

$$A(N, T, D) = -kT \ln Q(N, T, D). \qquad (11\text{-}8)$$

---

[1] Loc. cit.
[2] See S.T., p. 203.

Equation (11-4) provides the Maxwell relations

$$\left(\frac{\partial S}{\partial D}\right)_{T,N} = \left(\frac{\partial \bar{M}}{\partial T}\right)_{D,N}, \qquad -\left(\frac{\partial S}{\partial N}\right)_{T,D} = \left(\frac{\partial \mu}{\partial T}\right)_{D,N},$$

$$-\left(\frac{\partial \bar{M}}{\partial N}\right)_{T,D} = \left(\frac{\partial \mu}{\partial D}\right)_{T,N}.$$

(11-9)

From these we find

$$d\hat{\mu} = -\frac{S}{N}dT - \frac{\bar{M}}{N}dD - \frac{\mathscr{E}}{N^2}dN \qquad (11\text{-}10)$$

$$d\mu = -\left(\frac{\partial S}{\partial N}\right)_{T,D}dT - \left(\frac{\partial \bar{M}}{\partial N}\right)_{T,D}dD - \frac{1}{N}\left(\frac{\partial \mathscr{E}}{\partial N}\right)_{T,D}dN \qquad (11\text{-}11)$$

$$d\mathscr{E} = -\left[S - N\left(\frac{\partial S}{\partial N}\right)_{T,D}\right]dT - \left[\bar{M} - N\left(\frac{\partial \bar{M}}{\partial N}\right)_{T,D}\right]dD$$

$$+ \left(\frac{\partial \mathscr{E}}{\partial N}\right)_{T,D}dN. \qquad (11\text{-}12)$$

The reader may wish to derive further general relations for an N, T, D system, using analogies with earlier chapters.

Example. Helix-Coil Transition. This is a very simple example.[1] Suppose the linear macromolecular helix-coil model on page 45 of Part I has charges $+q$ and $-q$ at the ends of the chain and is in a uniform external electric field D. We take $D \geqslant 0$ and $q \geqslant 0$. The macromolecule

$$\boxed{-q}\ CCCHHHHHHCC\ \boxed{+q}$$
$$D \to$$

is assumed to be oriented with the field. Hence the field tends to stretch the system by converting H units into longer C units ($l_C > l_H$). The dipole moment is lq and the potential energy of the dipole in the field is $-lqD$.

For simplicity, we assume that C and H units have the same polarizability α. The associated potential energy in the field, per unit, is $-\alpha D^2/2$. With this assumption, the polarizability will make no

[1] More complicated examples of similar type, but for macroscopic systems, are discussed in T. L. Hill, *J. Am. Chem. Soc.*, **80**, 2142 (1958).

contribution to the effect of D on the transition $H \to C$. A more general situation is obviously $\alpha_C \neq \alpha_H$.

If $Q(N, l, T)$ is the canonical ensemble partition function of a macromolecule in the absence of a field (as on page 45 of Part I), in the presence of a field it is

$$Q(N, l, T, D) = Q(N, l, T) \, e^{lqD/kT} \, e^{N\alpha D^2/2kT}.$$

Also, if $\Delta(N, f, T)$ is the N, f, T partition function in the absence of a field, in the presence of a field we have

$$\Delta(N, f, T, D) = \sum_l Q(N, l, T, D) \, e^{fl/kT}$$

$$= e^{N\alpha D^2/2kT} \sum_l Q(N, l, T) \, e^{(f+qD)l/kT}$$

$$= e^{N\alpha D^2/2kT} \, \Delta(N, f + qD, T). \qquad (11\text{-}13)$$

Specifically, in the "unzipper-from-the-ends" model,[1]

$$\Delta(N, f, T, D) = e^{N\alpha D^2/2kT} \, r_C^N \, \frac{Nr(1 - r) + 1 - 2r + r^{N+2}}{(1 - r)^2},$$

$$\qquad (11\text{-}14)$$

where

$$r_C = q_C(T) \, e^{(f+qD)l_C/kT}, \qquad r_H = q_H(T) \, e^{(f+qD)l_H/kT},$$

$$r(f, T, D) = \frac{r_H}{r_C}.$$

This follows from Eqs. (2-86) and (11-13).

The basic thermodynamic equations are

$$d\bar{E} = T \, dS + f \, d\bar{l} - \bar{M} \, dD + \mu \, dN \qquad (11\text{-}15)$$

$$d(\hat{\mu}N) = - S \, dT - \bar{l} \, df - \bar{M} \, dD + \mu \, dN \qquad (11\text{-}16)$$

$$\hat{\mu}N = \bar{E} - TS - f\bar{l} \qquad (11\text{-}17)$$

$$= \mu N + \mathscr{E} \qquad (11\text{-}18)$$

$$= - kT \ln \Delta(N, f, T, D). \qquad (11\text{-}19)$$

These are obvious generalizations of Eqs. (11-3) to (11-8). These relations, together with Eq. (11-14), lead to all the thermodynamic properties of the "unzipper" model in an electric field.

[1] Equation (11-13) is more general and applies to other HC models as well.

Equations (2-92) and (2-93) for the mean number of helical units in the chain still hold, but with r redefined as in Eq. (11-14). If we take $f = 0$, then the expression at the top of page 47 of Part I becomes

$$\ln r = \ln \frac{\omega_H}{\omega_C} + \frac{\epsilon_C - \epsilon_H}{kT} - \frac{qD(l_C - l_H)}{kT}.$$

Figure 2-2 is still applicable. If $D =$ constant, Fig. 2-2 is essentially a plot of the fraction of helical units $(\bar{n}/N)$ against $1/T$. When $D = 0$, the helical form predominates at low temperatures $(\epsilon_C - \epsilon_H > 0, \; 1/T \to \infty)$. But if D is sufficiently large,

$$qD(l_C - l_H) > \epsilon_C - \epsilon_H$$

and the longer coil form is favored at low temperatures $(\ln r \to -\infty)$. That is, the relative energetic stability of H and C units can be reversed by the electric field.

If T is held constant, Fig. 2-2 may be regarded as a plot of $\bar{n}/N$ against $-D$. As $D \to \infty$, $\ln r \to -\infty$ and the coil form is obtained, as expected. Thus, the helix to coil transition can be induced by an electric field at constant T, if the macromolecule is charged, as assumed.

For the moment $\bar{M}$ we find easily, from Eqs. (11-13), (11-16), and (11-19),

$$\bar{M} = -\left(\frac{\partial \hat{\mu} N}{\partial D} \right)_{T, f, N} = N\alpha D + \bar{l}q. \qquad (11\text{-}20)$$

DILUTE GAS OF SMALL SYSTEMS. Here we consider a very dilute gas of small systems in a uniform, external electric field D. This involves a simple extension of Section 3-3. We have to add a term $-M_t \, dD$ to Eq. (3-26), but Eq. (3-27) is unchanged. The definitions of $\hat{\mu}$ and S are the same [Eqs. (3-28) and (3-30)]. We then find that Eqs. (11-3) to (11-7), above, are again the basic equations for a small system. Since the gas is infinitely dilute $(\mathcal{N}/V \to 0)$, we may again replace D by E if desired (i.e., $D = \mathsf{E}$).

Example. Rigid Linear Aggregate. In this example we have the same model as on page 69 of Part I, except that here the gas[1] of

---

[1] As on p. 69 of Part I, we could have in mind here, instead, an incompressible small system in an inert solvent. In this case D should be replaced in the basic thermodynamic equations by E, where $D = \epsilon^* \mathsf{E}$ and ϵ^* is the dielectric constant of the solvent. The definitions of E_t and p are then different [compare Koenig's Eqs. (35.1) and (37.8)]. See also Section 11-2.

aggregates is in an external field D. We assume that each unit of an aggregate, as, for example, in

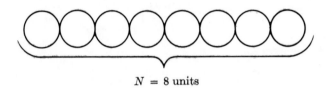

$$N = 8 \text{ units}$$

has polarizability α and a permanent moment μ_0 pointing along the chain. The total dipole moment of an aggregate is $N\mu_0$. Then, in Eq. (3-54),[1]

$$q(N, V, T, D) = q_0(N, V, T)\, e^{N\alpha D^2/2kT}\, \frac{\sinh y}{y}, \qquad (11\text{-}21)$$

where q_0 is the expression on the right-hand side of Eq. (3-55) and $y = N\mu_0 D/kT$. Note that q is an even function of D, as required on physical grounds.

With $q(N, V, T, D)$ available, Eq. (3-54) and

$$A_t = -\,kT \ln Q(N, V, T, \mathscr{N}, D) \qquad (11\text{-}22)$$

$$dA_t = -\,S_t\, dT - p\, dV - M_t\, dD + \mu_t\, d\mathscr{N} + \mu\mathscr{N}\, dN \qquad (11\text{-}23)$$

make possible the calculation of all the thermodynamic functions of a small system (aggregate). We consider explicitly two limiting cases.

In the *macroscopic limit*, we let $N \to \infty$ and take D positive, for definiteness. Because of the large dipole moment, $N\mu_0$, the aggregate is almost completely oriented in the field. We find

$$\ln q = \ln q_0 + \frac{N\alpha D^2}{2kT} + \frac{N\mu_0 D}{kT} - \ln \frac{2N\mu_0 D}{kT} + \cdots . \qquad (11\text{-}24)$$

There are terms here in N and in $\ln N$ ($\ln q_0$ has terms in N and $\ln N$). The macroscopic expression is

$$\ln q = \left(-\frac{\epsilon}{kT} + \frac{\alpha D^2}{2kT} + \frac{\mu_0 D}{kT} \right) N. \qquad (11\text{-}25)$$

[1] Compare S.T., Eq. (12-25).

From Eq. (11-24) and

$$M_t = \bar{M} \mathcal{N} = kT \left(\frac{\partial \ln Q}{\partial D} \right)_{T,V,\mathcal{N},N}$$

$$\mu \mathcal{N} = - kT \left(\frac{\partial \ln Q}{\partial N} \right)_{T,V,\mathcal{N},D}$$

we find, for example,

$$\bar{M}(N, T, D) = N\alpha D + N\mu_0 - \frac{kT}{D} \qquad (11\text{-}26)$$

$$\mu(N, T, D) = \epsilon - \frac{7kT}{2N} - \frac{\alpha D^2}{2} - \mu_0 D. \qquad (11\text{-}27)$$

These are consistent with Eq. (11-9c).

In the *small-field limit* $(D \to 0)$, there is little orientation of the dipolar aggregates in the field. In this case N is finite (i.e., we do not allow $N \to \infty$ because of the expansion used). On expanding $y^{-1} \sinh y$ in powers of y, we obtain

$$\ln q = \ln q_0 + \frac{N\alpha D^2}{2kT} + \frac{1}{6} \left(\frac{N\mu_0 D}{kT} \right)^2 + O(D^4). \qquad (11\text{-}28)$$

Note that there is a nonlinear term here in N^2, but this is not alarming since $N \to \infty$ is not permissible. By the same procedure as above, we deduce

$$\bar{M}(N, T, D) = N\alpha D + \frac{1}{3} \frac{N^2 \mu_0^2 D}{kT} + O(D^3) \qquad (11\text{-}29)$$

$$\mu = \epsilon - \frac{9kT}{2N} - \frac{\alpha D^2}{2} - \frac{N\mu_0^2 D^2}{3kT} + O(D^4). \qquad (11\text{-}30)$$

Instead of calculating thermodynamic functions directly from Eq. (11-23), one could of course find μ_t from Eq. (11-23), then $\hat{\mu}$ from Eq. (3-28), and finally other functions from Eq. (11-4).

We have considered so far in this chapter only closed small systems (N units) in an electric field. Of course open systems in an electric field can be treated as well, as in Chapter 10, for example. One interesting effect, with an open system, is that the electric field will influence the distribution in aggregate sizes. This is easily illustrated by the present example of rigid linear aggregates. From Eqs. (10-298) and (10-302), we see that if aggregates of different sizes are in equilibrium with each other, the fraction of aggregates of size N in the presence of a field D is given by

$$P_N(\mu, T, D) = \frac{\psi_N(T, D)\, e^{N\mu/kT}}{\sum\limits_{N} \psi_N\, e^{N\mu/kT}},\qquad (11\text{-}31)$$

where μ is the monomer chemical potential in the gas,

$$\psi_N(T, D) = \left(\frac{2\pi m N kT}{h^2}\right)^{3/2} \frac{\pi^2 kT m a^2 N^3}{3h^2}\, e^{-(N-1)\epsilon/kT}\, e^{N\alpha D^2/2kT}\, \frac{\sinh y}{y},$$

$$(11\text{-}32)$$

and $y = N\mu_0 D/kT$. Because P_N is a complicated function of N, even for this simple model, we have not made any numerical calculations.

11-2. SOLVENT EFFECTS IN AN ELECTRIC FIELD

We show here that it is easy to include an electric field in the treatment of solvent effects which was given in Section 2-3. We use the notation of that section.

The solvent is a dielectric with components 1, 2, ..., c (we can drop the usual superscript s here). The small systems (macromolecules, for example) are an additional, infinitely dilute component in the solution. The small systems are "closed," each with N units or monomers. There is a uniform external field D imposed on the solution.

Because of the presence of the solvent, a small system is subject to the field E, not D, where $\epsilon^*\mathsf{E} = D$ and ϵ^* is the dielectric constant of the solvent. The generalization of Eq. (2-117) which we choose is therefore[1]

$$dE_T = T\, dS_T - p\, dV_T - M_T\, d\mathsf{E}$$

$$+ \sum_{i=1}^{c} \mu_i\, dN_i + \mu^{\square}\, d\mathcal{N} + \mu\mathcal{N}\, dN,\qquad (11\text{-}33)$$

where M_T is the total dipole moment of the macroscopic solution. The precise definitions of E_T and p are those given in Koenig's[2]

[1] See T. L. Hill, *J. Chem. Phys.*, **28**, 61 (1958); **30**, 1114 (1959).
[2] Loc. cit.

Eq. (37.8). It then follows that

$$F_T = E_T - TS_T + pV_T = \sum_i \mu_i N_i + \mu^\square \mathcal{N} \tag{11-34}$$

$$dF_T = - S_T \, dT + V_T \, dp - M_T \, d\mathsf{E}$$
$$+ \sum_i \mu_i \, dN_i + \mu^\square \, d\mathcal{N} + \mu \mathcal{N} \, dN \tag{11-35}$$

$$\sum_i N_i \, d\mu_i + \mathcal{N} \, d\mu^\square = - S_T \, dT + V_T \, dp - M_T \, d\mathsf{E} + \mu \mathcal{N} \, dN. \tag{11-36}$$

Partial molal quantities are defined by

$$\widetilde{\mathrm{G}} = \left(\frac{\partial G_T}{\partial \mathcal{N}} \right)_{T, \, p, \, \mathsf{E}, \, N_i, \, N},$$

etc. Then

$$dG_T = \widetilde{\mathrm{G}} \, d\mathcal{N} + \sum_i \widetilde{\mathrm{G}}_i \, dN_i \qquad (T, p, \mathsf{E}, N \text{ constant})$$

$$G_T = \widetilde{\mathrm{G}} \mathcal{N} + \sum_i \widetilde{\mathrm{G}}_i N_i,$$

as usual.

On differentiating Eq. (11-34) with respect to $\mathcal{N}$,

$$\mu^\square = \widetilde{\mathrm{E}}^\square - T\widetilde{\mathrm{s}}^\square + p\widetilde{\mathrm{v}}^\square. \tag{11-37}$$

Also, using Maxwell relations from Eq. (11-35), we find

$$d\mu^\square = - \widetilde{\mathrm{s}}^\square \, dT + \widetilde{\mathrm{v}}^\square \, dp - \widetilde{\mathrm{M}}^\square \, d\mathsf{E} + \frac{\partial \mu^\square}{\partial x'} \, dx' + \frac{\partial \mu^\square}{\partial N} \, dN \qquad (sc). \tag{11-38}$$

The argument in Eqs. (7-70) to (7-75) is applicable here and shows that $\partial \mu^\square / \partial N$ in Eq. (11-38) is equal to μ, as defined by Eq. (11-33).

We then define F, $\hat{\mu}$, and S for a small system by

$$\mu^\square = F(N, p, T, \mathsf{E}, sc) + kT \ln x'$$
$$= N\hat{\mu}(N, p, T, \mathsf{E}, sc) + kT \ln x' \tag{11-39}$$

$$\widetilde{\mathrm{s}}^\square = S(N, p, T, \mathsf{E}, sc) - k \ln x'. \tag{11-40}$$

We also define

$$\bar{V} \equiv \widetilde{\mathrm{v}}^\square, \qquad \bar{M} \equiv \widetilde{\mathrm{M}}^\square, \qquad \bar{E} \equiv \widetilde{\mathrm{E}}^\square. \tag{11-41}$$

Thus $\bar{M}$ is the mean change in M_T brought about by the addition of one small system to the infinitely dilute solution (with T, p, E,

N_i, and N held constant). There will be contributions to $\bar{M}$ associated with the small system itself (permanent moment, polarizability) and also contributions from the effect the presence of the small system has on neighboring solvent molecules.

On combining Eqs. (11-37) to (11-41), we obtain the following fundamental relations for a small system:

$$F = N\hat{\mu} = \bar{E} - TS + p\bar{V} \tag{11-42}$$

$$d\bar{E} = T\,dS - p\,d\bar{V} - \bar{M}\,d\mathsf{E} + \mu\,dN \qquad (sc) \tag{11-43}$$

$$d(N\hat{\mu}) = -S\,dT + \bar{V}\,dp - \bar{M}\,d\mathsf{E} + \mu\,dN \qquad (sc) \tag{11-44}$$

$$d\mathscr{E} = d[N(\hat{\mu} - \mu)] = -S\,dT + \bar{V}\,dp - \bar{M}\,d\mathsf{E} - N\,d\mu \qquad (sc). \tag{11-45}$$

These should be compared with Eqs. (11-3) to (11-7) and (11-15) to (11-18). We leave it to the reader to continue from this point.

As a final topic, we derive a relation, which may have some practical value, between $\bar{M}$ and the change of the dielectric constant ϵ with x'. From

$$\epsilon\mathsf{E} = D = \mathsf{E} + \frac{4\pi M_T}{V_T}, \tag{11-46}$$

we have

$$4\pi M_T = (\epsilon - 1)\,\mathsf{E}\,V_T.$$

Then, on differentiating with respect to $\mathscr{N}$,

$$4\pi\tilde{\mathsf{M}} = (\epsilon - 1)\mathsf{E}\tilde{\mathsf{v}} + \mathsf{E}V_T\left(\frac{\partial\epsilon}{\partial\mathscr{N}}\right)_{T,p,\mathsf{E},N_i,N}. \tag{11-47}$$

We are interested in the infinitely dilute solution ($x' \to 0$):

$$4\pi\bar{M} = \left[(\epsilon^* - 1)\bar{V} + \mathsf{v}^*\left(\frac{\partial\epsilon}{\partial x'}\right)^{\square}_{T,p,\mathsf{E},N,sc}\right]\mathsf{E}, \tag{11-48}$$

where $\mathsf{v}^* = V^*/\Sigma_i N_i$. At ordinary field strengths the quantity in brackets is independent of E (it can be expanded in even powers of E) and $\bar{M}$ is proportional to E. Measurement of $(\partial\epsilon/\partial x')^{\square}$ would allow calculation of $\bar{M}$.

11-3. MAGNETIC FIELD

The thermodynamics of a magnetic field is formally identical with the thermodynamics of an electric field. Hence the preceding sections apply to a magnetic field provided we replace D by B (magnetic induction), E by H (magnetic field strength), and M by I (intensity of magnetization). Section 11-2 is applicable only to a dielectric (nonelectrolyte) solution. This restriction is not necessary here: The solution may be electrolytic.

Example. Ising Model. We conclude by rephrasing the general lattice-gas problem in "magnetic language" (the Ising model).

An approximate treatment of a finite lattice gas is given on pages 143 to 149 of Part I. Also, an exact treatment of a special case is considered on pages 62 to 64 and 70 to 72 of Part II. But there is no point in repeating this discussion for the magnetic case.

Let the small system be a lattice of B magnetic dipoles,[1] associated with the electron spins, each of which can exist in only two orientations or states: $\uparrow$, in the direction of the magnetic field H; or $\downarrow$, against the field. The potential energy of a dipole or spin is $-mH$ if oriented with the field ($\uparrow$) and $+mH$ if oriented against the field ($\downarrow$), where m is the magnetic moment.

Let N be the number of $\downarrow$ states and $B - N$ the number of $\uparrow$ states. For a given value of N, the potential energy of the dipoles in the field is then

$$mHN - mH(B - N) = (2N - B)mH.$$

For given H,B,T (the environmental variables), let $\bar{N}$ be the mean value of N ($0 \leqslant N \leqslant B$). Then the mean work necessary to increase H by dH is $-\bar{I}\,dH$, where

$$\bar{I} = (B - 2\bar{N})m. \tag{11-49}$$

The range of I values is $-Bm \leqslant I \leqslant +Bm$.

There is an additional contribution to the potential energy: nearest-neighbor parallel spins ($\uparrow\uparrow$ or $\downarrow\downarrow$) are assumed to have an interaction energy $-J$, whereas nearest-neighbor antiparallel

---

[1] To maintain the lattice-gas notation, we use B for the number of dipoles rather than for the magnetic induction. In this example, the magnetic induction is equal to the magnetic field strength, so we use the symbol H for the field. We follow the discussion in S.T., pp. 209–211 and 250–252, where applicable.

spins ($\uparrow\downarrow$) have an interaction energy $+J$. These interaction energies are due to quantum mechanical exchange forces; they are not diple–dipole interactions (which are neglected). If $J > 0$, we have the ferromagnetic case, whereas if $J < 0$, we have the anti-ferromagnetic case.

In a small system, all the B dipoles may not be equivalent because of edge effects (a different number of nearest neighbors).

Since there are B spins in the system and each spin can be $\uparrow$ or $\downarrow$, there are a total of 2^B possible configurations for the whole system. In any one of these configurations, N has a definite value and we let $N_{\uparrow\uparrow}$ be the number of nearest-neighbor $\uparrow\uparrow$ pairs, etc. Then, in this configuration, the energy of the system is (we omit kinetic energy and other degrees of freedom)

$$E = (2N - B)mH + N_{\uparrow\downarrow}J - (N_{\uparrow\uparrow} + N_{\downarrow\downarrow})J. \tag{11-50}$$

The canonical ensemble partition function is then

$$Q(B, T, H) = \sum_{2^B} e^{-E/kT}, \tag{11-51}$$

where the sum is over all 2^B configurations.

From Eqs. (11-3) to (11-5), the basic thermodynamic equations are

$$d\bar{E} = T\,dS - \bar{I}\,dH + \mu\,dB \tag{11-52}$$

$$A = \bar{E} - TS = \hat{\mu}B, \qquad \mathscr{E} = (\hat{\mu} - \mu)B \tag{11-53}$$

$$dA = d(\hat{\mu}B) = -S\,dT - \bar{I}\,dH + \mu\,dB \tag{11-54}$$

$$d\mathscr{E} = -S\,dT - \bar{I}\,dH - B\,d\mu \tag{11-55}$$

$$A = \hat{\mu}B = -kT\ln Q. \tag{11-56}$$

Note that the number of "units" in the system is B, instead of N as in Eq. (11-3).

We can easily verify the self-consistency of Eqs. (11-49) and (11-54):

$$\bar{I} = \frac{kT}{Q}\left(\frac{\partial Q}{\partial H}\right)_{B,\,T} = \frac{1}{Q}\sum_{2^B}(B - 2N)me^{-E/kT}$$

$$= (B - 2\bar{N})m.$$

Different definitions of E are possible, as we have already mentioned on page 151. A common alternate choice is

$$E' = E + IH.$$

This leads to

$$d\bar{E}' = T\,dS + H\,d\bar{I} + \mu\,dB$$

$$d(\bar{E}' - TS - \bar{I}H) = -S\,dT - \bar{I}\,dH + \mu\,dB, \qquad \text{etc.}$$

A great deal of exact work has been done on the above system, for both finite and infinite systems. Readers interested in pursuing the subject further should consult the recent review article by Domb, referred to above. Also, it should now be apparent[1] that the Ising (magnetic) problem is identical with the lattice-gas problem, which we have already discussed to some extent, except for notation. For example, the environmental variables H, B, T here are equivalent to μ, B, T for a lattice gas.

In conclusion we consider the "ideal" Ising model: That is, we take the interaction energy $J = 0$. Then

$$Q(B, T, H) = \sum_{2^B} e^{-(2N - B)mH/kT}$$

$$= \sum_{N=0}^{B} \frac{B!\,e^{-(2N - B)mH/kT}}{N!(B - N)!}$$

$$= (e^{mH/kT} + e^{-mH/kT})^B. \tag{11-57}$$

Equations (11-49), (11-54), and (11-56) give

$$\frac{\bar{N}}{B} = \frac{e^{-2mH/kT}}{1 + e^{-2mH/kT}} \tag{11-58}$$

$$\mu = -kT \ln(e^{mH/kT} + e^{-mH/kT})$$

$$= -mH + kT \ln\left(1 - \frac{\bar{N}}{B}\right) = \hat{\mu} \tag{11-59}$$

$$\mathscr{E} = 0 \tag{11-60}$$

$$\frac{S}{k} = B \ln B - (B - \bar{N}) \ln(B - \bar{N}) - \bar{N} \ln \bar{N}. \tag{11-61}$$

These results are equivalent to those on page 142 of Part I for an

[1] See also S.M., Chapter 7.

ideal lattice gas. The correspondence in notation is:

Ideal Ising model	Ideal lattice gas
$\mu + mH$	$-p$
$\hat{\mu} + mH$	$-\hat{p}$
$-2mH$	μ

B, $\bar{N}$, S, and T are the same in the two cases.

CHAPTER 12

SPHERICAL DROPS AND
BUBBLES

This chapter is concerned with the properties of a spherical, isotropic nucleus of a stable phase (α) forming within a macroscopic metastable phase (β). For definiteness, we shall use language appropriate to a liquid drop forming in a vapor. But the discussion could just as well be applied to bubbles in a liquid, or to the nucleation of melting or freezing. On the other hand, Section 10-6 has to do with the formation of aggregates within a stable equilibrium phase.

Our main object here is to show the relation between Gibbs' treatment of spherical surfaces and the "small system" approach which is being developed in this book. The two methods are equivalent but different when applied to the present problem. Of course small system thermodynamics is much more general in that it is not restricted to surface problems (see the other chapters in this book).

The small system method uses thermodynamic functions which pertain to the entire drop or small system. The Gibbs method uses excess functions (similar to those introduced on pages 38, 78, and 136 of Part I) which are defined by comparing small system functions with bulk functions. It is necessary to introduce the concept of a dividing surface in the Gibbs method but not in the small system method.

12-1. SMALL SYSTEM THERMODYNAMIC FUNCTIONS

Consider a spherical drop in a spherical container of volume V (Fig. 12-1). The center of mass of the drop is imagined restrained to the origin ($r = 0$). The drop is in contact with a metastable vapor (β) characterized by $T, \mu_1, \ldots, \mu_c$. These variables completely determine the nature of the drop. The entire system (drop plus surrounding vapor) is an open one. There is a continuous transition, at the interface, from drop to vapor. There is no restriction on the size of the drop; it may be so small that properties of bulk liquid (at $T, \mu_1, \ldots, \mu_c$) do not obtain even at $r = 0$. Figure 12-1 illustrates this case. The interior phase (drop) is denoted by α. The bulk liquid is indicated by α^0. Ordinarily, though, the center of the drop has

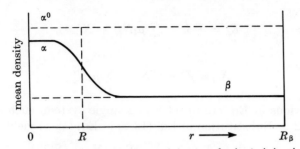

FIGURE 12-1. Radial dependence of density of spherical droplet. Bulk properties do not obtain at center ($r = 0$).

bulk properties so that α and α^0 coincide, as in Fig. 12-2. The volume V is taken as macroscopic and large enough that properties of bulk metastable vapor (at T, μ_1, ..., μ_c) are reached at least at the periphery of V; otherwise V is arbitrary. The pressure at the periphery is p_β (determined by T, μ_1, ..., μ_c).

For an ensemble of $\mathcal{N}$ of these open systems [compare Eq. (1-4)], we have

$$dE_t = T\,dS_t - p_\beta \mathcal{N}\,dV + \sum_{i=1}^{c} \mu_i\,dN_{ti} + X'\,d\mathcal{N}, \qquad (12\text{-}1)$$

where $X' = (\partial E_t / \partial \mathcal{N})_{S_t, V, N_{ti}}$. Use of a macroscopic ensemble ($\mathcal{N} \to \infty$) allows us to consider very small drops with large relative fluctuations in properties. Integration of Eq. (12-1) at constant T,

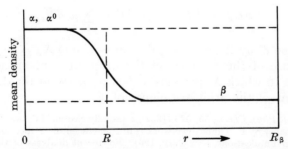

FIGURE 12-2. Radial dependence of density of spherical droplet. Bulk properties obtain at center ($r = 0$).

μ_i, V gives

$$E_t = TS_t + \sum_i \mu_i N_{ti} + X' \mathcal{N},$$

or

$$X' = \bar{E}' - TS' - \sum_i \mu_i \bar{N}'_i. \tag{12-2}$$

The functions in Eq. (12-2) refer to a single system, such as in Fig. 12-1 or 12-2. Substitution of Eq. (12-2) in Eq. (12-1) yields

$$d\bar{E}' = T\,dS' - p_\beta\,dV + \sum_i \mu_i\,d\bar{N}'_i. \tag{12-3}$$

We have given a treatment of the present problem from the Gibbs point of view elsewhere.[1] Equation (12-3) is the same as Eq. (P40).

Now consider, for reference, $\mathcal{N}$ systems containing the same vapor at T, μ_i but with no drop in the center. Actually, since such a system is macroscopic and homogeneous, it would suffice to treat only one system. Then, for the ensemble of reference systems, in obvious notation.

$$dE_t^\beta = T\,dS_t^\beta - p_\beta \mathcal{N}\,dV + \sum_i \mu_i\,dN_{ti}^\beta + X_\beta\,d\mathcal{N} \tag{12-4}$$

$$E_t^\beta = TS_t^\beta + \sum_i \mu_i N_{ti}^\beta + X_\beta \mathcal{N}$$

$$X_\beta = \bar{E}_\beta - TS_\beta - \sum_i \mu_i \bar{N}_{i\beta}. \tag{12-5}$$

These last functions refer to a single system (volume V) completely filled with vapor (β), that is, with no drop in the center. Therefore, from ordinary thermodynamics, $X_\beta = -p_\beta V$. Substitution of Eq. (12-5) in Eq. (12-4) gives the macroscopic expression

$$d\bar{E}_\beta = T\,dS_\beta - p_\beta\,dV + \sum_i \mu_i\,d\bar{N}_{i\beta}. \tag{12-6}$$

We define $\mathscr{E}$ by $X' = \mathscr{E} - p_\beta V$. Since X' and $X_\beta = -p_\beta V$ differ only because of the presence of the drop, or nonhomogeneity, in the system to which X' pertains, $\mathscr{E}$ is a property of the drop and is independent of the arbitrary choice of V.

---

[1] T. L. Hill, *J. Phys. Chem.*, **56**, 526 (1952), especially Section IV; we denote equations in this paper by P. Gibbs' own work is in "The Scientific Papers of J. Willard Gibbs," Dover Publications, New York, 1961. For recent analyses of this problem, with references, see the chapters by S. Ono and S. Kondo and by F. P. Buff in "Handbuch der Physik," S. Flügge (ed.), Springer-Verlag, Berlin, 1960, Vol. 10.

We subtract Eq. (12-5) from Eq. (12-2) and find

$$\mathscr{E} = \bar{E} - TS - \sum_i \mu_i \bar{N}_i, \qquad (12\text{-}7)$$

where $\bar{E} = \bar{E}' - \bar{E}_\beta$, etc. Similarly, from Eqs. (12-3) and (12-6),

$$d\bar{E} = T\,dS + \sum_i \mu_i\,d\bar{N}_i. \qquad (12\text{-}8)$$

All the functions appearing in the last two equations are characteristic of the drop (with the vapor subtracted out) and are independent of the arbitrary choice of V. They are determined (experimentally or from molecular theory) by the variables T, μ_i. Also, they do *not* depend on the choice of a Gibbs "dividing surface." If T, μ_i are chosen so as to make the drop become vanishingly small, then $\mathscr{E}$, $\bar{E}$, S, and $\bar{N}_i$ approach zero.

The drop, with properties $\mathscr{E}$, $\bar{E}$, S, etc., may be regarded as a completely open, small system with independent environmental variables T, μ_i, as in Chapter 10. The pressure p_β is not independent; in the notation of Section 10-2 we would denote it by $p^{(0)}(T, \mu_i)$ for the macroscopic metastable vapor.

In the case of a bubble, the $\bar{N}_i$ would of course be negative.

The equation

$$d\mathscr{E} = -S\,dT - \sum_i \bar{N}_i\,d\mu_i, \qquad (12\text{-}9)$$

which follows from Eqs. (12-7) and (12-8), has the environmental variables as independent variables. It is therefore the fundamental differential relation. From it we deduce

$$-S = \left(\frac{\partial \mathscr{E}}{\partial T}\right)_{\mu_i}, \qquad -\bar{N}_i = \left(\frac{\partial \mathscr{E}}{\partial \mu_i}\right)_{T,\,\mu_j} \qquad (12\text{-}10)$$

$$\left(\frac{\partial \bar{N}_k}{\partial T}\right)_{\mu_i} = \left(\frac{\partial S}{\partial \mu_k}\right)_{T,\,\mu_j}. \qquad (12\text{-}11)$$

Other relations of interest are

$$dA = d(\bar{E} - TS) = -S\,dT + \sum_i \mu_i\,d\bar{N}_i \qquad (12\text{-}12)$$

$$d(\mathscr{E} + TS) = T\,dS - \sum_i \bar{N}_i\,d\mu_i. \qquad (12\text{-}13)$$

These lead to equations analogous to (12-10) and (12-11).

The connection with statistical mechanics is

$$- dX' = d(kT \ln \Xi') = S' \, dT + p_\beta \, dV + \sum_i \bar{N}'_i \, d\mu_i \qquad (12\text{-}14)$$

$$- dX_\beta = d(p_\beta V) = d(kT \ln \Xi_\beta) = S_\beta \, dT + p_\beta \, dV + \sum_i \bar{N}_{i\beta} \, d\mu_i \qquad (12\text{-}15)$$

$$- d\mathscr{E} = d\left(kT \ln \frac{\Xi'}{\Xi_\beta}\right) = S \, dT + \sum_i \bar{N}_i \, d\mu_i, \qquad (12\text{-}16)$$

where Ξ' and Ξ_β are grand partition functions for the volume V, with and without a central drop, respectively.

12-2. RELATION TO THE GIBBS METHOD

The functions $\mathscr{E}, S, \bar{E}$, etc., above, pertain to the drop (small system). In earlier chapters we found it useful to introduce excess functions which exhibit the difference between the small system functions and corresponding bulk or macroscopic functions. When we do this here, in a natural way, we find that our excess functions (for the present problem) are exactly the Gibbs surface excess functions.

Let us consider the entropy as an example of an extensive property. Let s_β be the entropy per unit volume of the metastable vapor β $(s_\beta = S_\beta/V)$. Similarly, let s_α^0 be the entropy per unit volume of the bulk liquid. Then $s_\alpha^0 - s_\beta$ is the "bulk" entropy per volume which should be compared with S (since S_β has been subtracted from S' to give S). For a multicomponent system, we have to introduce a Gibbs dividing surface in order to complete the definition of the excess entropy $S^{(x)}$. The specification of the dividing-surface condition is left arbitrary for the moment, but let us suppose that the surface is at $r = R$ (Fig. 12-1). Then we write

$$V_\alpha = \tfrac{4}{3}\pi R^3, \qquad V_\beta = \tfrac{4}{3}\pi(R_\beta^3 - R^3), \qquad V = \tfrac{4}{3}\pi R_\beta^3 = V_\alpha + V_\beta.$$

Since V_α is the "volume of the drop," using the dividing surface $r = R$, we define $S^{(x)}$ by

$$S = V_\alpha(s_\alpha^0 - s_\beta) + S^{(x)}. \qquad (12\text{-}17)$$

This is the analogue of Eq. (6-19). Although S, s_α^0, and s_β do not depend on the location chosen for the dividing surface, V_α and $S^{(x)}$ do depend on this choice.

Now we have

$$S = S' - S_\beta = S' - (V_\alpha + V_\beta)s_\beta$$

and hence, from Eq. (12-17),

$$S^{(x)} = [S' - (V_\alpha + V_\beta)s_\beta] - V_\alpha(s_\alpha^0 - s_\beta)$$
$$= S' - V_\alpha s_\alpha^0 - V_\beta s_\beta. \qquad (12\text{-}18)$$

But this is just the Gibbs definition of a surface excess. Hence we use the notation $S^{(x)}$, $\bar{N}_i^{(x)}$, etc., for Gibbs surface excesses below.

The surface tension γ, for an arbitrary dividing-surface condition, is defined by [see Eq. (P42)]

$$\gamma\mathscr{A} = p_\alpha^0 V_\alpha + p_\beta V_\beta - \sum_i \mu_i \bar{N}_i' + \bar{E}' - TS', \qquad (12\text{-}19)$$

where the surface area $\mathscr{A} = 4\pi R^2$. The first two terms on the right depend on the location of the dividing surface, but the rest of the right-hand terms do not. If we use Eq. (12-5) (recalling that $X_\beta = -p_\beta V$) to eliminate $p_\beta V_\beta$ above, and then introduce Eq. (12-7), we find

$$\gamma\mathscr{A} = V_\alpha(p_\alpha^0 - p_\beta) + \mathscr{E}, \qquad (12\text{-}20)$$

where the first two terms depend on the dividing surface, but the last one does not.

If now we adopt the so-called surface of tension (s.o.t.) as a specific choice of dividing-surface condition [see Eq. (P45)], we have

$$\frac{2\gamma}{R} = p_\alpha^0 - p_\beta \qquad \text{(s.o.t.)} \qquad (12\text{-}21)$$

and hence

$$\mathscr{E} = \tfrac{1}{3}\gamma\mathscr{A} \qquad \text{(s.o.t.)}. \qquad (12\text{-}22)$$

Gibbs[1] introduced a quantity W, which, as he showed, is the work required to form a drop in the vapor. The definition of W [Gibbs' Eq. (552)] is the same as our definition of $\mathscr{E}$ in Eq. (12-7), although Gibbs does not seem to have derived a relation equivalent to our Eq. (12-9). Equation (12-22) above is the same as Gibbs' Eq. (560). The work property of $\mathscr{E}$ is obvious from

$$\mathscr{E} = X' - X_\beta = \left(\frac{\partial E_t}{\partial \mathscr{N}}\right)_{S_t, V, N_{ti}} - \left(\frac{\partial E_t^\beta}{\partial \mathscr{N}}\right)_{S_t^\beta, V, N_{ti}^\beta}. \qquad (12\text{-}23)$$

[1] Loc. cit., pp. 254–258.

The discussion of Eq. (10-107a) should be noted in this connection.

For the surface of tension [Eq. (P26)],

$$\mathscr{A} \, d\gamma = - \, S^{(x)} \, dT - \sum_i \bar{N}_i^{(x)} \, d\mu_i \qquad \text{(s.o.t.).} \qquad (12\text{-}24)$$

Equation (12-9) is the basic differential relation for the small system functions. Equation (12-24) is the corresponding relation for the excess functions. In Eq. (12-9), the first term is of order $\bar{N}^{2/3} kT$, whereas the other two terms are of order $\bar{N} kT$. All terms in Eq. (12-24) are of order $\bar{N}^{2/3} kT$.

It is probably worthwhile to verify the self-consistency of Eqs. (12-9) and (12-24). One way to do this is as follows. From Eq. (12-20),

$$\gamma \, d\mathscr{A} + \mathscr{A} \, d\gamma = V_\alpha (dp_\alpha^0 - dp_\beta) + (p_\alpha^0 - p_\beta) \, dV_\alpha + d\mathscr{E},$$

or

$$\mathscr{A} d\gamma = V_\alpha (dp_\alpha^0 - dp_\beta) + d\mathscr{E} \qquad \text{(s.o.t.).} \qquad (12\text{-}25)$$

We now substitute Eq. (12-9) and the macroscopic relationships

$$dp_\alpha^0 = s_\alpha^0 \, dT + \sum_i n_{\alpha i}^0 \, d\mu_i$$

$$dp_\beta = s_\beta \, dT + \sum_i n_{\beta i} \, d\mu_i$$

into Eq. (12-25) to obtain the desired result:

$$\mathscr{A} \, d\gamma = (V_\alpha s_\alpha^0 - V_\alpha s_\beta - S) \, dT + \sum_i (V_\alpha n_{\alpha i}^0 - V_\alpha n_{\beta i} - \bar{N}_i) \, d\mu_i$$

$$\text{(s.o.t.)}$$

$$= - \, S^{(x)} \, dT - \sum_i \bar{N}_i^{(x)} \, d\mu_i \qquad \text{(s.o.t.).} \qquad (12\text{-}26)$$

Alternatively, if we start with Eq. (12-9) and substitute equations of the type (12-17) for S and $\bar{N}_i$, we find

$$d\mathscr{E} = - \, S^{(x)} \, dT - \sum_i \bar{N}_i^{(x)} \, d\mu_i - V_\alpha (dp_\alpha^0 - dp_\beta) \qquad (12\text{-}27)$$

for an arbitrary dividing-surface condition. The difference $dp_\alpha^0 - dp_\beta$ is independent of dividing surface, so the term in V_α never drops out. Equations (12-25) and (12-27) give Eq. (12-26).

Very interesting approximate numerical calculations for one-component spherical drops of various sizes have been made by Plesner[1], using the Gibbs approach.

[1] I. Plesner, *J. Chem. Phys.*, in press.

To recapitulate: In Section 12-1 it is shown that small system functions can be defined for spherical drops in such a way that equations of the same type [(12-7) and (12-9)] as in Chapter 10 result. The drops can be arbitrarily small. This formulation has the advantage of avoiding the dividing-surface concept. But, if we introduce a dividing surface, it is easy to establish the connection with Gibbs' treatment of spherical surfaces.

CHAPTER 13

POLYDISPERSE SYSTEMS

More often than not, an experimental polymeric or colloidal system is polydisperse rather than monodisperse. Up to this point in the book, only monodisperse samples have been considered. But we can still define thermodynamic functions for a small system, in the polydisperse case, by averaging over the degree of polymerization. The monodisperse situation then becomes a limiting case.

We are referring here, of course, to a polydisperse mixture of *closed* small systems. An ensemble of open small systems has polydispersity of a different kind (dynamic aggregation equilibrium). This type of system was analyzed in Chapter 10.

In Section 13-1 we discuss a polydisperse N, p, T system. Examples are polymer molecules in solution, colloidal particles in solution or gas, and a colloidal powder sample. We start with small system equations for the monodisperse case and simply introduce averaging. The same analysis applies to all the examples just referred to (except that p drops out as a variable in some cases). But separate discussions are required if one wants to examine explicit connections with macroscopic thermodynamics. We illustrate such connections, for a solution, in Section 13-2.

Another important case is binding on a polydisperse macromolecule in solution. This is an N_1, μ_2, p, T system which is polydisperse in N_1. A synthesis of Sections 7-2 and 13-2 is required in order to treat such a system. This task is left to the interested reader.

13-1. SMALL SYSTEM EQUATIONS

The basic equations (see Chapter 2) for a monodisperse N, p, T small system with a fixed value of N are

and
$$F_N = N\hat{\mu}_N = \bar{E}_N - TS_N + p\bar{V}_N \tag{13-1}$$
$$dF_N = -S_N\,dT + \bar{V}_N\,dp \qquad (N \text{ constant}). \tag{13-2}$$

The subscript N is introduced for clarity below. These functions refer to the average *intrinsic* properties of a small system [see, for example, Eq. (2-108)]. If we have a polydisperse sample, we are still interested in average intrinsic properties, but now the averaging must be extended over N as well. If P_N is the fraction of small systems in the ensemble with size N, we choose not to include an entropy $-k\Sigma_N P_N \ln P_N$ in the definition of S (and F) for a small system in the polydisperse case, on grounds that this entropy is not an "intrinsic" property. Note that this choice differs from that made in Eqs. (10-240) and (10-247) where $-k\Sigma_N P_N \ln P_N$ was included for open systems. But this is as it should be: Any one *open* small system can take on the various values of N; its entropy is higher because there is an additional set of states (values of N) available to the system. In a polydisperse sample, on the other hand, each small system has a permanent value of N.

We therefore define the following properties per small system:

$$F = \sum_N P_N F_N, \qquad S = \sum_N P_N S_N,$$
$$\bar{E} = \sum_N P_N \bar{E}_N, \qquad \bar{V} = \sum_N P_N \bar{V}_N. \tag{13-3}$$

If we multiply Eq. (13-1) by P_N and sum, we have

$$F = \bar{E} - TS + p\bar{V}. \tag{13-4}$$

We regard P_N as a function of a set of parameters $\alpha_1, \alpha_2, \ldots$[1] For example, if the distribution is Gaussian and assumed continuous, there would be two parameters, the mean value $\bar{N}$ and the standard deviation σ:

$$P_N(\bar{N}, \sigma) = \frac{\exp[-(N-\bar{N})^2/2\sigma^2]}{(2\pi)^{1/2}\sigma}. \tag{13-5}$$

In practical cases the number of parameters might range, say, from one to four. For convenience, we shall always make the assignment $\alpha_1 = \bar{N}$. The complete list of independent parameters determining the form of P_N is then $\bar{N}, \alpha_2, \alpha_3, \ldots$.

Now from $F = \Sigma_N P_N F_N$, we deduce

$$dF = \sum_N P_N \, dF_N + \sum_N F_N \, dP_N$$
$$= \sum_N P_N(-S_N \, dT + \bar{V}_N \, dp)$$
$$\quad + \sum_N F_N\left(\frac{\partial P_N}{\partial \bar{N}} \, d\bar{N} + \frac{\partial P_N}{\partial \alpha_2} \, d\alpha_2 + \cdots\right)$$
$$= -S \, dT + \bar{V} \, dp + \mu \, d\bar{N} + \Phi_2 \, d\alpha_2 + \cdots, \tag{13-6}$$

---

[1] See T. L. Hill, *J. Chem. Phys.*, **34**, 1974 (1961). This paper anticipates the present chapter in some respects and goes beyond it.

where we have introduced

$$\mu \equiv \sum_N F_N\left(\frac{\partial P_N}{\partial \bar{N}}\right)_{\alpha_2,\,\dots}, \qquad \Phi_2 \equiv \sum_N F_N\left(\frac{\partial P_N}{\partial \alpha_2}\right)_{\bar{N},\,\alpha_3,\,\dots}, \quad \dots. \tag{13-7}$$

Equations (13-4) and (13-6) are the basic equations for a polydisperse small system. Compared to Eq. (2-3) for a monodisperse N, p, T system, Eq. (13-6) requires extra terms in α_2, α_3, ... , because of the dispersion of the distribution about the mean value $\bar{N}$. The variables F, S, $\bar{V}$, $\bar{E}$, μ, etc., are functions of p, T, $\bar{N}$, α_2 .... One is interested not only in the dependence of various properties on the average size $\bar{N}$ of the small systems but also in the dependence on the shape of the distribution, determined by α_2, α_3, ...

We can define $\hat{\mu}$ and $\mathscr{E}$ by

$$\bar{N}\hat{\mu} \equiv F \qquad \text{and} \qquad \mathscr{E} \equiv \bar{N}(\hat{\mu} - \mu). \tag{13-8}$$

Then

$$\hat{\mu} = \frac{F}{\bar{N}} = \frac{1}{\bar{N}}\sum_N P_N N \hat{\mu}_N \tag{13-9}$$

and

$$d\mathscr{E} = -S\,dT + \bar{V}\,dp - \bar{N}\,d\mu + \Phi_2\,d\alpha_2 + \cdots. \tag{13-10}$$

By differentiating $\bar{N} = \Sigma_N P_N N$, we obtain the following properties which we shall need below:

$$1 = \sum_N N\frac{\partial P_N}{\partial \bar{N}}, \qquad 0 = \sum_N N\frac{\partial P_N}{\partial \alpha_2}, \qquad \cdots. \tag{13-11}$$

The "macroscopic limit" here means that, even though there is a distribution in small system sizes, all small systems become very large. An example would be $\bar{N} \to \infty$ with α_2, α_3, ... held constant. In this case the distribution function P_N shifts toward large values of N without changing its shape. For systems of size N in the macroscopic limit, $F_N = N\mu^{(0)}(p, T)$ [see Eq. (2-55)]. Then

$$F = \sum_N P_N N \mu^{(0)} = \bar{N}\mu^{(0)},$$

with a similar result for S, $\bar{V}$, etc. Also,

$$\mu = \sum_N N\mu^{(0)}\frac{\partial P_N}{\partial \bar{N}} = \mu^{(0)}, \qquad \Phi_2 = \sum_N N\mu^{(0)}\frac{\partial P_N}{\partial \alpha_2} = 0, \qquad \cdots.$$

Thus we have the usual macroscopic relations (despite the distribution):

$$F = \bar{E} - TS + p\bar{V}$$
$$\mu^{(0)} = \mathrm{E}^{(0)} - T\mathrm{S}^{(0)} + p\mathrm{v}^{(0)} \qquad (13\text{-}12)$$
$$dF = -S\,dT + \bar{V}\,dp + \mu^{(0)}\,d\bar{N}.$$

Since

$$\hat{\mu} = F/\bar{N} = \mu^{(0)}, \quad \mathscr{E} = 0.$$

The equations in Section 2-1 are applicable here if the shape of the distribution (α_2, α_3, $\cdots$) is held constant [see Eq. 13-6)]. In addition, there will be various new relations involving changes in α_2, α_3, ... Examples are

$$\Phi_2 = \left(\frac{\partial F}{\partial \alpha_2}\right)_{T,\,p,\,\bar{N},\,\alpha_3,\,\ldots} = \left(\frac{\partial \mathscr{E}}{\partial \alpha_2}\right)_{T,\,p,\,\mu,\,\alpha_3,\,\ldots} \qquad (13\text{-}13)$$

$$\left(\frac{\partial S}{\partial \alpha_2}\right)_{T,\,p,\,\bar{N},\,\alpha_3,\,\ldots} = -\left(\frac{\partial \Phi_2}{\partial T}\right)_{p,\,\bar{N},\,\alpha_2,\,\ldots}$$
$$\left(\frac{\partial \Phi_2}{\partial \alpha_3}\right)_{T,\,p,\,\bar{N},\,\alpha_j} = \left(\frac{\partial \Phi_3}{\partial \alpha_2}\right)_{T,\,p,\,\bar{N},\,\alpha_j} \qquad (13\text{-}14)$$

$$\left(\frac{\partial \mu}{\partial \alpha_2}\right)_{T,\,p,\,\bar{N},\,\alpha_3,\,\ldots} = \left(\frac{\partial \Phi_2}{\partial \bar{N}}\right)_{T,\,p,\,\alpha_2,\,\ldots}. \qquad (13\text{-}15)$$

Example. Polydisperse Colloidal Particles. Suppose we have a sample of colloidal particles with Gaussian polydispersity. We assume that (see pages 41 and 129 to 132 of Part I)

$$F_N = Nf(p, T) + a(p, T)N^{2/3} \qquad (13\text{-}16)$$

and use Eq. (13-5) for P_N. If σ is small, we are interested only in values of N near $N = \bar{N}$. Hence we expand F_N about $N = \bar{N}$:

$$F_N = F_{\bar{N}} + \left(\frac{\partial F_N}{\partial N}\right)_{N=\bar{N}}(N - \bar{N}) + \frac{1}{2!}\left(\frac{\partial^2 F_N}{\partial N^2}\right)_{N=\bar{N}}(N - \bar{N})^2 + \cdots. \qquad (13\text{-}17)$$

Then we find, from Eqs. (13-3a), (13-5), and (13-17),

$$F(\bar{N}, p, T, \sigma) = \bar{N}f(p, T)$$
$$+ a(p, T)\bar{N}^{2/3}\left[1 - \frac{1}{9}\left(\frac{\sigma}{\bar{N}}\right)^2 - \frac{7}{81}\left(\frac{\sigma}{\bar{N}}\right)^4 - \cdots\right]. \qquad (13\text{-}18)$$

When $\sigma/\bar{N} \to 0$ (monodisperse system), this reduces to the applicable terms in Eq. (2-68).

We use the notation $\alpha_2 = \sigma$ and $\Phi_2 = \Phi$ in Eq. (13-6). Equations (13-6) and (13-18) then give

$$- S = \bar{N}\frac{\partial f}{\partial T} + \frac{\partial a}{\partial T}\bar{N}^{2/3}\left[1 - \frac{1}{9}\left(\frac{\sigma}{\bar{N}}\right)^2 - \frac{7}{81}\left(\frac{\sigma}{\bar{N}}\right)^4 - \cdots\right] \qquad (13\text{-}19)$$

$$\bar{V} = \bar{N}\frac{\partial f}{\partial p} + \frac{\partial a}{\partial p}\bar{N}^{2/3}\left[1 - \frac{1}{9}\left(\frac{\sigma}{\bar{N}}\right)^2 - \frac{7}{81}\left(\frac{\sigma}{\bar{N}}\right)^4 - \cdots\right] \qquad (13\text{-}20)$$

$$\mu = f + \frac{2}{3}a\bar{N}^{-1/3}\left[1 + \frac{2}{9}\left(\frac{\sigma}{\bar{N}}\right)^2 + \frac{35}{81}\left(\frac{\sigma}{\bar{N}}\right)^4 + \cdots\right] \qquad (13\text{-}21)$$

$$\Phi = -\frac{2}{9}a\bar{N}^{-1/3}\left[\left(\frac{\sigma}{\bar{N}}\right) + \frac{14}{9}\left(\frac{\sigma}{\bar{N}}\right)^3 + \cdots\right] \qquad (13\text{-}22)$$

$$\mathscr{E} = \frac{1}{3}a\bar{N}^{2/3}\left[1 - \frac{7}{9}\left(\frac{\sigma}{\bar{N}}\right)^2 - \frac{91}{81}\left(\frac{\sigma}{\bar{N}}\right)^4 - \cdots\right]. \qquad (13\text{-}23)$$

The self-consistency of these equations can be checked by Maxwell relations such as Eqs. (13-14a) and (13-15).

13-2. SMALL SYSTEMS IN SOLUTION

In this section we show, as an illustration, the explicit connections between the small system functions of the previous section and the usual functions of macroscopic solution thermodynamics, in the case that the small systems are in a solution. This is an extension of Section 2-3, which should be referred to.

We have, for the macroscopic solution,

$$dF_T = -S_T\,dT + V_T\,dp + \sum_{i=1}^{c} \mu_i^s\,dN_i^s + \sum_N \mu_N^{\square}\,d\mathscr{N}_N, \quad (13\text{-}24)$$

where $\mathscr{N}_N$ is the number of small systems of size N and $\mu_N^{\square}$ is the chemical potential of these small systems. The solution is infinitely dilute in all components N but not (usually) in the solvent components i. The integrated form of Eq. (13-24) is

$$F_T = \sum_i \mu_i^s N_i^s + \sum_N \mu_N^{\square}\mathscr{N}_N. \qquad (13\text{-}25)$$

The chemical potential of component N has the properties

$$\mu_N^\square = \tilde{\mathrm{E}}_N^\square - T\tilde{\mathrm{s}}_N^\square + p\tilde{\mathrm{v}}_N^\square \tag{13-26}$$

$$d\mu_N^\square = -\tilde{\mathrm{s}}_N^\square\, dT + \tilde{\mathrm{v}}_N^\square\, dp + \frac{kT}{x_N'}\, dx_N' \quad (sc), \tag{13-27}$$

where $x_N' = \mathcal{N}_N/(N_1^s + \cdots + N_c^s)$. These expressions are the same as if N were the only small system component because all small system components are infinitely dilute in the solution. If we now define $\hat{\mu}_N$, S_N, etc., by

$$\mu_N^\square = N\hat{\mu}_N(p, T, sc) + kT \ln x_N' \tag{13-28}$$

$$\tilde{\mathrm{s}}_N^\square = S_N(p, T, sc) - k \ln x_N' \tag{13-29}$$

$$\tilde{\mathrm{E}}_N^\square = \bar{E}_N, \qquad \tilde{\mathrm{v}}_N^\square = \bar{V}_N, \tag{13-30}$$

just as in Section 2-3, and substitute these in Eqs. (13-26) and (13-27), we obtain Eqs. (13-1) and (13-2), the starting points of the preceding section.

This completes the necessary part of the argument, but it is instructive to consider an alternative point of view as well. Instead of using the $\mathcal{N}_N$ as independent variables in Eq. (13-24), we introduce[1] the set of variables $\mathcal{N}$, $\bar{N}$, α_2, α_3, $\cdots$. Then

$$dF_T = -S_T\, dT + V_T\, dp + \sum_i \mu_i^s\, dN_i^s + \mu^\square\, d\mathcal{N}$$

$$+ \mu'\mathcal{N}\, d\bar{N} + \Phi_2'\mathcal{N}\, d\alpha_2 + \cdots . \tag{13-31}$$

This equation defines $\mu^\square$, μ', Φ_2', $\cdots$. The mixture of components N is treated here as a pseudo single component just as in Eq. (13-3)ff. Integration of Eq. (13-31) yields

$$F_T = \sum_i \mu_i^s N_i^s + \mu^\square \mathcal{N}. \tag{13-32}$$

Comparison with Eq. (13-25) shows that

$$\mu^\square = \sum_N P_N \mu_N^\square$$

$$= \sum_N P_N(N\hat{\mu}_N + kT \ln P_N + kT \ln x')$$

$$= \bar{N}\hat{\mu} + kT \sum_N P_N \ln P_N + kT \ln x', \tag{13-33}$$

[1] See T. L. Hill, loc. cit.

where $x' = \mathcal{N}/(N_1^s + \cdots + N_c^s)$. If we regard Eq. (13-33) as the definition of $\hat{\mu}$ in terms of $\mu^\square$, we note that the two entropy terms $- k \, \Sigma_N P_N \ln P_N$ and $- k \ln x'$, which are both present in $\mu^\square$, are subtracted out of this quantity in order to define an intrinsic $\hat{\mu}$.

By differentiating

$$F_T = E_T - TS_T + pV_T,$$

we obtain

$$\mu^\square = \left(\frac{\partial F_T}{\partial \mathcal{N}}\right)_{T,\,p,\,N_i^s,\,\bar{N},\,\alpha_2,\,\ldots} = \tilde{E}^\square - T\tilde{S}^\square + p\tilde{V}^\square. \tag{13-34}$$

Since

$$\mu^\square = \sum_N P_N \mu_N^\square = \sum_N P_N \tilde{E}_N^\square - T \sum_N P_N \tilde{S}_N^\square + p \sum_N P_N \tilde{V}_N^\square,$$

we then have

$$\tilde{E}^\square = \sum_N P_N \tilde{E}_N^\square = \sum_N P_N \bar{E}_N = \bar{E} \tag{13-35}$$

$$\tilde{V}^\square = \sum_N P_N \tilde{V}_N^\square = \sum_N P_N \bar{V}_N = \bar{V} \tag{13-36}$$

$$\tilde{S}^\square = \sum_N P_N \tilde{S}_N^\square = \sum_N P_N S_N - k \sum_N P_N \ln(P_N x')$$
$$= S - k \sum_N P_N \ln P_N - k \ln x'. \tag{13-37}$$

This last result is consistent with the comments we made above about Eq. (13-33).

Finally, we have to establish the connections between the coefficients μ, $\Phi_2, \ldots$ in Eq. (13-6) and μ', $\Phi_2', \ldots$ in Eq. (13-31). The argument is essentially the same as that beginning with Eq. (7-70). We find, instead of Eqs. (7-71) and (7-72),

$$\mu_k^s = \mu_k^* + \sum_N P_N \left[(N_1^s + \cdots + N_c^s) \frac{\partial N \hat{\mu}_N}{\partial N_k^s} - kT \right] x' \tag{13-38}$$

and

$$\sum_k N_k^s \sum_N P_N \frac{\partial N \hat{\mu}_N}{\partial N_k^s} = 0, \tag{13-39}$$

respectively, but Eq. (7-73) is unchanged. Then, from Eq. (13-32),

$$\mu' = \left(\frac{\partial \mu^\square}{\partial \bar{N}}\right)_{T,\,p,\,N_i^s,\,\mathcal{N},\,\alpha_2,\,\ldots}$$

$$= \sum_N \frac{\partial P_N}{\partial \bar{N}}(N\bar{\mu}_N + kT \ln x_N') + kT \sum_N \frac{\partial P_N}{\partial \bar{N}}$$

$$= \sum_N \frac{\partial P_N}{\partial \bar{N}}(N\bar{\mu}_N + kT \ln P_N)$$

$$= \sum_N \frac{\partial P_N}{\partial \bar{N}}N\bar{\mu}_N + kT\frac{\partial}{\partial \bar{N}}\sum_N P_N \ln P_N = \mu, \quad (13\text{-}40)$$

since $\Sigma_N P_N \ln P_N$ depends only on the shape (α_2, α_3, ...) of the distribution and not on the value of the mean $\bar{N}$. In the same way we find

$$\Phi_j' = \sum_N \frac{\partial P_N}{\partial \alpha_j}N\bar{\mu}_N + kT\frac{\partial}{\partial \alpha_j}\sum_N P_N \ln P_N$$

$$= \Phi_j + kT\frac{\partial}{\partial \alpha_j}\sum_N P_N \ln P_N \qquad (j = 2, 3, \ldots). \quad (13\text{-}41)$$

CHAPTER 14

HIGHER MOMENTS OF
DISTRIBUTION FUNCTIONS

Macroscopic thermodynamics is concerned with mean values of fluctuating extensive variables (E, N, V, etc.). But a variable that fluctuates has a probability distribution of possible values, and the mean is only one property of the distribution. The complete distribution can be characterized, for example, by the mean and the second and higher central moments. The second central moment is the square of the standard deviation. The neglect of second and higher moments in macroscopic thermodynamics is justified by the fact that relative fluctuations about mean values are extremely small indeed, except in very special circumstances.

On the other hand, small systems have appreciable fluctuations about mean values. In this book we have so far confined ourselves to "mean-value thermodynamics" as in macroscopic thermodynamics. That is, fluctuating extensive variables are represented in the basic small system thermodynamic equations by mean values only. It thus appears that we may be overlooking a "higher-order" thermodynamics of small systems (although not of macroscopic systems): There may be equations connecting higher moments of fluctuating extensive properties of small systems which are higher analogues of the mean-value equations already encountered.

Such equations do exist and we derive some examples in this chapter. However, we do not pursue the subject very far because, at least in one important respect (see below), nothing fundamentally new comes out of the analysis. Also, the equations found are rather cumbersome.

We confine ourselves to one special but important type of small system: The small system has one extensive and two intensive environmental variables (e.g., N, p, T and μ, V, T systems). We use a generalized notation applicable to any such case.

Consider a system with environmental variables g_1, g_2 (small g = intensive), and G_3 (large G = extensive), chosen so that[1]

---

[1] The brackets are inserted for purposes of comparison with other groups of terms below. We use special numbering on some equations in order to associate those equations belonging to the same hierarchy. For example: I, $I^{(1)}$, $I^{(2)}$, ...; II, $II^{(1)}$, $II^{(2)}$, ...; etc.

$$\left[\frac{S}{k} + \hat{g}_3 G_3\right] + g_1\bar{G}_1 + g_2\bar{G}_2 = 0. \qquad (14\text{-}I)$$

For example:

$$g_1 = -\frac{1}{kT}, \qquad g_2 = \frac{\mu}{kT}, \qquad G_3 = V,$$

$$(14\text{-}1)$$

$$G_1 = E, \qquad G_2 = N, \qquad g_3 = -\frac{p}{kT};$$

or

$$g_1 = -\frac{1}{kT}, \qquad g_2 = -\frac{p}{kT}, \qquad G_3 = N,$$

$$(14\text{-}2)$$

$$G_1 = E, \qquad G_2 = V \qquad g_3 = \frac{\mu}{kT};$$

or

$$g_1 = -\frac{p}{kT}, \qquad g_2 = \frac{\mu}{kT}, \qquad G_3 = E,$$

$$(14\text{-}3)$$

$$G_1 = V, \qquad G_2 = N, \qquad g_3 = -\frac{1}{kT}.$$

That is, G_1 and G_2 fluctuate, but G_3 does not. The assignment (14-1) corresponds to Chapter 6, whereas (14-2) corresponds to Chapter 2.

Equation (14-I) is a basic "mean-value" equation [see Eq. (2-2), for example]. Besides Eq. (14-I), other important mean-value equations are

$$d\left(\frac{S}{k}\right) + g_1\, d\bar{G}_1 + g_2\, d\bar{G}_2 + g_3\, dG_3 = 0 \qquad (14\text{-}II)$$

$$d(\hat{g}_3 G_3) + \bar{G}_1\, dg_1 + \bar{G}_2\, dg_2 - g_3\, dG_3 = 0 \qquad (14\text{-}III)$$

$$d[(\hat{g}_3 - g_3)G_3] + \bar{G}_1\, dg_1 + \bar{G}_2\, dg_2 + G_3\, dg_3 = 0. \qquad (14\text{-}IV)$$

These are generalizations, for example, of Eqs. (2-1), (2-3), and (2-4), respectively. Our object, in this chapter, is to derive higher-moment analogues of Eqs. (14-I) to (14-IV).

We have to appeal to statistical mechanics in order to relate probability distribution moments to thermodynamics. Thus, in so far as higher moments are brought in, the argument is no longer purely thermodynamic. The appropriate partition function here is

$$e^{-\hat{g}_3 G_3} = \sum_{G_1, G_2} \Omega(G_1,\ G_2,\ G_3)\ e^{g_1 G_1}\ e^{g_2 G_2} \tag{14-4}$$

and the probability of observing a g_1, g_2, G_3 system with particular values of G_1 and G_2 is

$$\frac{\Omega(G_1,\ G_2,\ G_3)\ e^{g_1 G_1}\ e^{g_2 G_2}}{e^{-\hat{g}_3 G_3}}.$$

Then,[1] for $n+m = 1$ or 2,

$$\left[\frac{\partial^{n+m}\bar{G}_1}{\partial g_1^n\, \partial g_2^m}\right]_{G_3} = \overline{(G_1 - \bar{G}_1)^{n+1}(G_2 - \bar{G}_2)^m}, \tag{14-5}$$

or we can exchange subscripts 1 and 2 in this equation. For $n+m \geqslant 3$, the left-hand side of Eq. (14-5) contains additional terms (lower-order derivatives of the same type). Hence the central moments of the G_1, G_2 distribution are related to derivatives of $\bar{G}_1$ and $\bar{G}_2$ with respect to g_1 and g_2. Therefore, if $\bar{G}_1(g_1, g_2, G_3)$ and $\bar{G}_2(g_1, g_2, G_3)$ are known, all higher central moments follow by differentiation. Thus, in a sense, the mean-value thermodynamic equations tell the whole story after all, and nothing basically new should be expected. But we still look for equations explicitly involving the higher moments [actually, we use the equivalent derivatives from Eq. (14-5)]. There does not appear to be a unique set of such equations, incidentally. We derive the simplest set we have encountered.

If Y is a function of g_1, g_2, and G_3, we define Y' by the operation

$$Y' = g_1\left(\frac{\partial Y}{\partial g_1}\right)_{g_2,\, G_3} + g_2\left(\frac{\partial Y}{\partial g_2}\right)_{g_1,\, G_3}, \tag{14-6}$$

and Y'' by $(Y')'$, etc. We also define

$$Y^{(1)} = g_1\frac{\partial Y}{\partial g_1} + g_2\frac{\partial Y}{\partial g_2} = Y' \tag{14-7}$$

$$Y^{(2)} = g_1^2\frac{\partial^2 Y}{\partial g_1^2} + 2g_1g_2\frac{\partial^2 Y}{\partial g_1\, \partial g_2} + g_2^2\frac{\partial^2 Y}{\partial g_2^2}$$

$$= Y'' - Y', \tag{14-8}$$

[1] R. F. Greene and H. B. Callen, *Phys. Rev.*, **83**, 1231 (1951).

and so forth (using binomial coefficients in the definition of $Y^{(n)}$).
Thus we find

$$Y^{(3)} = Y''' - 3Y'' + 2Y' \tag{14-9}$$

$$Y^{(4)} = Y'''' - 6Y''' + 11Y'' - 6Y', \tag{14-10}$$

and so forth.

We start with Eq. (14-I) and apply to each term the "prime" operation defined in Eq. (14-6). We use the fact that

$$(-\hat{g}_3 G_3)' = g_1 \bar{G}_1 + g_2 \bar{G}_2 = -\left[\frac{S}{k} + \hat{g}_3 G_3\right]$$

and find

$$\left[\frac{S^{(1)}}{k}\right] + g_1 \bar{G}_1^{(1)} + g_2 \bar{G}_2^{(1)} = 0. \tag{14-I$^{(1)}$}$$

By repeating the "prime" operation we also find

$$\left[\frac{S^{(2)} - S^{(1)}}{k}\right] + g_1 \bar{G}_1^{(2)} + g_2 \bar{G}_2^{(2)} = 0 \tag{14-I$^{(2)}$}$$

$$\left[\frac{S^{(3)} - 2S^{(2)} + 2S^{(1)}}{k}\right] + g_1 \bar{G}_1^{(3)} + g_2 \bar{G}_2^{(3)} = 0 \tag{14-I$^{(3)}$}$$

$$\left[\frac{S^{(4)} - 3S^{(3)} + 6S^{(2)} - 6S^{(1)}}{k}\right] + g_1 \bar{G}_1^{(4)} + g_2 \bar{G}_2^{(4)} = 0. \tag{14-I$^{(4)}$}$$

These equations are the higher-moment analogues of Eq. (14-I). The coefficients in the first terms are simply related to binomial coefficients.

From Eq. (14-I$^{(1)}$) we have

$$-\frac{S'}{k} = g_1 \bar{G}_1' + g_2 \bar{G}_2' = g_1 \frac{\partial(-S/k)}{\partial g_1} + g_2 \frac{\partial(-S/k)}{\partial g_2}.$$

Therefore

$$\frac{\partial(-S/k)}{\partial g_1} = \bar{G}_1', \qquad \frac{\partial(-S/k)}{\partial g_2} = \bar{G}_2',$$

and

$$d\left(-\frac{S}{k}\right) = \bar{G}_1' \, dg_1 + \bar{G}_2' \, dg_2 + \frac{\partial(-S/k)}{\partial G_3} \, dG_3.$$

This is similar to Eq. (14-III) above. If we use Eq. (14-I) for S/k, we find

$$\frac{\partial(-S/k)}{\partial G_3} = g_1\frac{\partial \bar{G}_1}{\partial G_3} + g_2\frac{\partial \bar{G}_2}{\partial G_3} + \frac{\partial(\hat{g}_3 G_3)}{\partial G_3}$$

$$= -g_1\frac{\partial g_3}{\partial g_1} - g_2\frac{\partial g_3}{\partial g_2} + g_3 = -g_3' + g_3.$$

Therefore,

$$d\left(\frac{S}{k}\right) + \bar{G}_1^{(1)}\, dg_1 + \bar{G}_2^{(1)}\, dg_2 + (-g_3^{(1)} + g_3)\, dG_3 = 0 \qquad \text{(14-III}^{(1)}\text{)}$$

is the next higher analogue of Eq. (14-III).

Similarly, if we start with Eqs. (14-I$^{(2)}$), (14-I$^{(3)}$), etc., we can derive

$$d\left(\frac{S^{(1)} - 2S}{k}\right) + \bar{G}_1^{(2)}\, dg_1 + \bar{G}_2^{(2)}\, dg_2$$

$$+ (-g_3^{(2)} + 2g_3^{(1)} - 2g_3)\, dG_3 = 0 \qquad \text{(14-III}^{(2)}\text{)}$$

$$d\left(\frac{S^{(2)} - 4S^{(1)} + 6S}{k}\right) + \bar{G}_1^{(3)}\, dg_1 + \bar{G}_2^{(3)}\, dg_2 + (-g_3^{(3)}$$

$$+ 3g_3^{(2)} - 6g_3^{(1)} + 6g_3)\, dG_3 = 0. \qquad \text{(14-III}^{(3)}\text{)}$$

The coefficients in Eq. (14-III$^{(4)}$) are $1, -6, +18, -24$ and $-1, +4,$ $-12, +24, -24$, respectively.

If we differentiate Eq. (14-I$^{(1)}$) and combine it with Eq. (14-III$^{(1)}$), we get

$$d\left(\frac{S^{(1)} - S}{k}\right) + g_1\, d\bar{G}_1^{(1)} + g_2\, d\bar{G}_2^{(1)}$$

$$+ (g_3^{(1)} - g_3)\, dG_3 = 0. \qquad \text{(14-II}^{(1)}\text{)}$$

Similarly, from Eqs. (14-I$^{(2)}$) and (14-III$^{(2)}$), etc.,

$$d\left(\frac{S^{(2)} - 2S^{(1)} + 2S}{k}\right) + g_1\, d\bar{G}_1^{(2)} + g_2\, d\bar{G}_2^{(2)}$$

$$+ (g_3^{(2)} - 2g_3^{(1)} + 2g_3)\, dG_3 = 0 \qquad \text{(14-II}^{(2)}\text{)}$$

$$d\left(\frac{S^{(3)} - 3S^{(2)} + 6S^{(1)} - 6S}{k}\right) + g_1\, d\bar{G}_1^{(3)} + g_2\, d\bar{G}_2^{(3)}$$

$$+ (g_3^{(3)} - 3g_3^{(2)} + 6g_3^{(1)} - 6g_3)\, dG_3 = 0. \qquad \text{(14-II}^{(3)}\text{)}$$

The coefficients in Eq. (14-II$^{(4)}$) are 1, -4, $+12$, -24, $+24$. These are the higher-moment analogues of Eq. (14-II).

Finally, from Eqs. (14-III$^{(1)}$), (14-III$^{(2)}$), etc., we have

$$d\left[\left(-g_3^{(1)} + g_3 + \frac{S}{G_3 k}\right)G_3\right] + \bar{G}_1^{(1)}\, dg_1 + \bar{G}_2^{(1)}\, dg_2$$

$$+ G_3\, d(g_3^{(1)} - g_3) = 0 \qquad (14\text{-IV}^{(1)})$$

$$d\left[\left(-g_3^{(2)} + 2g_3^{(2)} - 2g_3 + \frac{S^{(1)} - 2S}{G_3 k}\right)G_3\right] + \bar{G}_1^{(2)}\, dg_1$$

$$+ \bar{G}_2^{(2)}\, dg_2 + G_3\, d(g_3^{(2)} - 2g_3^{(1)} + 2g_3) = 0, \qquad (14\text{-IV}^{(2)})$$

and so forth. These are the analogues of Eq. (14-IV).

On comparing the functions playing equivalent roles in the above hierarchies of equations, we note the sequences

$$\bar{G}_1, \qquad \bar{G}_1^{(1)}, \qquad \bar{G}_1^{(2)}, \qquad \cdots$$

$$\bar{G}_2, \qquad \bar{G}_2^{(1)}, \qquad \bar{G}_2^{(2)}, \qquad \cdots$$

$$\hat{g}_3 G_3, \qquad \frac{S}{k}, \qquad \frac{S^{(1)} - 2S}{k}, \qquad \frac{S^{(2)} - 4S^{(1)} + 6S}{k}, \qquad \cdots$$

$$g_3, \qquad g_3^{(1)} - g_3, \qquad g_3^{(2)} - 2g_3^{(1)} + 2g_3, \qquad \cdots,$$

from which the other sequences can be constructed.

There is some simplification in these equations in the case of macroscopic systems. In Eqs. (14-I), (14-III), and (14-IV), $\hat{g}_3$ is replaced by g_3. In the sequences of equations beginning with (14-III$^{(1)}$), (14-II$^{(1)}$), and (14-IV$^{(1)}$), we replace

$$g_3^{(1)} - g_3, \qquad g_3^{(2)} - 2g_3^{(1)} + 2g_3, \qquad g_3^{(3)} - 3g_3^{(2)} + 6g_3^{(1)} - 6g_3, \qquad \cdots$$

by

$$\frac{S}{G_3 k}, \qquad \frac{S^{(1)} - 2S}{G_3 k}, \qquad \frac{S^{(2)} - 4S^{(1)} + 6S}{G_3 k}, \qquad \cdots,$$

as is apparent from the sequence (14-III$^{(1)}$), (14-III$^{(2)}$), $\ldots$. Thus the leading term in each of the equations (14-IV), (14-IV$^{(1)}$), $\ldots$, vanishes.

It may be that more compact higher-order equations exist, but we have not found them.

In summary, we have derived the hierarchies beginning with Eqs. (14-I$^{(1)}$), (14-II$^{(1)}$), (14-III$^{(1)}$), and (14-IV$^{(1)}$). These are higher analogues of Eqs. (14-I) to (14-IV), respectively. Quantities of the type $\bar{G}_1^{(n)}$ and $\bar{G}_2^{(n)}$ appear. These involve nth derivatives of $\bar{G}_1$ and $\bar{G}_2$ with respect to g_1 and g_2. These derivatives, in turn, are related to higher central moments in the G_1, G_2 distribution.

CHAPTER 15

DIFFERENCE EQUATIONS AND VERY SMALL SYSTEMS

Differential equations are used in macroscopic thermodynamics and we have carried over their use to small systems. However, as has been mentioned several times in earlier chapters, this cannot be done indiscriminately. Specifically, the concept of the *differential* of a *discrete* thermodynamic variable cannot be extended to arbitrarily small values of the variable. For very small values, it is necessary to employ differences instead of differentials. Hence we have the task, in this chapter, of introducing some new definitions of thermodynamic functions for very small systems and of deriving new equations interrelating these and other functions. The new equations provide an extension of small system thermodynamics in much the same way that small system thermodynamics extends ordinary thermodynamics.

There are some cases, incidentally, for which, on letting the system become small, it is necessary to make the transition directly from macroscopic thermodynamics to very small system thermodynamics (omitting the intermediate stage). This arises when discreteness influences first-order small terms. Some examples are given in the present chapter.

Discrete extensive environmental variables are the ones of primary concern to us. Examples are: the variable N in an N, p, T system; the variable B in a μ, B, T system (B = number of sites, as in Chapter 6); the variable N in an N, V, T system (V continuous); the variables N and B in an N, B, T system (Chapter 8); and the variables N, B, and E in an N, B, E system (Chapter 9). The first four of these cases serve as the subjects of the respective sections of this chapter.

An extensive variable that fluctuates, and is averaged, is of course continuous, not discrete. Examples are: the variables $\bar{E}$ and $\bar{V}$ in an N, p, T system; $\bar{N}$ and $\bar{E}$ in a μ, B, T system; etc. The variables μ, p, and T are also continuous. Thus, in a μ, p, T system, all variables are continuous.

One could discuss the thermodynamics of very small systems with discrete variables in considerable detail, much as small systems have been treated in Chapters 1 to 14. But we intend just the opposite here. We shall merely choose a few special cases and indicate some of the new features that arise. One important point might be mentioned at the outset: the thermodynamic equations are no longer the same for all environments.

15-1. N, p, T SYSTEMS

The basic equations of Chapter 2 are valid here, and can be used as a starting point, *provided* we hold N (the only discrete environmental variable) constant. This statement applies to a theoretical ensemble of small systems or to experimental small systems in a solvent. It can be verified by dropping the term in dN in Eq. (1-49) or Eq. (2-122), but otherwise using the same arguments as before. We then have [Eqs. (2-2) and (2-3)], in obvious notation,

$$F_N = \hat{\mu}_N N = \bar{E}_N - TS_N + p\bar{V}_N \qquad (15\text{-}1)$$

$$dF_N = d(\hat{\mu}_N N) = -S_N\,dT + \bar{V}_N\,dp \qquad (N \text{ constant}). \qquad (15\text{-}2)$$

Of course $\hat{\mu}_N$, $\bar{E}_N$, S_N, and $\bar{V}_N$ are all continuous functions of p and T.

We now want to introduce variations in N in Eq. (15-2). But when N is sufficiently small,[1] it must be treated as a discrete rather than continuous variable. Let us digress to consider the effect of discrete variations in N on an arbitrary variable $f_N(p, T)$.

If N, p, and T are all treated as continuous variables (N large),

$$df_N = \left(\frac{\partial f_N}{\partial T}\right)_{p,\,N} dT + \left(\frac{\partial f_N}{\partial p}\right)_{T,\,N} dp + \left(\frac{\partial f_N}{\partial N}\right)_{T,\,p} dN. \qquad (15\text{-}3)$$

The three terms on the right are additive because the variations dT, dp, and dN are infinitesimals. Any or all of dT, dp, and dN may be nonzero in this equation. The situation is somewhat different when N is discrete. Without loss of generality, we let the variation ΔN have only two possible values: $\Delta N = 0$ or $\Delta N = +1$. If $\Delta N = +1$ and T, $p = $ constant, we use the notation $\delta f_N = f_{N+1} - f_N$ for the variation in f_N. The variation in f_N when N decreases from N to $N - 1$ would then be written $-\delta f_{N-1}$. If we allow variations

---

[1] This depends on the accuracy desired or experimental error involved. For example, if the value of N is accurate to two per cent, the smallest possible change in N, $\Delta N = 1$, could be considered a differential change (N is effectively continuous) for $N > O(50)$. But N should be regarded as discrete for $N < O(50)$.

in any or all of T, p, and N, the complete expression for δf_N, which replaces Eq. (15-3), is easily seen to be

$$\delta f_N = \left(\frac{\partial f_N}{\partial T}\right)_{p,\,N} dT + \left(\frac{\partial f_N}{\partial p}\right)_{T,\,N} dp + (f_{N+1} - f_N)\,\Delta N$$

$$+ \left[\frac{\partial(f_{N+1} - f_N)}{\partial T} dT + \frac{\partial(f_{N+1} - f_N)}{\partial p} dp\right]\Delta N, \qquad (15\text{-}4)$$

where, as always, $\Delta N = 0$ or $+1$. Thus if dT and dp are nonzero and $\Delta N = +1$,

$$\delta f_N = f_{N+1} - f_N + \frac{\partial f_{N+1}}{\partial T} dT + \frac{\partial f_{N+1}}{\partial p} dp \qquad (\Delta N = +1) \atop (15\text{-}5)$$

as it should be.

The differing uses of the three symbols Δ, δ, and d, above, should be noted. Whenever $\Delta N = +1$, δf_N represents a finite change and not a differential.

In view of

$$\delta f_N = \left(\frac{\partial f_N}{\partial T}\right)_{p,\,N} dT \qquad (p, N \text{ constant})$$

and

$$\delta f_N = (f_{N+1} - f_N)\Delta N \qquad (p, T \text{ constant}),$$

we introduce the notation

$$\left(\frac{\delta f_N}{\partial T}\right)_{p,\,N} = \left(\frac{\partial f_N}{\partial T}\right)_{p,\,N}, \qquad \left(\frac{\delta f_N}{\partial p}\right)_{T,\,N} = \left(\frac{\partial f_N}{\partial p}\right)_{T,\,N},$$

$$\left(\frac{\delta f_N}{\Delta N}\right)_{T,\,p} = f_{N+1} - f_N. \qquad (15\text{-}6)$$

Since

$$\left[\frac{\delta}{\Delta N}\left(\frac{\partial f_N}{\partial p}\right)_{T,\,N}\right]_{T,\,p} = \left(\frac{\partial f_{N+1}}{\partial p}\right)_{T,\,N} - \left(\frac{\partial f_N}{\partial p}\right)_{T,\,N}, \qquad (15\text{-}7)$$

we have the Maxwell relation

$$\left[\frac{\delta}{\Delta N}\left(\frac{\partial f_N}{\partial p}\right)_{T,\,N}\right]_{T,\,p} = \left[\frac{\delta(f_{N+1} - f_N)}{\partial p}\right]_{T,\,N}, \qquad (15\text{-}8)$$

and a similar one between T and N (the conventional relation between T and p is of course also valid).

For most purposes it suffices to consider variations in *either* the continuous variables *or* the discrete variable, but not both [as allowed in Eq. (15-4)]. In this case we write

$$\delta f_N \overset{*}{=} \left(\frac{\partial f_N}{\partial T}\right)_{p,\,N} dT + \left(\frac{\partial f_N}{\partial p}\right)_{T,\,N} dp + (f_{N+1} - f_N)\Delta N, \tag{15-9}$$

where the asterisk indicates the restriction just referred to. Equations (15-6) to (15-8), for example, follow from Eq. (15-9) as well as from Eq. (15-4).

A derivative such as $(\partial p/\Delta N)_{T,\,f_N}$ is meaningless in the present calculus, although not in ordinary calculus. The reason for this is that when $\Delta N = +1$ and $T = $ constant, a *finite* change in p, δp, would be required in order to hold f_N constant, i.e., in order that $f_N(T, p) = f_{N+1}(T, p + \delta p)$. But Eq. (15-4) is restricted to infinitesimal changes in p. Equation (15-9) would not apply in any case since both N and p are varied.

We can verify from the definition of δf_N in Eq. (15-4) that

$$\delta(f_N + g_N) = \delta f_N + \delta g_N,$$

a property which we shall need presently.

Let us return now to Eqs. (15-1) and (15-2). If we apply Eq. (15-4) to the function $F_N(p, T)$ and define[1] the chemical potential

$$\mu_N(p, T) \equiv F_{N+1}(p, T) - F_N(p, T), \tag{15-10}$$

then we have

$$\delta F_N = -S_N\,dT + \bar{V}_N\,dp + \mu_N\,\Delta N$$
$$+ \left[\left(\frac{\partial \mu_N}{\partial T}\right)_{p,\,N} dT + \left(\frac{\partial \mu_N}{\partial p}\right)_{T,\,N} dp\right]\Delta N \tag{15-11}$$

and also

$$\left(\frac{\delta F_N}{\partial T}\right)_{p,\,N} = \left(\frac{\partial F_N}{\partial T}\right)_{p,\,N} = -S_N$$
$$\left(\frac{\delta F_N}{\partial p}\right)_{T,\,N} = \left(\frac{\partial F_N}{\partial p}\right)_{T,\,N} = \bar{V}_N \tag{15-12}$$

[1] The choice between $F_N - F_{N-1}$ and $F_{N+1} - F_N$ is of course arbitrary. The two quantities are not quite equivalent. The difference $F_{N+1/2} - F_{N-1/2}$ is closer in value to the derivative (see the Appendix), but this definition is excluded because the number of molecules or units in the system must be an integer.

$$\left(\frac{\delta F_N}{\Delta N}\right)_{T,\,p} = \mu_N, \qquad \left(\frac{\partial \bar{V}_N}{\partial T}\right)_{p,\,N} = -\left(\frac{\partial S_N}{\partial p}\right)_{T,\,N} \qquad (15\text{-}13)$$

$$-\left(\frac{\delta S_N}{\Delta N}\right)_{T,\,p} = \left(\frac{\partial \mu_N}{\partial T}\right)_{p,\,N} = -S_{N+1} + S_N \qquad (15\text{-}14)$$

$$\left(\frac{\delta \bar{V}_N}{\Delta N}\right)_{T,\,p} = \left(\frac{\partial \mu_N}{\partial p}\right)_{T,\,N} = \bar{V}_{N+1} - \bar{V}_N. \qquad (15\text{-}15)$$

Thus alternative forms of Eq. (15-11) are

$$\delta F_N = -S_N\,dT + \bar{V}_N\,dp + \mu_N\,\Delta N$$

$$+ \left[-\left(\frac{\delta S_N}{\Delta N}\right)_{T,\,p} dT + \left(\frac{\delta \bar{V}_N}{\Delta N}\right)_{T,\,p} dp \right] \Delta N \qquad (15\text{-}16)$$

$$\overset{*}{=} -S_N\,dT + \bar{V}_N\,dp + \mu_N\,\Delta N. \qquad (15\text{-}17)$$

Equations (15-11) and (15-16) are the extensions of Eq. (2-3) to very small systems. They reduce to Eq. (2-3) when N is large enough for ΔN to be considered a differential.[1]

At this point, the reader may wish to consult the Appendix to this chapter. It compares the difference μ_N and the derivative $\mu(N)$ for a number of simple types of small terms.

It might also be mentioned here that μ_N for a very small system does not have the conventional physical significance of a potential which determines the approach to, and point of, material transport equilibrium. The primary reason for this is that the system under discussion is closed, not open. The same comment applies, of course, to a closed, small N, p, T system. One should view μ_N as merely an interesting property that provides a logical mathematical extension of the function $\mu(N)$ to very small systems.

From Eq. (15-4) we have

$$\delta(TS_N) = T\,\delta S_N + S_N\,dT + \left(\frac{\delta S_N}{\Delta N}\right)_{T,\,p} dT\,\Delta N \qquad (15\text{-}18)$$

$$\delta(p\bar{V}_N) = p\,\delta \bar{V}_N + \bar{V}_N\,dp + \left(\frac{\delta \bar{V}_N}{\Delta N}\right)_{T,\,p} dp\,\Delta N. \qquad (15\text{-}19)$$

[1] See the footnote on p. 188.

Then

$$\delta A_N = \delta(\bar{E}_N - TS_N) = \delta(F_N - p\bar{V}_N)$$

$$= -S_N\, dT - p\, \delta\bar{V}_N + \mu_N\, \Delta N - \left(\frac{\delta S_N}{\Delta N}\right)_{T,\,p} dT\, \Delta N$$

$$\tag{15-20}$$

$$\delta H_N = \delta(\bar{E}_N + p\bar{V}_N) = \delta(F_N + TS_N)$$

$$= T\, \delta S_N + \bar{V}_N\, dp + \mu_N\, \Delta N + \left(\frac{\delta \bar{V}_N}{\Delta N}\right)_{T,\,p} dp\, \Delta N \tag{15-21}$$

$$\delta\bar{E}_N = \delta(F_N + TS_N - p\bar{V}_N)$$

$$= T\, \delta S_N - p\, \delta\bar{V}_N + \mu_N\, \Delta N. \tag{15-22}$$

It should be noted that, for example,

$$\left(\frac{\delta A_N}{\delta \bar{V}_N}\right)_{T,\,N} = \left(\frac{\partial A_N}{\partial \bar{V}_N}\right)_{T,\,N} = -p$$

$$\left(\frac{\delta A_N}{\partial T}\right)_{\bar{V}_N,\,N} = \left(\frac{\partial A_N}{\partial T}\right)_{\bar{V}_N,\,N} = -S_N$$

$$\left(\frac{\delta \bar{E}_N}{\delta S_N}\right)_{\bar{V}_N,\,N} = \left(\frac{\partial \bar{E}_N}{\partial S_N}\right)_{\bar{V}_N,\,N} = T,$$

because only ordinary differentials are encountered when N is constant. But quantities like $(\delta A_N/\Delta N)_{T,\bar{V}_N}$, etc., are not defined, for a finite δp is required to keep $\bar{V}_N$ constant and only differentials of p and T are allowed in Eq. (15-20).

We define $\mathscr{E}_N$ by

$$\mathscr{E}_N \equiv F_N - \mu_N N = N(\hat{\mu}_N - \mu_N), \tag{15-23}$$

and seek expressions for $\delta\mathscr{E}_N$. We find

$$\delta\mathscr{E}_N = \delta F_N - \delta(\mu_N N)$$

$$= -\left[S_N - N\left(\frac{\delta S_N}{\Delta N}\right)_{T,\,p}\right] dT + \left[\bar{V}_N - N\left(\frac{\delta \bar{V}_N}{\Delta N}\right)_{T,\,p}\right] dp$$

$$- (N+1)\,(\mu_{N+1} - \mu_N)\, \Delta N$$

$$- (N+1)\left[\frac{\partial(\mu_{N+1} - \mu_N)}{\partial T} dT + \frac{\partial(\mu_{N+1} - \mu_N)}{\partial p} dp\right] \Delta N$$

$$\tag{15-24}$$

$$\overset{*}{=} - \left[S_N - N \left(\frac{\delta S_N}{\Delta N} \right)_{T,\,p} \right] dT + \left[\bar{V}_N - N \left(\frac{\delta \bar{V}_N}{\Delta N} \right)_{T,\,p} \right] dp$$

$$+ \left(\frac{\delta \mathscr{E}_N}{\Delta N} \right)_{T,\,p} \Delta N, \qquad (15\text{-}25)$$

where

$$\left(\frac{\delta \mathscr{E}_N}{\Delta N} \right)_{T,\,p} = - (N + 1)(\mu_{N+1} - \mu_N). \qquad (15\text{-}26)$$

Equations (15-24) and (15-25) should be compared with Eq. (2-23). Since [compare Eq. (2-17)]

$$\delta\mu_N = - \left(\frac{\delta S_N}{\Delta N} \right)_{T,\,p} dT + \left(\frac{\delta \bar{V}_N}{\Delta N} \right)_{T,\,p} dp + (\mu_{N+1} - \mu_N)\,\Delta N$$

$$+ \left[\frac{\partial(\mu_{N+1} - \mu_N)}{\partial T} dT + \frac{\partial(\mu_{N+1} - \mu_N)}{\partial p} dp \right] \Delta N \quad (15\text{-}27)$$

$$\overset{*}{=} - \left(\frac{\delta S_N}{\Delta N} \right)_{T,\,p} dT + \left(\frac{\delta \bar{V}_N}{\Delta N} \right)_{T,\,p} dp$$

$$- \frac{1}{(N+1)} \left(\frac{\delta \mathscr{E}_N}{\Delta N} \right)_{T,\,p} \Delta N, \qquad (15\text{-}28)$$

we can write Eq. (15-24) in the alternative form

$$\delta \mathscr{E}_N = - S_{N+1}\, dT + \bar{V}_{N+1}\, dp - (N + 1)\, \delta\mu_N. \qquad (15\text{-}29)$$

A similar relation which is easy to prove is

$$\delta(F_{N+1} - \mu_N N) = - S_{N+1}\, dT + \bar{V}_{N+1}\, dp - N\, \delta\mu_N. \qquad (15\text{-}30)$$

The derivatives $(\delta \mathscr{E}_N / \partial T)_{p,\,\mu_N}$ and $(\delta \mathscr{E}_N / \partial p)_{T,\,\mu_N}$ are meaningless but, in view of

$$\delta \mathscr{E}_N = - (N + 1)(\mu_{N+1} - \mu_N)\,\Delta N \qquad (T, p \text{ constant})$$

and

$$\delta\mu_N = (\mu_{N+1} - \mu_N)\,\Delta N \qquad (T, p \text{ constant}),$$

we have

$$\left(\frac{\delta \mathscr{E}_N}{\delta\mu_N} \right)_{T,\,p} = - (N + 1). \qquad (15\text{-}31)$$

The expressions for $\delta\hat{\mu}_N$ are

$$\delta\hat{\mu}_N = -\frac{S_N}{N}\,dT + \frac{\bar{V}_N}{N}\,dp - \frac{\mathscr{E}_N}{N(N+1)}\,\Delta N$$

$$+ \left[\frac{\partial(\hat{\mu}_{N+1} - \hat{\mu}_N)}{\partial T}\,dT + \frac{\partial\,(\hat{\mu}_{N+1} - \hat{\mu}_N)}{\partial p}\,dp\right]\Delta N \tag{15-32}$$

$$\overset{*}{=} -\frac{S_N}{N}\,dT + \frac{\bar{V}_N}{N}\,dp - \frac{\mathscr{E}_N}{N(N+1)}\,\Delta N. \tag{15-33}$$

These are the extensions of Eq. (2-13). Thus

$$\left(\frac{\delta\hat{\mu}_N}{\Delta N}\right)_{T,\,p} = -\frac{\mathscr{E}_N}{N(N+1)}$$

$$= \hat{\mu}_{N+1} - \hat{\mu}_N = \frac{\mu_N - \hat{\mu}_{N+1}}{N} = \frac{\mu_N - \hat{\mu}_N}{N+1}. \tag{15-34}$$

As an example of the effect of size on an intensive variable of the type G_N/N (see page 34 of Part I), we consider $\bar{V}_N/N$. We have

$$\left(\frac{\delta(\bar{V}_N/N)}{\Delta N}\right)_{T,\,p} = \frac{\bar{V}_{N+1}}{N+1} - \frac{\bar{V}_N}{N} = \frac{N\bar{V}_{N+1} - (N+1)\bar{V}_N}{N(N+1)}$$

and

$$\left(\frac{\delta\mathscr{E}_N}{\partial p}\right)_{T,\,N} = \bar{V}_N - N\left(\frac{\delta\bar{V}_N}{\Delta N}\right)_{T,\,p} = -N\bar{V}_{N+1} + (N+1)\bar{V}_N.$$

Therefore

$$\left(\frac{\delta\bar{V}_N/N}{\Delta N}\right)_{T,\,p} = -\frac{1}{N(N+1)}\left(\frac{\delta\mathscr{E}_N}{\partial p}\right)_{T,\,N}. \tag{15-35}$$

For the heat capacity (see page 33 of Part I) we write

$$DQ_N = C_N\,dT = T\,dS_N \qquad (p,\,N \text{ constant}),$$

or

$$C_N = T\left(\frac{\partial S_N}{\partial T}\right)_{p,\,N} = -NT\left(\frac{\partial^2\hat{\mu}_N}{\partial T^2}\right)_{p,\,N}. \tag{15-36}$$

Then

$$\left[\frac{\delta(C_N/N)}{\Delta N}\right]_{p,\,T} = \frac{C_{N+1}}{N+1} - \frac{C_N}{N} = T\,\frac{\partial^2(\hat{\mu}_N - \hat{\mu}_{N+1})}{\partial T^2}$$

$$= \frac{T}{N(N+1)}\left(\frac{\partial^2\mathscr{E}_N}{\partial T^2}\right)_{p,\,N}. \tag{15-37}$$

EXPANSIONS IN POWERS OF N^{-1}. In some cases, an expansion of $\hat{\mu}_N$ in powers of N^{-1} may exist (compare page 136 of Part I):

$$\hat{\mu}_N(p, T) = \mu^{(0)}(p, T) + N^{-1}\hat{\mu}^{(1)}(p, T) + N^{-2}\hat{\mu}^{(2)}(p, T) + \cdots .$$
$$(15\text{-}38)$$

The smaller the system, the greater the number of terms required. But if the system is small enough, the equations satisfied by $\hat{\mu}_N$ are those of the present section rather than of Chapter 2. Therefore, even if the expansion exists, Eq. (15-38) should not in general be used in Chapter 2. For example,

$$\mu_N = (N + 1)\,\hat{\mu}_{N+1} - N\hat{\mu}_N$$
$$= \mu^{(0)} - N^{-2}\hat{\mu}^{(2)} + N^{-3}(\hat{\mu}^{(2)} - 2\hat{\mu}^{(3)}) - \cdots , \qquad (15\text{-}39)$$

whereas, from Chapter 2,

$$\mu = \left(\frac{\partial N\hat{\mu}_N}{\partial N}\right)_{T,\,p} = \mu^{(0)} - N^{-2}\hat{\mu}^{(2)} - 2N^{-3}\hat{\mu}^{(3)} - \cdots . \quad (15\text{-}40)$$

A discrepancy between μ_N and μ appears beginning with the term in N^{-3}. Thus, for a system that allows expansions in powers of N^{-1}, difference equations must be employed if the system is small enough that the N^{-3} term in $\hat{\mu}_N$, or the N^{-2} term in F_N, is required in order to achieve sufficient accuracy.

Other functions are

$$\mathscr{E}_N = N(\hat{\mu}_N - \mu_N) = \hat{\mu}^{(1)} + 2N^{-1}\hat{\mu}^{(2)} + N^{-2}(-\hat{\mu}^{(2)} + 3\hat{\mu}^{(3)}) + \cdots$$
$$(15\text{-}41)$$

$$-\frac{S_N}{N} = \left(\frac{\partial \hat{\mu}_N}{\partial T}\right)_{p,\,N} = \frac{\partial \mu^{(0)}}{\partial T} + N^{-1}\frac{\partial \hat{\mu}^{(1)}}{\partial T} + N^{-2}\frac{\partial \hat{\mu}^{(2)}}{\partial T} + \cdots$$
$$(15\text{-}42)$$

$$\frac{\bar{V}_N}{N} = \left(\frac{\partial \hat{\mu}_N}{\partial p}\right)_{T,\,N} = \frac{\partial \mu^{(0)}}{\partial p} + N^{-1}\frac{\partial \hat{\mu}^{(1)}}{\partial p} + N^{-2}\frac{\partial \hat{\mu}^{(2)}}{\partial p} + \cdots .$$
$$(15\text{-}43)$$

Examples. In treating simple examples on pages 43 and 69 of Part I, it was necessary to point out that differentiation with respect to N could not be carried to arbitrarily small N. We have eliminated this restriction in the present section by replacing the derivative μ by the difference μ_N. But it happens that in the two examples referred to above, $\hat{\mu}_N N$ is *linear* in N. In such a case, μ and μ_N are identical. Hence we now find that our earlier precautionary remarks, in these two cases, happened to be unnecessary. In general, of course, μ and μ_N will differ, and μ_N must be used for very small N.

Pages 46 and 48 of Part I provide simple examples of models in which μ and μ_N differ. We leave it to the reader to write out the expressions for μ_N. Note that the formula for $\bar{n}$ involves differentiation with respect to r at constant N [this is equivalent to Eq. (15-12b)] and hence is valid, as it stands, for very small N.

15-2. μ, B, T SYSTEMS

This case is formally identical with that treated in the preceding section. We can take over all the equations[1] of Section 15-1 by using the transcription [see (6-5)]

$$\begin{aligned}
\bar{E}_N &\to \bar{E}_B, & T &\to T, & S_N &\to S_B \\
N &\to B, & \bar{V}_N &\to \bar{N}_B, & \mathscr{E}_N &\to \mathscr{E}_B \\
\mu_N &\to -p_B, & \hat{\mu}_N &\to -\hat{p}_B, & p &\to -\mu.
\end{aligned} \tag{15-44}$$

Examples. The function $\hat{p}B$ for an ideal lattice gas (page 142 of Part I) is linear in B. Hence p and p_B are identical. This situation is analogous to that on pages 43 and 69 of Part I, referred to above.

In the treatment of a Bragg–Williams lattice gas on pages 145 to 149 of Part I, B and N are regarded as continuous variables. There seems to be little point, however, in "improving" this treatment by the introduction of discreteness because the potential energy term, $\alpha N^2/B$, is an approximation which itself is based on a "continuous" argument.

15-3. N, V, T SYSTEMS

Here N is a discrete variable but we consider V to be continuous, as in many theoretical models. Because there is one discrete variable, the situation is quite similar to that in Sections 15-1 and 15-2.

The fundamental equations are (page 18, Part I)

$$A_N = \bar{E}_N - TS_N \tag{15-45}$$

$$dA_N = -S_N\,dT - p_N\,dV \qquad (N \text{ constant}), \tag{15-46}$$

---

[1] But DQ_B has to be omitted from the equation preceding (15-36). See the bottom of p. 135, Part I.

where A_N, $\bar{E}_N$, S_N, and p_N are all functions of V and T. For the variation in an arbitrary function $f_N(V, T)$, we have

$$\delta f_N = \left(\frac{\partial f_N}{\partial T}\right)_{V,\,N} dT + \left(\frac{\partial f_N}{\partial V}\right)_{T,\,N} dV + (f_{N+1} - f_N)\,\Delta N$$

$$+ \left[\frac{\partial(f_{N+1} - f_N)}{\partial T} dT + \frac{\partial(f_{N+1} - f_N)}{\partial V} dV\right]\Delta N. \qquad (15\text{-}47)$$

We define

$$\mu_N(V, T) \equiv A_{N+1}(V, T) - A_N(V, T). \qquad (15\text{-}48)$$

Then

$$\delta A_N = -\,S_N\,dT - p_N\,dV + \mu_N\,\Delta N$$

$$+ \left[\left(\frac{\partial \mu_N}{\partial T}\right)_V dT + \left(\frac{\partial \mu_N}{\partial V}\right)_T dV\right]\Delta N \qquad (15\text{-}49)$$

$$\overset{*}{=}\; -\,S_N\,dT - p_N\,dV + \mu_N\,\Delta N. \qquad (15\text{-}50)$$

All the deductions made directly from Eq. (15-11) follow as well from Eq. (15-49), if we introduce the transcription

$$F_N \to A_N, \qquad S_N \to S_N, \qquad T \to T, \qquad \bar{V}_N \to -p_N$$

$$p \to V, \qquad \mu_N \to \mu_N, \qquad N \to N. \qquad (15\text{-}51)$$

For example,

$$\left(\frac{\delta p_N}{\Delta N}\right)_{T,\,V} = -\left(\frac{\partial \mu_N}{\partial V}\right)_{T,\,N} = p_{N+1} - p_N. \qquad (15\text{-}52)$$

From the expressions for $\delta(TS_N)$ and $\delta(p_N V)$ we deduce

$$\delta(A_N + p_N V) = \delta F_N$$

$$= -\,S_N\,dT + V\,\delta p_N + \mu_N\,\Delta N - \left(\frac{\delta S_N}{\Delta N}\right)_{T,\,V} dT\,\Delta N \qquad (15\text{-}53)$$

$$\delta(A_N + TS_N) = \delta \bar{E}_N$$

$$= T\,\delta S_N - p_N\,dV + \mu_N\,\Delta N - \left(\frac{\delta p_N}{\Delta N}\right)_{T,\,V} dV\,\Delta N \qquad (15\text{-}54)$$

$$\delta(A_N + TS_N + p_N V) = \delta H_N$$

$$= T\,\delta S_N + V\,\delta p_N + \mu_N\,\Delta N. \qquad (15\text{-}55)$$

Let us define $\mathscr{E}_N$ by

$$\mathscr{E}_N \equiv A_N + p_N V - \mu_N N = F_N - \mu_N N. \qquad (15\text{-}56)$$

This leads to

$$\delta\mathscr{E}_N \overset{*}{=} - \left[S_N - N\left(\frac{\delta S_N}{\Delta N}\right)_{T,V} - V\left(\frac{\delta S_N}{\partial V}\right)_{T,N} \right] dT$$

$$+ \left[N\left(\frac{\delta p_N}{\Delta N}\right)_{T,V} + V\left(\frac{\delta p_N}{\partial V}\right)_{T,N} \right] dV$$

$$- \left[(N+1)\left(\frac{\delta \mu_N}{\Delta N}\right)_{T,V} + V\left(\frac{\delta \mu_N}{\partial V}\right)_{T,N} \right] \Delta N. \qquad (15\text{-}57)$$

Closely related is the expression

$$\delta(A_N + p_{N+1} V - \mu_N N) \overset{*}{=} - S_{N+1}\, dT + V\, \delta p_{N+1} - (N+1)\, \delta\mu_N. \qquad (15\text{-}58)$$

Example. Gas of Hard Spheres. We shall consider here the first few terms in the exact virial expansion of a finite gas of hard spheres in a cube with periodic boundary conditions.[1] But first we have to investigate the limit $V \to \infty$ for N large but finite, where the gas would behave ideally.

In the above limit,

$$Q_N(V, T) = \frac{V^N}{N! \Lambda^{3N}} \qquad (V \to \infty), \qquad (15\text{-}59)$$

where

$$\Lambda = \frac{h}{(2\pi m k T)^{1/2}}.$$

For N large but not infinite,

$$-\frac{A_N}{kT} = \ln Q_N = N \ln V - N \ln \Lambda^3 - N \ln N + N - \tfrac{1}{2} \ln 2\pi N$$

$$- \frac{1}{12N} + \cdots. \qquad (15\text{-}60)$$

---

[1] I. Oppenheim and P. Mazur, *Physica*, **23**, 197 (1957); B. J. Alder and T. E. Wainwright, *J. Chem. Phys.*, **33**, 1439 (1960); *Phys. Rev.*, **127**, 359 (1962); J. L. Lebowitz and J. K. Percus, *Phys. Rev.*, **124**, 1673 (1961). This problem is also referred to at the end of Chapter 6, Part I.

Then, from Eq. (15-48),

$$- \frac{\mu_N}{kT} = \ln \frac{V}{\Lambda^3 N} - \frac{1}{N} + \frac{1}{2N^2} + \cdots . \qquad (15\text{-}61)$$

Let us compare this with

$$- \frac{\mu}{kT} = \left(\frac{\partial \ln Q_N}{\partial N} \right)_{T,V} = \ln \frac{V}{\Lambda^3 N} - \frac{1}{2N} + \frac{1}{12N^2} + \cdots . \qquad (15\text{-}62)$$

We note that here we have a case in which discreteness influences the first small term. This occurs because the "macroscopic" term $-N \ln N$ in Eq. (15-60) contributes to the N^{-1} term[1] in Eq. (15-61). As a check on Eq. (15-61), we can work with Eq. (15-59) directly, without introducing Stirling's approximation. We find

$$- \frac{\mu_N}{kT} = \ln \frac{Q_{N+1}}{Q_N} = \ln \frac{V}{\Lambda^3 (N+1)} = \ln \frac{V}{\Lambda^3 N} - \frac{1}{N} + \frac{1}{2N^2} + \cdots .$$

Other functions are

$$\frac{p_N}{kT} = \left(\frac{\partial - A_N/kT}{\partial V} \right)_{T,N} = \frac{N}{V} \qquad (15\text{-}63)$$

$$\frac{\mathscr{E}_N}{kT} = \frac{A_N}{kT} + \frac{p_N V}{kT} - \frac{\mu_N N}{kT} = \ln \frac{N! e^N}{(N+1)^N} = \tfrac{1}{2} \ln \frac{2\pi N}{e^2} + \frac{7}{12N} + \cdots . \qquad (15\text{-}64)$$

When V is not infinite, a virial expansion of p is required. The first terms[2] are

$$\frac{pV}{NkT} = 1 + B_2^{(0)} \left(1 - \frac{1}{N} \right) \frac{N}{V} + B_3^{(0)} \left(1 + \frac{1}{5N} - \frac{6}{5N^2} \right) \left(\frac{N}{V} \right)^2 + \cdots , \qquad (15\text{-}65)$$

where $B_2^{(0)}$ and $B_3^{(0)}$ are the macroscopic virial coefficients for hard spheres,

$$B_2^{(0)} = \frac{2\pi a^3}{3}, \qquad B_3^{(0)} = \tfrac{5}{8} (B_2^{(0)})^2,$$

---

[1] This cannot happen with an N, p, T system because the macroscopic term in F_N has the form $Nf(p, T)$. For such a term, the difference and derivative (p and T constant) are the same for all N. In Eq. (15-60) for A_N, the macroscopic term has the form $Nf(N/V, T)$. In this case, the difference and derivative (V and T constant) are not, in general, the same for small N.

[2] Loc. cit.

with a = diameter of hard sphere. The functions of N^{-1} in parentheses are polynomials, not infinite series.

With the information given by statistical mechanics in Eq. (15-65), we proceed to derive the other thermodynamic functions. We start with

$$\frac{A_N(V)}{kT} - \frac{A_N(V^*)}{kT} = - \int_{V^*}^{V} \frac{p_N}{kT} \, dV, \qquad (15\text{-}66)$$

where V^* is a very large volume. Equation (15-60) gives $A_N(V^*)$. Then, from Eqs. (15-65) and (15-66), we have

$$\frac{A_N(V, T)}{NkT} = \ln \frac{\Lambda^3 N}{Ve} + \frac{1}{2N} \ln 2\pi N + \frac{1}{12N^2} + \cdots$$

$$+ B_2^{(0)}\left(1 - \frac{1}{N}\right)\left(\frac{N}{V}\right) + \tfrac{1}{2}B_3^{(0)}\left(1 + \frac{1}{5N} - \frac{6}{5N^2}\right)\left(\frac{N}{V}\right)^2 + \cdots .$$
$$(15\text{-}67)$$

This leads to

$$\frac{\mu_N}{kT} = \ln \frac{\Lambda^3 N}{V} + \frac{1}{N} - \frac{1}{2N^2} + \cdots$$

$$+ \tfrac{2}{1}B_2^{(0)}\left(\frac{N}{V}\right) + \tfrac{3}{2}B_3^{(0)}\left(1 + \frac{17}{15N}\right)\left(\frac{N}{V}\right)^2 + \cdots \qquad (15\text{-}68)$$

$$\frac{\mathscr{E}_N}{kT} = \tfrac{1}{2} \ln \frac{2\pi N}{e^2} + \frac{7}{12N} + \cdots$$

$$- 2B_2^{(0)}\left(\frac{N}{V}\right) - \tfrac{1}{5}B_3^{(0)}\left(7 + \frac{9}{N}\right)\left(\frac{N}{V}\right)^2 + \cdots \qquad (15\text{-}69)$$

and

$$\bar{E}_N = - T^2 \left(\frac{\partial A_N/T}{\partial T}\right)_{V,N} = \frac{3NkT}{2}. \qquad (15\text{-}70)$$

As a check on self-consistency, we find that both sides of [see Eq. (15-57)]

$$\left(\frac{\delta \mathscr{E}_N}{\Delta N}\right)_{T,V} = - \left[(N + 1)\left(\frac{\delta \mu_N}{\Delta N}\right)_{T,V} + V\left(\frac{\delta \mu_N}{\partial V}\right)_{T,N}\right]$$

are equal to

$$- \frac{2B_2^{(0)}}{V} - \frac{2B_3^{(0)}}{5V^2}(7N + 8).$$

15-4. N, B, T SYSTEMS

Here we have two discrete variables—for example, N molecules on B sites of a lattice gas. Rather obviously, the variation of an arbitrary function $f_{N,B}(T)$ is given by

$$\delta f_{N,B} = \left(\frac{\partial f_{N,B}}{\partial T}\right)_{N,B} dT$$

$$+ \left[f_{N,B+1} - f_{N,B} + \frac{\partial(f_{N,B+1} - f_{N,B})}{\partial T} dT \right] \Delta B$$

$$+ \left[f_{N+1,B} - f_{N,B} + \frac{\partial(f_{N+1,B} - f_{N,B})}{\partial T} dT \right] \Delta N$$

$$+ \left[\left\{ f_{N+1,B+1} - f_{N,B+1} - f_{N+1,B} + f_{N,B} \right\} + \frac{\partial\{\}}{\partial T} dT \right] \Delta B \, \Delta N,$$
$$(15\text{-}71)$$

where ΔB, $\Delta N = 0$ or $+1$. If $\Delta B = \Delta N = +1$,

$$\delta f_{N,B}(T) = f_{N+1,B+1} - f_{N,B} + \frac{\partial f_{N+1,B+1}}{\partial T} dT.$$

Because of the complexity of Eq. (15-71), we turn to

$$\delta f_{N,B} \overset{*}{=} \left(\frac{\partial f_{N,B}}{\partial T}\right)_{N,B} dT + (f_{N,B+1} - f_{N,B}) \Delta B$$

$$+ (f_{N+1,B} - f_{N,B}) \Delta N, \qquad (15\text{-}72)$$

where the asterisk means that only one of dT, ΔB, and ΔN can be nonzero at a time.

Our starting point is [see Eqs. (15-45) and (15-46)]

$$A_{N,B} = \bar{E}_{N,B} - TS_{N,B} \qquad (15\text{-}73)$$

$$dA_{N,B} = -S_{N,B} \, dT \qquad (N, B \text{ constant}). \qquad (15\text{-}74)$$

We define

$$-p_{N,B} \equiv A_{N,B+1} - A_{N,B}$$
and
$$\mu_{N,B} \equiv A_{N+1,B} - A_{N,B}. \qquad (15\text{-}75)$$

Then

$$\delta A_{N,B} \overset{*}{=} -S_{N,B} \, dT - p_{N,B} \Delta B + \mu_{N,B} \Delta N \qquad (15\text{-}76)$$

and

$$\left(\frac{\delta A_{N,B}}{\partial T}\right)_{N,B} = \left(\frac{\partial A_{N,B}}{\partial T}\right)_{N,B} = -S_{N,B}$$

$$\left(\frac{\delta A_{N,B}}{\Delta B}\right)_{T,N} = -p_{N,B}, \qquad \left(\frac{\delta A_{N,B}}{\Delta N}\right)_{T,B} = \mu_{N,B}. \tag{15-77}$$

Also, we have the Maxwell relations

$$\left(\frac{\delta p_{N,B}}{\partial T}\right)_{N,B} = S_{N,B+1} - S_{N,B} = \left(\frac{\delta S_{N,B}}{\Delta B}\right)_{T,N} \tag{15-78}$$

$$\left(\frac{\partial \mu_{N,B}}{\partial T}\right)_{N,B} = -S_{N+1,B} + S_{N,B} = -\left(\frac{\delta S_{N,B}}{\Delta N}\right)_{T,B}. \tag{15-79}$$

It is also true that

$$\left(\frac{\delta \mu_{N,B}}{\Delta B}\right)_{T,N} = -\left(\frac{\delta p_{N,B}}{\Delta N}\right)_{T,B}, \tag{15-80}$$

for each of these "derivatives" is equal to $A_{N+1,\,B+1} - A_{N+1,\,B} - A_{N,\,B+1} + A_{N,\,B}$. An alternative form of Eq. (15-80) is

$$\mu_{N,\,B+1} - \mu_{N,\,B} = -(p_{N+1,\,B} - p_{N,\,B}). \tag{15-81}$$

The same sorts of comments can be made here about $p_{N,\,B}$ and $\mu_{N,\,B}$ as were made about μ_N in the paragraph preceding Eq. (15-18). Thus, a pressure p determines the approach to, and point of, mechanical equilibrium only for a system which is open with respect to volume changes. Here B is the environmental variable, not p. Furthermore, $p_{N,\,B}\Delta B$ cannot be associated with a reversible work because a variation $\Delta B = +1$ (even for an ensemble of very small systems) cannot be carried out reversibly.

We shall have need below for

$$\delta(p_{N,\,B}B) \overset{*}{=} B\frac{\delta S_{N,\,B}}{\Delta B}\,dT + \left(B\frac{\delta p_{N,\,B}}{\Delta B} + p_{N,\,B+1}\right)\Delta B$$

$$- B\frac{\delta \mu_{N,\,B}}{\Delta B}\Delta N \tag{15-82}$$

$$\overset{*}{=} B\,\delta p_{N,\,B} + p_{N,\,B+1}\,\Delta B \tag{15-83}$$

and

$$\delta(\mu_{N,\,B}N) \overset{*}{=} -N\,\frac{\delta S_{N,\,B}}{\Delta N}\,dT - N\,\frac{\delta p_{N,\,B}}{\Delta N}\,\Delta B$$

$$+ \left(N\,\frac{\delta \mu_{N,\,B}}{\Delta N} + \mu_{N+1,\,B}\right)\Delta N \qquad (15\text{-}84)$$

$$\overset{*}{=} N\,\delta\mu_{N,\,B} + \mu_{N+1,\,B}\,\Delta N. \qquad (15\text{-}85)$$

Using the above relations we can now derive the following:

$$\delta\mathscr{E}_{N,\,B} = \delta(A_{N,\,B} + p_{N,\,B}\,B - \mu_{N,\,B}\,N)$$

$$\overset{*}{=} -\left(S_{N,\,B} - N\,\frac{\delta S_{N,\,B}}{\Delta N} - B\,\frac{\delta S_{N,\,B}}{\Delta B}\right)dT$$

$$+ \left[N\,\frac{\delta p_{N,\,B}}{\Delta N} + (B+1)\,\frac{\delta p_{N,\,B}}{\Delta B}\right]\Delta B$$

$$- \left[(N+1)\,\frac{\delta \mu_{N,\,B}}{\Delta N} + B\,\frac{\delta \mu_{N,\,B}}{\Delta B}\right]\Delta N \qquad (15\text{-}86)$$

$$\delta(A_{N+1,\,B+1} + p_{N+1,\,B}B - \mu_{N,\,B+1}N)$$

$$\overset{*}{=} -S_{N+1,\,B+1}\,dT + B\,\delta p_{N+1,\,B} - N\,\delta\mu_{N,\,B+1} \qquad (15\text{-}87)$$

$$\delta(A_{N,\,B} + TS_{N,\,B}) = \delta\bar{E}_{N,\,B}$$

$$\overset{*}{=} T\,\delta S_{N,\,B} - p_{N,\,B}\,\Delta B + \mu_{N,\,B}\,\Delta N. \qquad (15\text{-}88)$$

Example. Ideal Lattice Gas. This simple model has already been discussed in Eqs. (2-77) to (2-84) and (6-51) to (6-57) for the environmental variables N, p/T and μ/T, B, respectively.

The energy of the system is $E = $ constant $= 0$ and the environmental variables are N, B. The partition function is

$$\Omega_{N,\,B} = \frac{B!}{N!(B-N)!}, \qquad (15\text{-}89)$$

and

$$S_{N,\,B} = k\ln\Omega_{N,\,B}. \qquad (15\text{-}90)$$

In place of Eq. (15-76), we have

$$\delta \left(\frac{S_{N, B}}{k} \right)^* = p'_{N, B} \, \Delta B - \mu'_{N, B} \, \Delta N, \tag{15-91}$$

where

$$p'_{N, B} = \frac{p_{N, B}}{kT} \qquad \text{and} \qquad \mu'_{N, B} = \frac{\mu_{N, B}}{kT}.$$

Equations (15-89) to (15-91) lead to

$$p'_{N, B} = \left(\frac{\delta \ln \Omega_{N, B}}{\Delta B} \right)_N = \ln \frac{\Omega_{N, B+1}}{\Omega_{N, B}} = \ln \frac{B + 1}{B + 1 - N} \tag{15-92}$$

$$- \mu'_{N, B} = \ln \frac{\Omega_{N+1, B}}{\Omega_{N, B}} = \ln \frac{B - N}{N + 1} \tag{15-93}$$

$$- \frac{\mathscr{E}_{N, B}}{kT} = \frac{S_{N, B}}{k} - p'_{N, B} \, B + \mu'_{N, B} \, N$$

$$= \ln \frac{B!}{N!(B - N)!} \left(\frac{B + 1 - N}{B + 1} \right)^B \left(\frac{N + 1}{B - N} \right)^N$$

$$= - \tfrac{1}{2} \ln \frac{2\pi N(B - N)}{B} + \frac{B}{B - N} + \cdots. \tag{15-94}$$

We can check these results using, for example,

$$\left(\frac{\delta p'_{N, B}}{\Delta N} \right)_B = - \left(\frac{\delta \mu'_{N, B}}{\Delta B} \right)_N \tag{15-95}$$

and [see Eq. (15-86)]

$$\left(\frac{\delta \mathscr{E}_{N, B}/kT}{\Delta N} \right)_B = - \left[(N + 1) \frac{\delta \mu'_{N, B}}{\Delta N} + B \frac{\delta \mu'_{N, B}}{\Delta B} \right]. \tag{15-96}$$

This is another example in which the first-order small term is affected by discreteness. To see this, we use the Stirling approximation and write

$$\frac{S_{N, B}}{k} = \ln \Omega_{N, B} = B \ln B - N \ln N - (B - N) \ln (B - N)$$

$$- \tfrac{1}{2} \ln \frac{2\pi N(B - N)}{B} + \cdots. \tag{15-97}$$

Then, if we treat N and B as continuous,

$$\frac{p}{kT} = \left[\frac{\partial(S/k)}{\partial B}\right]_N = \ln\frac{B}{B-N} - \frac{N}{2B(B-N)} + \cdots$$

(15-98)

$$-\frac{\mu}{kT} = \left[\frac{\partial(S/k)}{\partial N}\right]_B = \ln\frac{B-N}{N} + \frac{2N-B}{2N(B-N)} + \cdots.$$

(15-99)

The corresponding expressions from Eqs. (15-92) and (15-93) [or from Eq. (15-97), using differences] are

$$p'_{N,B} = \ln\frac{B}{B-N} - \frac{N}{B(B-N)} + \cdots$$

(15-100)

and

$$-\mu'_{N,B} = \ln\frac{B-N}{N} - \frac{1}{N} + \cdots.$$

(15-101)

Hence the small terms in Eqs. (15-98) and (15-99) have no proper range of validity. Incidentally, Eq. (15-99) can easily be shown to be equivalent to Eq. (5.35) of James and Guth,[1] which gives the force as a function of length for a finite one-dimensional freely folding ruler model of a polymer chain.

Example. Ideal Binary Mixture. This example is considered on pages 87 and 88 of Part I, with N_1 and N_2 continuous. In view of the discussion above, a correction for discreteness is in order. The problem is practically identical with the preceding example.

The basic equations are

$$\delta A_{N_1,N_2} \overset{*}{=} -S_{N_1,N_2}\,dT + \mu^{(1)}_{N_1,N_2}\,\Delta N_1 + \mu^{(2)}_{N_1,N_2}\,\Delta N_2$$

(15-102)

$$\mu^{(1)}_{N_1,N_2} = A_{N_1+1,N_2} - A_{N_1,N_2}, \qquad \text{etc.,} \qquad (15\text{-}103)$$

$$A_{N_1,N_2} = -kT\ln Q_{N_1,N_2}, \qquad (15\text{-}104)$$

where Q_{N_1,N_2} is given by Eqs. (4-77) and (4-79). Then

$$\frac{\mu^{(1)}_{N_1,N_2}}{kT} = \ln\frac{(N_1+1)}{j_1(N_1+N_2+1)} = -\ln j_1 + \ln x_1 + \frac{1}{N}\frac{x_2}{1-x_2} + \cdots,$$

(15-105)

[1] H. M. James and E. Guth, *J. Chem. Phys.*, **11**, 455 (1943).

with a similar expression for $\mu_{N_1, N_2}^{(2)}$. Also

$$\frac{\mathscr{E}_{N_1, N_2}}{kT} = \frac{A_{N_1, N_2} - N_1\mu_{N_1, N_2}^{(1)} - N_2\mu_{N_1, N_2}^{(2)}}{kT}$$

$$= \ln \frac{N_1!N_2!(N_1 + N_2 + 1)^{N_1+N_2}}{N!(N_1 + 1)^{N_1} (N_2 + 1)^{N_2}} = \tfrac{1}{2} \ln \frac{2\pi N_1 N_2}{Ne^2} + \cdots .$$

$$(15\text{-}106)$$

Other Examples. We recall that the "twelve-site spherical lattice gas" is a good example of a very small N, B, T system. It is discussed on pages 62 to 64.

The Bragg–Williams lattice gas for an N, B, T system is considered on pages 67 and 68, using continuous variables. We do not correct this treatment for the reason given on page 196.

APPENDIX

It is instructive to compare differences with derivatives in a few simple cases. For example, in an N, p, T system, $F_N(p, T)$ might have terms, among others, with N dependences of the following types: N (macroscopic), constant, $N^{2/3}$, $N^{1/3}$, $\ln N$, $1/N$, etc. We can omit the coefficients (functions of p and T), in each case, without loss of generality. For each term, let us compare $\mu_N = F_{N+1} - F_N$ with $\mu = \partial F/\partial N$.

In the first two cases $\mu_N = \mu$.

If $F_N = N^{2/3}$, then

$$\mu = \tfrac{2}{3}N^{-1/3}, \qquad \mu_N = \tfrac{2}{3}N^{-1/3} + O(N^{-4/3})$$

$$F_{N+1/2} - F_{N-1/2} = \tfrac{2}{3}N^{-1/3} + O(N^{-7/3}).$$

If $F_N = N^{1/3}$, then

$$\mu = \tfrac{1}{3}N^{-2/3}, \qquad \mu_N = \tfrac{1}{3}N^{-2/3} + O(N^{-5/3})$$

$$F_{N+1/2} - F_{N-1/2} = \tfrac{1}{3}N^{-2/3} + O(N^{-8/3}).$$

If $F_N = \ln N$,

$$\mu = \frac{1}{N}, \qquad \mu_N = \frac{1}{N} - \frac{1}{2N^2} + \cdots$$

$$F_N - F_{N-1} = \frac{1}{N} + \frac{1}{2N^2} + \cdots$$

$$F_{N+1/2} - F_{N-1/2} = \frac{1}{N} + O(N^{-3}).$$

If $F_N = 1/N$,

$$\mu = -\frac{1}{N^2}, \qquad \mu_N = -\frac{1}{N^2} + O(N^{-3})$$

$$F_{N+1/2} - F_{N-1/2} = -\frac{1}{N^2} + O(N^{-4}).$$

In each of these cases we see that the first "small system term" is the same for μ and μ_N, but the next smaller term differs. Also, in each case, as expected, the difference between μ and $F_{N+1/2} - F_{N-1/2}$ is of smaller order than the difference between μ and μ_N.

INDEX